C000295803

# British
# Railways
# Locomotives

## Combined Volume 1953

IAN ALLAN *Publishing*

First published 1953
This impression 1996

ISBN 0 7110 2435 9

All rights reserved. No part of this book may be reproduced
or transmitted in any form or by any means, electronic or
mechanical, including photocopying, recording or by any
information storage and retrieval system, without permission
from the Publisher in writing.

© Ian Allan Ltd 1953, 1996

Published by Ian Allan Publishing

an imprint of Ian Allan Ltd, Terminal House,
Station Approach, Shepperton, Surrey TW17 8AS.
Printed by Ian Allan Printing Ltd,
Coombelands House, Coombelands Lane,
Addlestone, Surrey KT15 1HY.

*Front cover:* 'West Country' class 4-6-2 No 34029 *Lundy*
seen in ex-works condition at Eastleigh. *Colour-Rail*

*Back cover, top:* 'King' class 4-6-0 No 6001 *King Edward VII*
seen at Iver with an express in June 1952. *E. R. Wetherset*

*Back cover, bottom:* Class 'A2' 4-6-2 No 60536
*Trimbush* heads past Prestonpans with the 9.10am Glasgow-
Newcastle in June 1952. *E. R. Wetherset*

# THE **ABC** OF

# BRITISH RAILWAYS

# LOCOMOTIVES

## PART 1 - Nos. 1-9999

SUMMER
1953
EDITION

# NOTES ON THE USE OF THIS BOOK

1. This booklet lists British Railways locomotives numbe between 1 and 9999 in service at February 21st, 1953. This rang numbers covers Western Region (ex-G.W.R.) engines with following exceptions :

  (i) Diesel and gas turbine locomotives, which are dealt wit the ABC OF BRITISH RAILWAYS LOCOMOTIV Part 2—Nos. 10000-39999.

  (ii) British Railways Standard classes and Class "WD" 2 locomotives in service on the Western Region. These listed in the ABC OF BRITISH RAILWAYS LOC MOTIVES Part 4—Nos. 60000-99999.

2. With the exception of Diesel locomotives, Western Reg locomotives retain their original Great Western numbers.

3. This book is divided into three parts :—

(a) An alphabetical list of classes, with dimensions and s divisions, and summary of locomotives in the class.

(b) A numerical list of locomotives showing the class of ea and the name, if any.

(c) A table of dimensions.

4. The aim of the book is that 1 (a) above shall provide a re reference to particulars of individual locomotives in a class : a that 1 (b) shall be used for observation purposes.

5. The following notes are a guide to the system of refere marks and other details given in the lists of dimensions shown each class in the alphabetical list of classes.

(a) In the lists of dimensions " Su " indicates a superhea locomotive, and " SS " indicates that some locomotives the class are superheated.

(b) Locomotives are fitted with two inside cylinders, slide val and Stephenson link motion, except where otherwise sho e.g. (O) indicates outside cylinders and " P.V." pis valves.

(c) The date on which a design of locomotive first appeare indicated by " Introduced."

6. All locomotives are of G.W.R. origin, except where oth wise shown.

7. The following is a list of abbreviations used to indicate pre-grouping owners of certain Western Region locomotives:

| | | | |
|---|---|---|---|
| AD | Alexandra (Newport and South Wales) Docks & Railway. | CMDP | Cleobury Mortimer and Di Priors Light Railway. |
| BM | Brecon and Merthyr Railway. | LMM | Llanelly & Mynydd M Railway. |
| BPGV | Burry Port & Gwendraeth Valley Railway. | MSWJ | Midland and South Wes Junction Railway. |
| Cam.R. | Cambrian Railways. | | |
| Car.R. | Cardiff Railway. | P & M | Powlesland & Mason (C tractor). |

2

| R | Rhymney Railway. | WCPR | Weston, Clevedon & Portishead Railway. |
| HT | Swansea Harbour Trust. | | |
| V | Taff Vale Railway. | W & L | Cambrian Railways (Welshpool and Llanfair). |
| of R | Cambrian Railways (Vale of Rheidol). | YTW | Ystalyfera Tin Works. |

# WESTERN REGION LOCOMOTIVE RUNNING SHEDS AND SHED CODES

| Depot No. | Depot | Depot No. | Depot | Depot No. | Depot |
|---|---|---|---|---|---|
| 81A | **Old Oak Common** | 84A | **Wolverhampton (Stafford Rd.)** | 87A | **Neath** |
| 81B | **Slough** | | | | Glyn Neath |
| | Aylesbury | 84B | Oxley | | Neath (N. & B.) |
| | Marlow | 84C | Banbury | 87B | Duffryn Yard |
| | Watlington | 84D | Leamington Spa | 87C | Danygraig |
| 81C | Southall | 84E | Tyseley | 87D | Swansea East Dock |
| 81D | Reading | | Stratford-on-Avon | 87E | Landore |
| | Henley-on-T. | 84F | Stourbridge | 87F | Llanelly |
| 81E | Didcot | 84G | Shrewsbury | | Burry Port |
| | Newbury | | Clee Hill | | Pantyfynnon |
| | Wallingford | | Craven Arms | 87G | Carmarthen |
| 81F | Oxford | | Knighton | 87H | Neyland |
| | Abingdon | | Builth Road | | Cardigan |
| | Fairford | 84H | Wellington (Salop) | | Milford Haven |
| 82A | **Bristol (Bath Road)** | 84J | Croes Newydd | | Pembroke Dock |
| | Bath | | Bala | | Whitland |
| | Weston-super-Mare | | Trawsfynydd | 87J | Goodwick |
| | Yatton | | Penmaenpool | 87K | Swansea Victoria |
| 82B | Bristol (S.P.M.) | 84K | Chester | | Upper Bank |
| 82C | Swindon | 85A | Worcester | | Gurnos |
| | Chippenham | | Evesham | | Llandovery |
| 82D | Westbury | | Kingham | | |
| | Frome | 85B | Gloucester | 88A | **Cardiff (Cathays)** |
| 82E | Yeovil | | Brimscombe | | Radyr |
| 82F | Weymouth | | Cheltenham | 88B | Cardiff East Dock |
| | Bridport | | Cirencester | 88C | Barry |
| 83A | **Newton Abbot** | | Lydney | 88D | Merthyr |
| | Ashburton | | Tetbury | | Cae Harris |
| | Kingsbridge | 85C | Hereford | | Dowlais Central |
| 83B | Taunton | | Leominster | | Rhymney |
| | Bridgwater | | Ross | 88E | Abercynon |
| | Minehead | 85D | Kidderminster | 88F | Treherbert |
| 83C | Exeter | 86A | **Newport (Ebbw Jc.)** | | Ferndale |
| | Tiverton Junc. | 86B | Newport (Pill) | 89A | **Oswestry** |
| 83D | Laira (Plymouth) | 86C | Cardiff (Canton) | | Llanidloes |
| | Launceston | 86D | Llantrisant | | Moat Lane |
| | Princetown | 86E | Severn Tunnel Junc. | | Welshpool (W&L) |
| 83E | St. Blazey | 86F | Tondu | 89B | Brecon |
| | Bodmin | 86G | Pontypool Road | | Builth Wells |
| | Moorswater | | Branches Fork | 89C | Machynlleth |
| 83F | Truro | 86H | Aberbeeg | | Aberayron |
| 83G | Penzance | 86J | Aberdare | | Aberystwyth |
| | Helston | 86K | Abergavenny | | Portmadoc |
| | St. Ives | | Tredegar | | Pwllheli |

# SUMMARY OF WESTERN REGION STEAM LOCOMOTIVE CLASSES

## WITH HISTORICAL NOTES AND DIMENSIONS

In this list the classes are arranged by wheel arrangement in following order : 4-6-0, 4-4-0, 2-8-0, 2-6-0, 2-4-0, 0-6-0, 2-8-‹ 2-8-0T, 2-6-2T, 0-6-2T, 0-6-0T, 0-4-2T, 0-4-0T.    Codes in sn bold type at the head of each class denote B.R. power classificati

---

### 4-6-0    6MT    1000 Class "County"

Introduced 1945: Hawksworth design
Weights: Loco.    76 tons 17 cwt.
        Tender 49 tons 0 cwt.
Pressure: 280 lb. Su.
Cyls.: (O) 18½″ × 30″
Driving Wheels: 6′ 3″
T.E.: 32,580 lb.
P.V.

1000–29                    Total 30

---

### 4-6-0    4P    2900 Class "Saint"

Introduced 1903: Churchward design, developed from No. 2900 (originally No. 100, introduced 1902), earlier locomotives subsequently fitted with new boilers and superheaters, remainder built as such.
Weights: Loco.    72 tons 0 cwt.
        Tender 40 tons 0 cwt.
Pressure: 225 lb. Su.
Cyls : (O) 18½″ × 30″
Driving Wheels: 6′ 8½″
T.E.: 24,395 lb.
P.V.

2920/37/45
                           Total 3

---

### 4-6-0    5P    4000 Cla "Star"

Introduced 1907: Churchward des developed from No. 4000 (origi No. 40, introduced 1906 as a 4-earlier locomotives subseque fitted with new boilers and su heaters, remainder built as such.
Weights: Loco.    75 tons 12 cwt.
        Tender 46 tons 14 cwt.
Pressure: 225 lb. Su.
Cyls.: (4) 15″ × 26″
Driving Wheels: 6′ 8½″
T.E.: 27,800 lb.
Inside Walschaerts gear and roc shafts.    P.V.

4049/52/3/6/61/2
                           Tota

---

### 4-6-0    7P    4073 Cl: "Castle"

Introduced 1923: Collett design, veloped from " Star " (4000 5083-92 converted from " Star," from 4-6-2).
Weights: Loco.    79 tons 17 cwt.
        Tender 46 tons 14 cwt.
Pressure: 225 lb. Su.
Cyls.: (4) 16″ × 26″
Driving Wheels: 6′ 8½″
T.E.: 31,625 lb.
Inside Walschaerts gear and roc shafts.    P.V.

111,    4000/37/73–99,    5000–
7000–37                    Total

## 4-6-0    5MT    4900 Class
### "Hall"

Introduced 1924: Collett rebuild with
6' driving wheels of "Saint" (built
1907).

Introduced 1928: Modified design for
new construction, with higher-
pitched boiler, modified footplating
and detail differences.

Weights: Loco. $\begin{cases} 72 \text{ tons } 10 \text{ cwt.*} \\ 75 \text{ tons } 0 \text{ cwt.†} \end{cases}$
            Tender 46 tons 14 cwt.

Pressure: 225 lb. Su.

Cyls.: (O) $18\frac{1}{2}'' \times 30''$

Driving Wheels: 6' 0"

T.E.: 27,275 lb.

4900

4901–10/2–99, 5900–99, 6900–
58                              **Total 258**

## 4-6-0    8P    6000 Class
### "King"

Introduced 1927: Collett design.

Weights: Loco.   89 tons 0 cwt.
            Tender 46 tons 14 cwt.

Pressure: 250 lb. Su.

Cyls.: (4) $16\frac{1}{4}'' \times 28''$

Driving Wheels: 6' 6"

T.E.: 40,285 lb.

Inside Walschaerts gear and rocking
shafts.    P.V.

6000–29                         **Total 30**

## 4-6-0    5MT    6800 Class
### "Grange"

Introduced 1936: Collett design, variation of "Hall" with smaller wheels,
incorporating certain parts of withdrawn 4300 2-6-0 locos.

Weights: Loco.   74 tons 0 cwt.
            Tender 40 tons 0 cwt.

Pressure: 225 lb. Su

Cyls.: (O) $18\frac{1}{2}'' \times 30''$

Driving Wheels: 5' 8"

T.E.: 28,875 lb.

P.V.

6800–79                         **Total 80**

## 4-6-0    5MT    6959 Class
### "Modified Hall"

Introduced 1944: Hawksworth development of "Hall," with larger superheater, "one-piece" main frames and
plate framed bogie.

Weights: Engine 75 tons 16 cwt.
            Tender 46 tons 14 cwt.

Pressure: 225 lb. Su.

Cyls.: (O) $18\frac{1}{2}'' \times 30''$

Driving Wheels: 6' 0"

T.E.: 27,275 lb.

P.V.

6959–99, 7900–29               **Total 71**

## 4-6-0    5MT    7800 Class
### "Manor"

Introduced 1938: Collett design for
secondary lines, incorporating certain
parts of withdrawn 4300 2-6-0 locos.

Weights: Loco.   68 tons 18 cwt.
            Tender 40 tons 0 cwt.

Pressure: 225 lb. Su.

Cyls.: (O) $18'' \times 30''$

Driving Wheels: 5' 8"

T.E.: 27,340 lb.

P.V.

7800–29                         **Total 30**

## 4-4-0    2P    9000 Class

Introduced 1936: Collett rebuild, incorporating "Duke" type boiler and
"Bulldog" frames, for light lines.

Weights: Loco.   49 tons 0 cwt.
            Tender 40 tons 0 cwt.

Pressure: 180 lb. SS.

Cyls.: $18'' \times 26''$

Driving Wheels: 5' 8"

T.E.: 18,955 lb.

9000–5/8–18/20–8               **Total 26**

## 2-8-0   8F   2800 Class

*Introduced 1903: Churchward design, earlier locos. subsequently fitted with new boilers and superheaters.
†Introduced 1938: Collett locos., with side window cabs and detail alterations.

Weights: Loco. $\begin{cases} 75 \text{ tons } 10 \text{ cwt.*} \\ 76 \text{ tons } 5 \text{ cwt.†} \end{cases}$
         Tender 40 tons 0 cwt.
Pressure: 225 lb. Su.
Cyls.: (O) 18½″ × 30″
Driving Wheels: 4′ 7½″
T.E.: 35,380 lb.
P.V.

*2800–2883
†2884–99, 3800–66

Total 167

## 2-8-0   7F   R.O.D. Class

Introduced 1911: Robinson G. C. design (L.N.E.R. O4), built from 1917 for Railway Operating Division, R.E., taken into G.W. stock from 1919, and subseqently fitted with G.W. boiler mountings and details.
Weights: Loco. 73 tons 11 cwt.
         Tender 47 tons 14 cwt.
Pressure: 185 lb. Su.
Cyls.: (O) 21″ × 26″
Driving Wheels: 4′ 8″
T.E.: 32,200 lb.
P.V.

3010–2/4–8/20/2–6/8/9/31–3/6/8/40–4/7/8

Total 28

## 2-8-0   7F   4700 Class

Introduced 1919: Churchward mixed traffic design (4700 built with smaller boiler and later rebuilt).
Weights: Loco. 82 tons 0 cwt.
         Tender 46 tons 14 cwt.
Pressure: 225 lb. Su.
Cyls.: (O) 19″ × 30″
Driving Wheels: 5′ 8″
T.E.: 30,460 lb.
P.V.

4700–8

Total 9

## 2-6-0   4MT   4300 Cla

*Introduced 1911: Churchward desi
†Introduced 1925: Locos. with de alterations affecting weight.
‡Introduced 1932: Locos. with s window cabs and detail alterations

Weights: Loco. $\begin{cases} 62 \text{ tons } 0 \text{ cwt.*} \\ 64 \text{ tons } 0 \text{ cwt.†} \\ 65 \text{ tons } 6 \text{ cwt.‡} \end{cases}$
         Tender 40 tons 0 cwt.
Pressure: 200 lb. Su.
Cyls.: (O) 18½″ × 30″
Driving Wheels: 5′ 8″
T.E.: 25,670 lb.
P.V

*4326/58/75/7/81, 5306/7/10–9,21–8/30–9/41/4/5/7/50/1/3/5–8/60–2/7–72/5–82/4–6/890–9, 6300–14/6–99, 7305–21
†7300–4
‡9300–19

Total 2

## 2-4-0   1MT   MSW

Introduced 1894: Dubs design M.S.W.J., reboilered by G.W.
Weights: Loco. 35 tons 5 cwt.
         Tender 30 tons 5 cwt.
Pressure: 165 lb.
Cyls.: 17″ × 24″
Driving Wheels: 5′ 6″
T.E.: 13,400 lb.

1336

Total

## 0-6-0   3MT   2251 Clas

Introduced 1930: Collett design.
Weights:
  Loco. 43 tons 8 cwt.
  Tender $\begin{cases} 36 \text{ tons } 15 \text{ cwt.} \\ 47 \text{ tons } 6 \text{ cwt (ex-R.O} \\ \text{tender from 3000 Class} \\ 2\text{-8-0).} \end{cases}$
Pressure: 200 lb. Su.
Cyls.: 17½″ × 24″
Driving Wheels: 5′ 2″
T.E.: 20,155 lb.

2200–99, 3200–19     Total 12

7

## -0  2MT  2301 Class

oduced 1883: Dean design, later
cted with superheaters.

ights: Loco.  36 tons 16 cwt.
   Tender 34 tons 5 cwt.

ssure: 180 lb. Su.

s.: $\begin{cases} 17'' \times 24'' \\ 17\frac{1}{2}'' \times 24'' \end{cases}$

ving Wheels : 5' 2''

: $\begin{cases} 17{,}120 \text{ lb.} \\ 18{,}140 \text{ lb.} \end{cases}$

3/7/40/54, 2409/11/26/58/
0/74/84, 2513/6/32/8/41/51/
/68/78/9

**Total 21**

## -0  2MT  Cam.

oduced 1903: Jones Cambrian " 89 "
ass, reboilered by G.W. from 1924.

ights: Loco.  38 tons 17 cwt.
   Tender 31 tons 13 cwt.

ssure: 160 lb. SS.

s.: 18'' × 26''

ving Wheels: 5' 1½''

: 18,625 lb.

4/9/55/73/92/4-6

**Total 8**

## -2T  8F  7200 Class

oduced 1934: Collett rebuild with
xtended bunker and trailing wheels
f .Churchward 4200 class 2-8-0T.

ight: 92 tons 2 cwt.

ssure: 200 lb. Su.

s.: (O) 19'' × 30''

ving Wheels: 4' 7½''

.: 33,170 lb.

00-53

**Total 54**

## 2-8-0T  $\left\{ \begin{smallmatrix} 7F* \\ 8F† \end{smallmatrix} \right\}$  4200 Class

*Introduced 1910: Churchward design.
†Introduced 1923: 5205 class, with
 enlarged cyls. and detail alterations.

Weight $\begin{cases} 81 \text{ tons } 12 \text{ cwt.*} \\ 82 \text{ tons } 2 \text{ cwt.†} \end{cases}$

Pressure: 200 lb. Su.

Cyls.: $\begin{cases} \text{(O) } 18\frac{1}{2}'' \times 30''* \\ \text{(O) } 19'' \times 30''† \end{cases}$

Driving Wheels: 4' 7½''

T.E.: $\begin{cases} 31.450 \text{ lb.*} \\ 33{,}170 \text{ lb.†} \end{cases}$

P.V.

*4200/1/3/6-8/11-5/7/8/21-33/5-
8/41-3/6-8/50-99, 5200-4
†5205-64 **Total 151**

## 2-6-2T  4MT  3100 Class

Introduced 1938: Collett rebuild with
higher pressure and smaller wheels of
Churchward 3150 class (introduced
1906).

Weight: 81 tons 9 cwt.
Pressure: 225 lb. Su.
Cyls.: (O) 18½'' × 30''
Driving Wheels: 5' 3''
T.E.: 31,170 lb.
P.V.

3100-4

**Total 5**

## 2-6-2T  4MT  3150 Class

Introduced 1906: Churchward design,
developed from his original 3100
class of 1903, but with larger boiler,
subsequently fitted with superheaters.

Weight: 81 tons 12 cwt.
Pressure: 200 lb. Su.
Cyls.: (O) 18½'' × 30''
Driving Wheels: 5' 8''
T.E.: 25,670 lb.
P.V.

3150/60/3/4/70-2/4/6/7/80/3/
5-7/90 **Total 16**

For full details of
B.R. CLASS " WD " 2-8-0s
running on the Western Region

see the

A.B.C. OF B.R. LOCOMOTIVES
PT. IV. Nos. 60000-99999

## 2-6-2T 3MT 4400 Class

Introduced 1904: Churchward design for light branches, subsequently fitted with superheaters.
Weight: 56 tons 13 cwt.
Pressure: 180 lb. Su.
Cyls.: (O) 17″ × 24″
Driving Wheels: 4′ 1½″
T.E.: 21,440 lb.
P.V.

4401/5/6/10      **Total 4**

## 2-6-2T 4MT 4500 Class

*Introduced 1906: Churchward design for light branches, developed from 4400 class with larger wheels, earlier locos. subsequently fitted with superheaters.
†Introduced 1927: **4575 class** with detail alterations and increased weight.
Weights $\begin{cases} 57 \text{ tons } 0 \text{ cwt.*} \\ 61 \text{ tons } 0 \text{ cwt.†} \end{cases}$
Pressure: 200 lb. Su.
Cyls.: (O) 17″ × 24″
Driving Wheels: 4′ 7½″
T.E.: 21,250 lb.
P.V.

*4500/5–8/11/5/9/21–6/30/2–42/5–74
†4575–99, 5500–74      **Total 156**

## 2-6-2T 4MT 5100 & 6100 Classes

*5100 class. Introduced 1928: Collett rebuild with detail alterations and increased weight of Churchward 3100 class (introduced 1903 and subsequently fitted with superheaters).
†5101 class. Introduced 1929: Modified design for new construction.
‡6100 class. Introduced 1931: Locos. for London suburban area with increased boiler pressure.
Weights $\begin{cases} 75 \text{ tons } 10 \text{ cwt.*} \\ 78 \text{ tons } 9 \text{ cwt.††} \end{cases}$
Pressure $\begin{cases} 200 \text{ lb. Su.*†} \\ 225 \text{ lb. Su.‡} \end{cases}$
Cyls.: (O) 18″ × 30″
Driving Wheels: 5′ 8″
T.E. $\begin{cases} 24,300 \text{ lb.*†} \\ 27,340 \text{ lb.‡} \end{cases}$
P.V.

*5112/3/40/8
†4100–79, 5101–10/50–99
‡6100–69

     **Total 213**

## 2-6-2T 4MT 8100 Class

Introduced 1938: Collett rebuild with higher pressure and smaller wheels of Churchward locos. in 5100 class.
Weight: 76 tons 11 cwt.
Pressure: 225 lb. Su.
Cyls.: (O) 18″ × 30″
Driving Wheels: 5′ 6″
T.E.: 28,165 lb.
P.V.

8100–9      **Total**

## 2-6-2T 4MT AD

Introduced 1920: Hawthorn Leslie design for A.D. Railway.
Weight: 65 tons 0 cwt.
Pressure: 160 lb.
Cyls.: (O) 19″ × 26″
Driving Wheels: 4′ 7″
T.E.: 23,210 lb.

1205      **Total**

## 2-6-2T unclass. V of

*Introduced 1902: Davies and Metcalf design for V. of R. 1′ 11½″ gauge.
†Introduced 1923: G.W. development of V. of R. design.
Weight: 25 tons 0 cwt.
Pressure: 165 lb.
Cyls. (O) $\begin{cases} 11″ \times 17″* \\ 11½″ \times 17″† \end{cases}$
Driving Wheels: 2′ 6″
T.E. $\begin{cases} 9,615 \text{ lb.*} \\ 10,510 \text{ lb.†} \end{cases}$

*9
†7/8      **Total**

## 0-6-2T 5MT 5600 Class

*Introduced 1924: Collett design for service in Welsh valleys.
†Introduced 1927: Locos. with detail alterations.
Weights $\begin{cases} 68 \text{ tons } 12 \text{ cwt.*} \\ 69 \text{ tons } 7 \text{ cwt.†} \end{cases}$
Pressure: 200 lb. Su.
Cyls.: 18″ × 26″
Driving Wheels: 4′ 7½″
T.E.: 25,800 lb.
P.V.

*5600–99
†6600–99      **Total 20**

## -6-2T 3F B & M

Introduced 1926: Dunbar design for B. & M., rebuilt by G.W. with taper boiler (Introduced 1915). Reboilered by G.W.R. with ex-Rhymney boiler.
Weight: 59 tons 5 cwt.
Pressure $\begin{cases} 175 \text{ lb. Su.*} \\ 175 \text{ lb.†} \end{cases}$
Cyls.: 18" × 26"
Driving Wheels: 5' 0"
T.E.: 20,885 lb.

431/2/4/5
436                                    **Total 5**

## -6-2T 4F Cardiff Rly.

Introduced 1928: G.W. rebuild with taper boiler of Ree Cardiff Railway design, introduced 1908.
Weight: 66 tons 12 cwt.
Pressure: 175 lb. Su.
Cyls.: 18" × 26"
Driving Wheels: 4' 6½"
T.E.: 22,990 lb.

55                                     **Total 1**

## -6-2T 4F Rhymney Rly.

Introduced 1921: Hurry Riches Rhymney "R1" class, development of "R." (Introduced 1907.)
Introduced 1926: Reboilered by G.W. with superheated taper boiler.
Weights $\begin{cases} 66 \text{ tons } 0 \text{ cwt.*} \\ 62 \text{ tons } 10 \text{ cwt.†} \end{cases}$
Pressure $\begin{cases} 175 \text{ lb.*} \\ 200 \text{ lb. Su.†} \end{cases}$
Cyls.: 18½" × 26"
Driving Wheels: 4' 6"
T.E. $\begin{cases} 24,520 \text{ lb.*} \\ 28,015 \text{ lb.†} \end{cases}$

35–8, 41–3
39, 40/4                               **Total 10**

### 4F

Introduced 1914: Hurry Riches Rhymney Class "A1," built with Belpaire boiler.
Introduced 1929: Reboilered by G.W. with superheated taper boiler.

Weights $\begin{cases} 64 \text{ tons } 3 \text{ cwt.*} \\ 63 \text{ tons } 0 \text{ cwt.†} \end{cases}$
Pressure $\begin{cases} 175 \text{ lb.*} \\ 175 \text{ lb. Su.†} \end{cases}$
Cyls.: 18" × 26"*†
Driving Wheels: 4' 4½"
T.E.: 23,870 lb.*†

*68
†56/8/9/65/6/9, 70/5                   **Total 9**

### 3P

*Introduced 1926: G.W. rebuild with superheated taper boiler of Hurry Riches Rhymney "P" class.
†Introduced 1928: Rebuild of Rhymney "AP" class (superheated development of "P," introduced 1921).
Weights $\begin{cases} 58 \text{ tons } 19 \text{ cwt.*} \\ 63 \text{ tons } 0 \text{ cwt.†} \end{cases}$
Pressure: 175 lb. Su.
Cyls.: $\begin{cases} 18" \times 26"* \\ 18\frac{1}{2}" \times 26"† \end{cases}$
Driving Wheels: 5' 0"
T.E.: $\begin{cases} 20,885 \text{ lb.*} \\ 21,700 \text{ lb.†} \end{cases}$

*82/3    †77–81                        **Total 7**

## 0-6-2T 4F TV

Introduced 1924: G.W. rebuild with superheated taper boiler of Hurry Riches T.V. "O4" class (introduced 1907).
Weight: 61 tons 0 cwt.
Pressure: 175 lb. Su
Cyls.: 17½" × 26"
Driving Wheels: 4' 6½"
T.E.: 21,730 lb.

204/5/8/10/1/5/6/79/82/5/90
                                       **Total 11**

For full details of

**B.R. STANDARD LOCOMOTIVES**

running on the Western Region,

**see the**

A.B.C. OF B.R. LOCOMOTIVES
PT. IV. Nos. 60000-99999

#### 4P

Introduced 1924: G.W. rebuild with superheated taper boiler of Cameron T.V. " A " class (introduced 1914). Two sizes of cylinder.
Weight: 65 tons 14 cwt.
Pressure $\begin{cases} 175 \text{ lb. Su.*} \\ 200 \text{ lb. Su.†} \end{cases}$
Cyls. $\begin{cases} 18\frac{1}{2}'' \times 26''* \\ 17\frac{1}{2}'' \times 26''† \end{cases}$
Driving Wheels: 5' 3"
T.E.: $\begin{cases} 21,000 \text{ lb.*} \\ 21,480 \text{ lb.†} \end{cases}$

*307/8/22/35/49/52/60/1/6/70–2/ 80/7/8
†303–6/12/6/43/5–8/51/6/7/62/4/ 5,7/8/73–9/81–6/9–91/3/4/7–9
                                    **Total 55**


#### 0-6-0PT  2F     850 Class

Introduced 1910: Rebuilt with pannier tanks.
Weight: 36 tons 3 cwt.
Pressure: 165 lb.
Cyls.: $16'' \times 24''$
Driving Wheels: 4' 1½"
T.E.: 17,410 lb.

1935,  2008/11/2

                                    **Total 4**


#### 0-6-0ST  0F    1361 Class

Introduced 1910: Churchward design for dock shunting.
Weight: 35 tons 4 cwt.
Pressure: 150 lb.
Cyls.: (O) $16'' \times 20''$
Driving Wheels: 3' 8"
T.E.: 14,835 lb.

1361–5                             **Total 5**


#### 0-6-0PT  1F    1366 Class

Introduced 1934: Collett development of 1361 class, with pannier tanks.
Weight: 35 tons 15 cwt.
Pressure: 165 lb.
Cyls.: (O) $16'' \times 20''$
Driving Wheels: 3' 8"
T.E.: 16,320 lb.

1366–71                            **Total 6**


#### 0-6-0PT  4F    1500 Class

Introduced 1949: Hawksworth short-wheelbase heavy shunting design.
Weight: 58 tons 4 cwt
Pressure: 200 lb.
Cyls.: (O) $17\frac{1}{2}'' \times 24''$
Driving Wheels: 4' 7½"
T.E.: 22,515 lb.
Walschaerts gear, P.V.

1500–9                             **Total 10**


#### 0-6-0PT  2F    1600 Class

Introduced 1949: Hawksworth light branch line and shunting design.
Weight: 41 tons 12 cwt
Pressure: 165 lb.
Cyls.: $16\frac{1}{2}'' \times 24''$
Driving Wheels: 4' 1½"
T.E.: 18,515 lb.

1600–49                            **Total 50**


#### 0-6-0PT         2F
####      2021 & 2181 Classes

*2021 class. Introduced 1897: Dean saddletank, subsequently rebuilt with pannier tanks. Nos. 2101 onwards built with domeless Belpaire boilers, interchanged later throughout the class.
†2181 class. Introduced 1939: 2021 class modified with increased brake power for heavy gradients.
Weight: 39 tons 15 cwt.
Pressure: 165 lb.
Cyls.: $16\frac{1}{2}'' \times 24''$
Driving Wheels: 4' 1½"
T.E.: 18,515 lb.

*2027/34/5/8/40/2/3/53/60/1/9/ 70/2/81/2/5/8/90/2/7/9, 2101/7, 8/12/34/6/8/44/60
†2182/3/6
            **Totals : 2021 Class 30**
            **          2181 Class 3**

## 0-6-0PT 1P 5400 Class

Introduced 1931: Collett design for light passenger work, push-and-pull fitted.

Weight: 46 tons 12 cwt.

Pressure: 165 lb.

Cyls.: $16\frac{1}{2}'' \times 24''$

Driving Wheels: 5' 2"

T.E.: 14,780 lb.

5400-24

Total 25

## 0-6-0PT 3F 5700 Class

Introduced 1929: Collett design for shunting and light goods work, developed from 2021 class.

Introduced 1930: Locos. with steam brake and no A.T.C. fittings, for shunting only.

Introduced 1933: Locos. with condensing gear for working over L.T.E. Metropolitan line.

Introduced 1933: Locos. with detail alterations, modified cab (except 8700) and increased weight.

*Introduced 1948: Steam brake locos. with increased weight.

Weights $\begin{cases} 47 \text{ tons } 10 \text{ cwt.} *\dagger \\ 50 \text{ tons } 15 \text{ cwt.} \ddagger \\ 49 \text{ tons } 0 \text{ cwt.} \S ** \end{cases}$

Pressure: 200 lb.

Cyls.: $17\frac{1}{2}'' \times 24''$

Driving Wheels: 4' $7\frac{1}{2}''$

T.E.: 22,515 lb.

5700-99, 7700-99, 8701-49

8700-49

9700-10

3600-3799, 4600-99, 8700/50-99, 9600-92, 9711-99

*6750-79

Total 863

## 0-6-0PT 2P* 2F†
## 6400 & 7400 Classes

6400 class. Introduced 1932: Collett design for light passenger work, variation of 5400 class with smaller wheels, push-and-pull fitted.

*7400 class. Introduced 1936: Non-push-and-pull fitted locos.

Weights $\begin{cases} 45 \text{ tons } 12 \text{ cwt.} * \\ 45 \text{ tons } 9 \text{ cwt.} \dagger \end{cases}$

Pressure: 180 lb.

Cyls.: $16\frac{1}{2}'' \times 24''$

Driving Wheels: 4' $7\frac{1}{2}''$

T.E.: 18,010 lb.

*6400-39

†7400-49

Totals : 6400 Class 40

7400 Class 50

## 0-6-0PT 4F 9400 Class

*Introduced 1947: Hawksworth taper-boiler design for heavy shunting.

†Introduced 1949: Locos. with non-superheated boilers.

Weight: 55 tons 7 cwt.

Pressure: 200 lb. SS.

Cyls.: $17\frac{1}{2}'' \times 24''$

Driving Wheels: 4' $7\frac{1}{2}''$

T.E.: 22,515 lb.

*9400-9

†8400-99, 9410-99

N.B.—Locos. of this class are still being delivered.

## 0-6-0T 3F AD

Introduced 1917: Kerr Stuart design for Railway Operating Division, R.E., purchased by A.D. Railway 1919.

Weight: 50 tons 0 cwt.

Pressure: 160 lb.

Cyls.: (O) $17'' \times 24''$

Driving Wheels: 4' 0"

T.E.: 19,650 lb.

666/7

Total 2

## 0-6-0T   1F    BPGV

Introduced 1910 : Hudswell Clarke
  design for B.P.G.V. rebuilt by
  G.W.R.
Weight : 37 tons 15 cwt.
Pressure : 165 lb.
Cyls: (O) 15″ × 22″
Driving wheels : 3′ 9″
T.E.: 15,430 lb.

2198             Total 1

### 2F

*Introduced 1912: Hudswell Clarke
  design for B.P.G.V.
†Rebuilt by G.W.R.
Weight: 37 tons 15 cwt.
Pressure: 160 lb.
Cyls.: (O) 16″ × 24″
Driving Wheels: 3′ 9″
T.E.: 18,570 lb.

*2166
†2162/5/8          Total 4

## 0-6-0ST   1F    BPGV

Introduced 1907: Avonside design for
  B.P.G.V., rebuilt by G.W.R.
Weight: 38 tons 5 cwt.
Pressure: 165 lb.
Cyls.: (O) 15″ × 22″
Driving Wheels: 3′ 6″
T.E.: 16,530 lb.

2176             Total 1

### 1F

Introduced 1906: Avonside design for
  B.P.G.V.
Weight: 38 tons 0 cwt.
Pressure: 170 lb.
Cyls.: (O) 15″ × 22″
Driving Wheels: 3′ 6″
T.E.: 17,030 lb.

2196             Total 1

## 0-6-0PT   4F    Cardiff Rly

Introduced 1920: Hope and Hudswell
  Clarke design for Cardiff Railway,
  reboilered by G.W. and fitted with
  pannier tanks.
Weight: 45 tons 6 cwt.
Pressure: 165 lb.
Cyls.: 18″ × 24″
Driving Wheels: 4′ 1½″
T.E.: 22,030 lb.

681–4             Total

## 0-6-0PT   2F    CMDP

Introduced 1905: M. Wardle saddle
  tank for C.M.D.P., reboilered by
  G.W. and fitted with pannier tanks.
Weight: 39 tons 18 cwt.
Pressure: 160 lb.
Cyls.: (O) 16″ × 22″
Driving Wheels: 3′ 6″
T.E.: 18,235 lb.

28/9             Total

## 0-6-0ST   1F    LMM

Introduced 1912: Hudswell Clarke de-
  sign for L.M.M., reboilered by G.W.
Weight: 34 tons 9 cwt.
Pressure: 160 lb.
Cyls.: (O) 15″ × 22″
Driving Wheels: 3′ 7½″
T.E.: 15,475 lb.

359             Total

## 0-6-0T   4F    Rhymney Rly

Introduced 1930: Hurry Riches
  Rhymney "S" class (introduced
  1908), rebuilt by G.W. with taper
  boiler.
Weight: 54 tons 8 cwt.
Pressure: 175 lb.
Cyls.: 18″ × 26″
Driving Wheels: 4′ 4½″
T.E.: 23,870 lb.

93–6             Total

**4F**

Introduced 1920: Hurry Riches Rhymney "S1" class.
Weight: 56 tons 8 cwt.
Pressure: 175 lb.
Cyls. $\begin{cases} 18'' \times 26''* \\ 18\frac{1}{2}'' \times 26''† \end{cases}$
Driving Wheels: 4' 4½"
T.E. $\begin{cases} 23,870 \text{ lb.*} \\ 25,210 \text{ lb.†} \end{cases}$
*91/2  †90  **Total 3**


**0-6-0T**  **1F**  **TV**

Introduced 1884: Hurry Riches T.V. "H" class with steeply tapered boiler for Pwllyrhebog incline, subsequently rebuilt twice.
Weight: 44 tons 15 cwt.
Pressure: 140 lb.
Cyls.: 17½" × 26"
Driving Wheels: 5' 3"
T.E.: 15,040 lb.
194  **Total 1**


**0-6-0T**  **0F**  **WCP**

Introduced 1911: Marsh rebuild of Stroudley L.B.S.C. A1. (loco. built 1877, rebuilt to A1X 1919, purchased W.C.P. 1925, acquired by G.W. 1940)
Weight: 28 tons 5 cwt.
Pressure: 150 lb.
Cyls.: 12" × 20"
Driving Wheels: 4' 0"
T.E.: 7,650 lb.
5  **Total 1**


**0-6-0T**  Unclass  **W & L**

Introduced 1902: Beyer Peacock design for 2' 6½" gauge W. & L. Section, Cam. Railways.
Weight: 19 tons 18 cwt.
Gauge: 2' 6½"
Pressure: 150 lb.
Cyls.: (O) 11½" × 16"
Driving Wheels: 2' 9"
T.E.: 8,175 lb.
822/3  **Total 2**


**0-4-2T**  **1P**
## 1400 & 5800 Classes

*1400 class introduced 1932: Collett design for light branch work (originally designated 4800 class). Push-and-pull fitted.
†5800 class introduced 1933: Non push-and-pull fitted locos.
Weight: 41 tons 6 cwt.
Pressure: 165 lb.
Cyls.: 16" × 24"
Driving Wheels: 5' 2"
T.E.: 13,900 lb.

*1400–74  †5800–19  **Total 95**


**0-4-0T**  **3F**  **1101 Class**

Introduced 1926: Avonside Engine Co., design to G.W requirements for dock shunting.
Weight: 38 tons 4 cwt.
Pressure: 170 lb.
Cyls.: (O) 16" × 24"
Driving Wheels: 3' 9½"
T.E.: 19,510 lb.
Walschaerts gear.

1101–6  **Total 6**


**0-4-0ST**  **0F**  **Car.R**

Introduced 1898: Kitson design for Car.R.
Weight: 25 tons 10 cwt.
Pressure: 160 lb.
Cyls.: (O) 14" × 21"
Driving wheels: 3' 2½"
T.E.: 14,540 lb.
Hawthorn Kitson valve gear.

1338  **Total 1**


**0-4-0ST**  **0F**  **P & M**

Introduced 1907: Peckett design for P. & M.
Weight: 33 tons 10 cwt.
Pressure: 150 lb.
Cyls.: (O) 15" × 21"
Driving Wheels: 3' 7"  T.E.: 14,010 lb.

1151/2  **Total 2**

Introduced 1903: Hawthorn Leslie design
for P. & M., reboilered by G.W.R.
Weight: 26 tons 13 cwt.
Pressure: 120 lb
Cyls.: (O) 14″ × 20″
Driving Wheels: 3′ 6″   T.E.: 9,520 lb.

1153 **Total 1**

## 0-4-0ST    OF    SHT

ntroduced 1905: Barclay design for
S.H.T.
Weight: 28 tons 0 cwt.
Pressure: 160 lb.
Cyls.: (O) 14″ × 22″
Driving Wheels: 3′ 5″   T.E.: 14,305 lb.

1140 **Total 1**

Introduced 1906: Peckett design for
S.H.T. (similar to 1150-2).
Weight: 33 tons 10 cwt.
Pressure: 150 lb.
Cyls.: (O) 15″ × 21″
Driving Wheels: 3′ 7″
T.E.: 14,010 lb.

1143/5 **Total 2**

Introduced 1909: Hawthorn Leslie de-
sign for S.H.T.
Weight: 26 tons 17 cwt.
Pressure: 150 lb.
Cyls.: (O) 14″ × 22″
Driving Wheels: 3′ 6″
T.E.: 13,090 lb.

1144 **Total**

Introduced 1911: Hudswell Clark
design for S.H.T.
Weight: 28 tons 15 cwt.
Pressure: 160 lb.
Cyls.: (O) 15″ × 22″
Driving Wheels: 3′ 4″
T.E.: 16,830 lb.

1142 **Total**

## 0-4-0ST    Unclass    YTW

Introduced 1900: Peckett design sup-
plied to Ystalyfera Tin Works.
Weight: 23 tons 0 cwt.
Pressure: 146 lb.
Cyls.: (O) 14½″ × 20″
Driving Wheels: 3′ 2″
T.E.: 13,000 lb.

1 (*Service Loco.*) **Total**

# NUMERICAL LIST OF WESTERN REGION
## STEAM LOCOMOTIVES

Locomotives are of G.W. origin except where
indicated by initials

**0-4-0ST**    **YTW**

Hercules (*Service Loco.*)

**0-6-0T**    **WCP**

5 Portishead

**2-6-2T**    **V of R**

| 7 | 8 | 9 |
|---|---|---|

**0-6-0PT**    **CMDP**

| 28 | 29 |
|----|----|

**0-6-2T**    **RR**

| 35 | 42 | 66 | 79 |
|----|----|----|----|
| 36 | 43 | 68 | 80 |
| 37 | 44 | 69 | 81 |
| 38 | 56 | 70 | 82 |
| 39 | 58 | 75 | 83 |
| 40 | 59 | 77 |    |
| 41 | 65 | 78 |    |

**0-6-0T**    **RR**

| 90 | 92 | 94 | 96 |
|----|----|----|----|
| 91 | 93 | 95 |    |

**4-6-0**    **4073 Class**

111 Viscount Churchill

**0-6-2T**    **Car.R.**

155

**0-6-0T**    **TV**

194

**0-6-2T**    **TV**

| 204 | 282 | 308 | 347 |
|-----|-----|-----|-----|
| 205 | 285 | 312 | 348 |
| 208 | 290 | 316 | 349 |
| 210 | 303 | 322 | 351 |
| 211 | 304 | 335 | 352 |
| 215 | 305 | 343 | 356 |
| 216 | 306 | 345 | 357 |
| 279 | 307 | 346 |     |

**0-6-0T**    **LMM**

359 Hilda

**0-6-2T**    **TV**

| 360 | 371 | 380 | 389 |
|-----|-----|-----|-----|
| 361 | 372 | 381 | 390 |
| 362 | 373 | 382 | 391 |
| 364 | 374 | 383 | 393 |
| 365 | 375 | 384 | 394 |
| 366 | 376 | 385 | 397 |
| 367 | 377 | 386 | 398 |
| 368 | 378 | 387 | 399 |
| 370 | 379 | 388 |     |

**0-6-2T**    **BM**

| 431 | 434 | 436 |
|-----|-----|-----|
| 432 | 435 |     |

666-1407

**0-6-0T**         **AD**

| 666 | 667 |

**0-6-0PT**       **Car.R.**

| 681 | 682 | 683 | 684 |

**0-6-0T**       **W & L.**

| 822 | 823 |

**0-6-0**       **Cam.R.**

| 844 | 855 | 892 | 895 |
| 849 | 873 | 894 | 896 |

**4-6-0**     **1000 Class**
       **" County "**

1000 County of Middlesex
1001 County of Bucks
1002 County of Berks
1003 County of Wilts
1004 County of Somerset
1005 County of Devon
1006 County of Cornwall
1007 County of Brecknock
1008 County of Cardigan
1009 County of Carmarthen
1010 County of Caernarvon
1011 County of Chester
1012 County of Denbigh
1013 County of Dorset
1014 County of Glamorgan
1015 County of Gloucester
1016 County of Hants
1017 County of Hereford
1018 County of Leicester
1019 County of Merioneth
1020 County of Monmouth
1021 County of Montgomery
1022 County of Northampton
1023 County of Oxford

1024 County of Pembroke
1025 County of Radnor
1026 County of Salop
1027 County of Stafford
1028 County of Warwick
1029 County of Worcester

**0-4-0T**     **1101 Class**

| 1101 | 1103 | 1105 |
| 1102 | 1104 | 1106 |

**0-4-0T**        **SH**

| 1140 | 1143 | 1145 |
| 1142 | 1144 | |

**0-4-0T**        **PN**

| 1151 | 1152 | 1153 |

**2-6-2T**        **AD**

1205

**2-4-0**       **MSW**

1336

**0-4-0ST**     **Car.R**

1338

**0-6-0ST**     **1361 Class**

| 1361 | 1363 | 1365 |
| 1362 | 1364 | |

**0-6-0PT**     **1366 Cl.**

| 1366 | 1368 | 1370 |
| 1367 | 1369 | 1371 |

**0-4-2T**     **1400 Class**

| 1400 | 1402 | 1404 | 1406 |
| 1401 | 1403 | 1405 | 1407 |

16

Top left: Ex-P. & M. 0-4-0ST No. 1152. Top right: Ex-Y.T.W.
0-4-0ST No. 1 Hercules. Bottom left: Ex-Car. R.0-4-0ST No. 1338.
Bottom right: Ex-S.H.T. 0-4-0ST No. 1143.
[P. Ransome-Wallis, C. H. S. Owen, R. H. G. Simpson, G. Oates

[G. Wheeler (2), R. C. Riley, A. Delicata.

Top left: 1101 Class 0-4-0T No. 1102. Top right: 1361 Class 0-6-0ST No. 1365. Bottom left: 1366 Class 0-6-0PT No. 1371. Bottom right: 1400 Class 0-4-2T No. 1409.

Top left: Ex-A.D. 0-6-0T No. 667. Top right: Ex-B.P.G.V. 0-6-0T No. 2198.
Bottom left: Ex-B.P.G.V. 0-6-0ST No. 2196 Gwendraeth. Bottom right:
Ex-B.P.G.V. 0-6-0T No. 2168. [A. Delicata (2), J. N. Westwood (2).

Top left: 850 Class 0-6-0PT No. 1935. Top right: Ex-Car. R. 0-6-0PT No. 683. Bottom left: Ex-A.D. 2-6-2T No. 1205. Bottom right: 2021 Class 0-6-0PT No. 2107.

[R. H. G. Simpson, P. C. Short, H. C. Casserley, B. E. Morrison]

Top left: 7400 Class 0-6-0PT No. 7406. Top right: 1600 Class 0-6-0PT No. 1636. Bottom right: 5700 Class 0-6-0PT No. 7782. Bottom left: 5700 Class 0-6-0PT No. 8759 (with later cab design).
[G. R. Wheeler, P. Ransome-Wallis, F. W. Day, C. R. L. Coles

Top left: Ex-T.V. " A " Class 0-6-2T No. 370. Top right: Ex-B. & M. 0-6-2T No. 436 (with ex-R.R. boiler). Bottom left: Ex-R.R.R. " RI " Class 0-6-2T No. 35. Bottom right: 5600 Class 0-6-2T No. 6697.

[F. J. Saunders (2), A. Delicata, B. E. Morrison

[B. E. Morrison

*Below left:* Diesel Railcar No. 14.
[T. Lakin

*Below right:* Diesel parcels Railcar No. 17.
[A. R. Carpenter

[G. Clarke

Above: 4073 Class 4-6-0s Nos. 5095 *Barbury Castle* and 5016 *Montgomery Castle*.

Below left: A self-weighing tender attached to 4073 Class 4-6-0 No. 5086 *Viscount Horne*. Below right: 1000 Class 4-6-0 No. 1021 *County of Montgomery*.

[H. C. Casserley, G. R. Wheeler

| | | | |
|---|---|---|---|
| 1408 | 1425 | 1442 | 1459 |
| 1409 | 1426 | 1443 | 1460 |
| 1410 | 1427 | 1444 | 1461 |
| 1411 | 1428 | 1445 | 1462 |
| 1412 | 1429 | 1446 | 1463 |
| 1413 | 1430 | 1447 | 1464 |
| 1414 | 1431 | 1448 | 1465 |
| 1415 | 1432 | 1449 | 1466 |
| 1416 | 1433 | 1450 | 1467 |
| 1417 | 1434 | 1451 | 1468 |
| 1418 | 1435 | 1452 | 1469 |
| 1419 | 1436 | 1453 | 1470 |
| 1420 | 1437 | 1454 | 1471 |
| 1421 | 1438 | 1455 | 1472 |
| 1422 | 1439 | 1456 | 1473 |
| 1423 | 1440 | 1457 | 1474 |
| 1424 | 1441 | 1458 | |

## 0-6-0PT 1500 Class

| | | | |
|---|---|---|---|
| 1500 | 1503 | 1506 | 1509 |
| 1501 | 1504 | 1507 | |
| 1502 | 1505 | 1508 | |

## 0-6-0PT 1600 Class

| | | | |
|---|---|---|---|
| 1600 | 1613 | 1626 | 1639 |
| 1601 | 1614 | 1627 | 1640 |
| 1602 | 1615 | 1628 | 1641 |
| 1603 | 1616 | 1629 | 1642 |
| 1604 | 1617 | 1630 | 1643 |
| 1605 | 1618 | 1631 | 1644 |
| 1606 | 1619 | 1632 | 1645 |
| 1607 | 1620 | 1633 | 1646 |
| 1608 | 1621 | 1634 | 1647 |
| 1609 | 1622 | 1635 | 1648 |
| 1610 | 1623 | 1636 | 1649 |
| 1611 | 1624 | 1637 | |
| 1612 | 1625 | 1638 | |

## 0-6-0PT 850 Class

| | | | |
|---|---|---|---|
| 1935 | 2008 | 2011 | 2012 |

## 0-6-0PT 2021 Class

| | | | |
|---|---|---|---|
| 2027 | 2060 | 2088 | 2112 |
| 2034 | 2061 | 2090 | 2134 |
| 2035 | 2069 | 2092 | 2136 |
| 2038 | 2070 | 2097 | 2138 |
| 2040 | 2072 | 2099 | 2144 |
| 2042 | 2081 | 2101 | 2160 |
| 2043 | 2082 | 2107 | |
| 2053 | 2085 | 2108 | |

## 0-6-0T BPGV Rly.

| | | | |
|---|---|---|---|
| 2162 | 2165 | 2166 | 2168 |

## 0-6-0ST BPGV Rly.

2176

## 0-6-0PT 2181 Class

| | | |
|---|---|---|
| 2182 | 2183 | 2186 |

## 0-6-0ST BPGV Rly.

2196 Gwendraeth

## 0-6-0T BPGV Rly.

2198

## 0-6-0 2251 Class

| | | | |
|---|---|---|---|
| 2200 | 2206 | 2212 | 2218 |
| 2201 | 2207 | 2213 | 2219 |
| 2202 | 2208 | 2214 | 2220 |
| 2203 | 2209 | 2215 | 2221 |
| 2204 | 2210 | 2216 | 2222 |
| 2205 | 2211 | 2217 | 2223 |

| | | | | | | | |
|---|---|---|---|---|---|---|---|
| 2224 | 2243 | 2262 | 2281 | 2844 | 2858 | 2872 | 2886 |
| 2225 | 2244 | 2263 | 2282 | 2845 | 2859 | 2873 | 2887 |
| 2226 | 2245 | 2264 | 2283 | 2846 | 2860 | 2874 | 2888 |
| 2227 | 2246 | 2265 | 2284 | 2847 | 2861 | 2875 | 2889 |
| 2228 | 2247 | 2266 | 2285 | 2848 | 2862 | 2876 | 2890 |
| 2229 | 2248 | 2267 | 2286 | 2849 | 2863 | 2877 | 2891 |
| 2230 | 2249 | 2268 | 2287 | 2850 | 2864 | 2878 | 2892 |
| 2231 | 2250 | 2269 | 2288 | 2851 | 2865 | 2879 | 2893 |
| 2232 | 2251 | 2270 | 2289 | 2852 | 2866 | 2880 | 2894 |
| 2233 | 2252 | 2271 | 2290 | 2853 | 2867 | 2881 | 2895 |
| 2234 | 2253 | 2272 | 2291 | 2854 | 2868 | 2882 | 2896 |
| 2235 | 2254 | 2273 | 2292 | 2855 | 2869 | 2883 | 2897 |
| 2236 | 2255 | 2274 | 2293 | 2856 | 2870 | 2884 | 2898 |
| 2237 | 2256 | 2275 | 2294 | 2857 | 2871 | 2885 | 2899 |
| 2238 | 2257 | 2276 | 2295 | | | | |
| 2239 | 2258 | 2277 | 2296 | | | | |
| 2240 | 2259 | 2278 | 2297 | | | | |
| 2241 | 2260 | 2279 | 2298 | | | | |
| 2242 | 2261 | 2280 | 2299 | | | | |

## 4-6-0      2900 Class

### " Saint "

2920 Saint David
2937 Clevedon Court
2945 Hillingdon Court

## 0-6-0      2301 Class

| | | | |
|---|---|---|---|
| 2323 | 2426 | 2516 | 2568 |
| 2327 | 2458 | 2532 | 2578 |
| 2340 | 2460 | 2538 | 2579 |
| 2354 | 2474 | 2541 | |
| 2409 | 2484 | 2551 | |
| 2411 | 2513 | 2556 | |

## 2-8-0      R.O.D. Clas

| | | | |
|---|---|---|---|
| 3010 | 3018 | 3028 | 3040 |
| 3011 | 3020 | 3029 | 3041 |
| 3012 | 3022 | 3031 | 3042 |
| 3014 | 3023 | 3032 | 3043 |
| 3015 | 3024 | 3033 | 3044 |
| 3016 | 3025 | 3036 | 3047 |
| 3017 | 3026 | 3038 | 3048 |

## 2-8-0      2800 Class

| | | | |
|---|---|---|---|
| 2800 | 2811 | 2822 | 2833 |
| 2801 | 2812 | 2823 | 2834 |
| 2802 | 2813 | 2824 | 2835 |
| 2803 | 2814 | 2825 | 2836 |
| 2804 | 2815 | 2826 | 2837 |
| 2805 | 2816 | 2827 | 2838 |
| 2806 | 2817 | 2828 | 2839 |
| 2807 | 2818 | 2829 | 2840 |
| 2808 | 2819 | 2830 | 2841 |
| 2809 | 2820 | 2831 | 2842 |
| 2810 | 2821 | 2832 | 2843 |

## 2-6-2T      3100 Clas

| | | | |
|---|---|---|---|
| 3100 | 3102 | 3103 | 3104 |
| 3101 | | | |

## 6-2T — 3150 Class

| | | | |
|---|---|---|---|
| 50 | 3170 | 3176 | 3185 |
| 60 | 3171 | 3177 | 3186 |
| 63 | 3172 | 3180 | 3187 |
| 64 | 3174 | 3183 | 3190 |

## 6-0 — 2251 Class

| | | | |
|---|---|---|---|
| 200 | 3205 | 3210 | 3215 |
| 201 | 3206 | 3211 | 3216 |
| 202 | 3207 | 3212 | 3217 |
| 203 | 3208 | 3213 | 3218 |
| 204 | 3209 | 3214 | 3219 |

## 6-0PT — 5700 Class

| | | | |
|---|---|---|---|
| 600 | 3628 | 3656 | 3684 |
| 601 | 3629 | 3657 | 3685 |
| 602 | 3630 | 3658 | 3686 |
| 603 | 3631 | 3659 | 3687 |
| 604 | 3632 | 3660 | 3688 |
| 605 | 3633 | 3661 | 3689 |
| 606 | 3634 | 3662 | 3690 |
| 607 | 3635 | 3663 | 3691 |
| 608 | 3636 | 3664 | 3692 |
| 609 | 3637 | 3665 | 3693 |
| 610 | 3638 | 3666 | 3694 |
| 611 | 3639 | 3667 | 3695 |
| 612 | 3640 | 3668 | 3696 |
| 613 | 3641 | 3669 | 3697 |
| 614 | 3642 | 3670 | 3698 |
| 615 | 3643 | 3671 | 3699 |
| 616 | 3644 | 3672 | 3700 |
| 617 | 3645 | 3673 | 3701 |
| 618 | 3646 | 3674 | 3702 |
| 619 | 3647 | 3675 | 3703 |
| 620 | 3648 | 3676 | 3704 |
| 621 | 3649 | 3677 | 3705 |
| 622 | 3650 | 3678 | 3706 |
| 623 | 3651 | 3679 | 3707 |
| 624 | 3652 | 3680 | 3708 |
| 625 | 3653 | 3681 | 3709 |
| 626 | 3654 | 3682 | 3710 |
| 627 | 3655 | 3683 | 3711 |

## 3150 Class (continued)

| | | | |
|---|---|---|---|
| 3712 | 3734 | 3756 | 3778 |
| 3713 | 3735 | 3757 | 3779 |
| 3714 | 3736 | 3758 | 3780 |
| 3715 | 3737 | 3759 | 3781 |
| 3716 | 3738 | 3760 | 3782 |
| 3717 | 3739 | 3761 | 3783 |
| 3718 | 3740 | 3762 | 3784 |
| 3719 | 3741 | 3763 | 3785 |
| 3720 | 3742 | 3764 | 3786 |
| 3721 | 3743 | 3765 | 3787 |
| 3722 | 3744 | 3766 | 3788 |
| 3723 | 3745 | 3767 | 3789 |
| 3724 | 3746 | 3768 | 3790 |
| 3725 | 3747 | 3769 | 3791 |
| 3726 | 3748 | 3770 | 3792 |
| 3727 | 3749 | 3771 | 3793 |
| 3728 | 3750 | 3772 | 3794 |
| 3729 | 3751 | 3773 | 3795 |
| 3730 | 3752 | 3774 | 3796 |
| 3731 | 3753 | 3775 | 3797 |
| 3732 | 3754 | 3776 | 3798 |
| 3733 | 3755 | 3777 | 3799 |

## 2-8-0 — 2800 Class

| | | | |
|---|---|---|---|
| 3800 | 3817 | 3834 | 3851 |
| 3801 | 3818 | 3835 | 3852 |
| 3802 | 3819 | 3836 | 3853 |
| 3803 | 3820 | 3837 | 3854 |
| 3804 | 3821 | 3838 | 3855 |
| 3805 | 3822 | 3839 | 3856 |
| 3806 | 3823 | 3840 | 3857 |
| 3807 | 3824 | 3841 | 3858 |
| 3808 | 3825 | 3842 | 3859 |
| 3809 | 3826 | 3843 | 3860 |
| 3810 | 3827 | 3844 | 3861 |
| 3811 | 3828 | 3845 | 3862 |
| 3812 | 3829 | 3846 | 3863 |
| 3813 | 3830 | 3847 | 3864 |
| 3814 | 3831 | 3848 | 3865 |
| 3815 | 3832 | 3849 | 3866 |
| 3816 | 3833 | 3850 | |

## 4-6-0  4073 Class

### " Castle "

4000 North Star
4037 The South Wales Borderers

## 4-6-0  4000 Class

### " Star "

4049 Princess Maud
4052 Princess Beatrice
4053 Princess Alexandra
4056 Princess Margaret
4061 Glastonbury Abbey
4062 Malmesbury Abbey

## 4-6-0  4073 Class

### " Castle "

4073 Caerphilly Castle
4074 Caldicot Castle
4075 Cardiff Castle
4076 Carmarthen Castle
4077 Chepstow Castle
4078 Pembroke Castle
4079 Pendennis Castle
4080 Powderham Castle
4081 Warwick Castle
4082 Windsor Castle
4083 Abbotsbury Castle
4084 Aberystwyth Castle
4085 Berkeley Castle
4086 Builth Castle
4087 Cardigan Castle
4088 Dartmouth Castle
4089 Donnington Castle
4090 Dorchester Castle
4091 Dudley Castle

4092 Dunraven Castle
4093 Dunster Castle
4094 Dynevor Castle
4095 Harlech Castle
4096 Highclere Castle
4097 Kenilworth Castle
4098 Kidwelly Castle
4099 Kilgerran Castle

## 2-6-2T  5100 Class

| | | | |
|------|------|------|------|
| 4100 | 4114 | 4128 | 4142 |
| 4101 | 4115 | 4129 | 4143 |
| 4102 | 4116 | 4130 | 4144 |
| 4103 | 4117 | 4131 | 4145 |
| 4104 | 4118 | 4132 | 4146 |
| 4105 | 4119 | 4133 | 4147 |
| 4106 | 4120 | 4134 | 4148 |
| 4107 | 4121 | 4135 | 4149 |
| 4108 | 4122 | 4136 | 4150 |
| 4109 | 4123 | 4137 | 4151 |
| 4110 | 4124 | 4138 | 4152 |
| 4111 | 4125 | 4139 | 4153 |
| 4112 | 4126 | 4140 | 4154 |
| 4113 | 4127 | 4141 | 4155 |

*For full details of*

GAS TURBINE & DIESEL LOCOS
*running on the Western Region*
**see the**

A.B.C. OF B.R. LOCOMOTIVES
PT. II Nos. 10000-39999

*For full details of*

B. R. STANDARD LOCOMOTIVE
and CLASS " WD " 2-8-0s
*running on the Western Region*
**see the**

A.B.C. OF B.R. LOCOMOTIVE
PT. IV. Nos. 60000-99999

| 156 | 4162 | 4168 | 4174 |
| 157 | 4163 | 4169 | 4175 |
| 158 | 4164 | 4170 | 4176 |
| 159 | 4165 | 4171 | 4177 |
| 160 | 4166 | 4172 | 4178 |
| 161 | 4167 | 4173 | 4179 |

## -8-0T     4200 Class

| 200 | 4230 | 4258 | 4280 |
| 201 | 4231 | 4259 | 4281 |
| 203 | 4232 | 4260 | 4282 |
| 206 | 4233 | 4261 | 4283 |
| 207 | 4235 | 4262 | 4284 |
| 208 | 4236 | 4263 | 4285 |
| 211 | 4237 | 4264 | 4286 |
| 212 | 4238 | 4265 | 4287 |
| 213 | 4241 | 4266 | 4288 |
| 214 | 4242 | 4267 | 4289 |
| 215 | 4243 | 4268 | 4290 |
| 217 | 4246 | 4269 | 4291 |
| 218 | 4247 | 4270 | 4292 |
| 221 | 4248 | 4271 | 4293 |
| 222 | 4250 | 4272 | 4294 |
| 223 | 4251 | 4273 | 4295 |
| 224 | 4252 | 4274 | 4296 |
| 225 | 4253 | 4275 | 4297 |
| 226 | 4254 | 4276 | 4298 |
| 227 | 4255 | 4277 | 4299 |
| 228 | 4256 | 4278 |  |
| 229 | 4257 | 4279 |  |

## -6-0     4300 Class

| 326 | 4375 | 4377 | 4381 |
| 358 |  |  |  |

## -6-2T     4400 Class

| 401 | 4405 | 4406 | 4410 |

## -6-2T     4500 Class

| 500 | 4507 | 4515 | 4522 |
| 505 | 4508 | 4519 | 4523 |
| 506 | 4511 | 4521 | 4524 |

| 4525 | 4549 | 4567 | 4585 |
| 4526 | 4550 | 4568 | 4586 |
| 4530 | 4551 | 4569 | 4587 |
| 4532 | 4552 | 4570 | 4588 |
| 4533 | 4553 | 4571 | 4589 |
| 4534 | 4554 | 4572 | 4590 |
| 4535 | 4555 | 4573 | 4591 |
| 4536 | 4556 | 4574 | 4592 |
| 4537 | 4557 | 4575 | 4593 |
| 4538 | 4558 | 4576 | 4594 |
| 4539 | 4559 | 4577 | 4595 |
| 4540 | 4560 | 4578 | 4596 |
| 4541 | 4561 | 4579 | 4597 |
| 4542 | 4562 | 4580 | 4598 |
| 4545 | 4563 | 4581 | 4599 |
| 4546 | 4564 | 4582 |  |
| 4547 | 4565 | 4583 |  |
| 4548 | 4566 | 4584 |  |

## 0-6-0PT     5700 Class

| 4600 | 4623 | 4646 | 4669 |
| 4601 | 4624 | 4647 | 4670 |
| 4602 | 4625 | 4648 | 4671 |
| 4603 | 4626 | 4649 | 4672 |
| 4604 | 4627 | 4650 | 4673 |
| 4605 | 4628 | 4651 | 4674 |
| 4606 | 4629 | 4652 | 4675 |
| 4607 | 4630 | 4653 | 4676 |
| 4608 | 4631 | 4654 | 4677 |
| 4609 | 4632 | 4655 | 4678 |
| 4610 | 4633 | 4656 | 4679 |
| 4611 | 4634 | 4657 | 4680 |
| 4612 | 4635 | 4658 | 4681 |
| 4613 | 4636 | 4659 | 4682 |
| 4614 | 4637 | 4660 | 4683 |
| 4615 | 4638 | 4661 | 4684 |
| 4616 | 4639 | 4662 | 4685 |
| 4617 | 4640 | 4663 | 4686 |
| 4618 | 4641 | 4664 | 4687 |
| 4619 | 4642 | 4665 | 4688 |
| 4620 | 4643 | 4666 | 4689 |
| 4621 | 4644 | 4667 | 4690 |
| 4622 | 4645 | 4668 | 4691 |

| 4692 | 4694 | 4696 | 4698 |
|------|------|------|------|
| 4693 | 4695 | 4697 | 4699 |

## 2-8-0      4700 Class

| 4700 | 4703 | 4705 | 4707 |
|------|------|------|------|
| 4701 | 4704 | 4706 | 4708 |
| 4702 |      |      |      |

## 4-6-0 "Hall" 4900 Classs

4900 Saint Martin
4901 Adderley Hall
4902 Aldenham Hall
4903 Astley Hall
4904 Binnegar Hall
4905 Barton Hall
4906 Bradfield Hall
4907 Broughton Hall
4908 Broome Hall
4909 Blakesley Hall
4910 Blaisdon Hall
4912 Berrington Hall
4913 Baglan Hall
4914 Cranmore Hall
4915 Condover Hall
4916 Crumlin Hall
4917 Crosswood Hall
4918 Dartington Hall
4919 Donnington Hall
4920 Dumbleton Hall
4921 Eaton Hall
4922 Enville Hall
4923 Evenley Hall
4924 Eydon Hall
4925 Eynsham Hall
4926 Fairleigh Hall
4927 Farnborough Hall
4928 Gatacre Hall
4929 Goytrey Hall
4930 Hagley Hall
4931 Hanbury Hall
4932 Hatherton Hall
4933 Himley Hall
4934 Hindlip Hall
4935 Ketley Hall
4936 Kinlet Hall
4937 Lanelay Hall
4938 Liddington Hall
4939 Littleton Hall
4940 Ludford Hall
4941 Llangedwyn Hall
4942 Maindy Hall
4943 Marrington Hall
4944 Middleton Hall
4945 Milligan Hall
4946 Moseley Hall
4947 Nanhoran Hall
4948 Northwick Hall
4949 Packwood Hall
4950 Patshull Hall
4951 Pendeford Hall
4952 Peplow Hall
4953 Pitchford Hall
4954 Plaish Hall
4955 Plaspower Hall
4956 Plowden Hall
4957 Postlip Hall
4958 Priory Hall
4959 Purley Hall
4960 Pyle Hall
4961 Pyrland Hall
4962 Ragley Hall
4963 Rignall Hall
4964 Rodwell Hall
4965 Rood Ashton Hall,
4966 Shakenhurst Hall
4967 Shirenewton Hall
4968 Shotton Hall
4969 Shrugborough Hall
4970 Sketty Hall
4971 Stanway Hall
4972 Saint Brides Hall
4973 Sweeney Hall
4974 Talgarth Hall
4975 Umberslade Hall
4976 Warfield Hall
4977 Watcombe Hall
4978 Westwood Hall
4979 Wootton Hall
4980 Wrottesley Hall
4981 Abberley Hall
4982 Acton Hall
4983 Albert Hall
4984 Albrighton Hall

| | |
|---|---|
| 4985 Allesley Hall | 5027 Farleigh Castle |
| 4986 Aston Hall | 5028 Llantilio Castle |
| 4987 Brockley Hall | 5029 Nunney Castle |
| 4988 Bulwell Hall | 5030 Shirburn Castle |
| 4989 Cherwell Hall | 5031 Totnes Castle |
| 4990 Clifton Hall | 5032 Usk Castle |
| 4991 Cobham Hall | 5033 Broughton Castle |
| 4992 Crosby Hall | 5034 Corfe Castle |
| 4993 Dalton Hall | 5035 Coity Castle |
| 4994 Downton Hall | 5036 Lyonshall Castle |
| 4995 Easton Hall | 5037 Monmouth Castle |
| 4996 Eden Hall | 5038 Morlais Castle |
| 4997 Elton Hall | 5039 Rhuddlan Castle |
| 4998 Eyton Hall | 5040 Stokesay Castle |
| 4999 Gopsal Hall | 5041 Tiverton Castle |
| | 5042 Winchester Castle |
| | 5043 Earl of Mount Edgcumbe |
| | 5044 Earl of Dunraven |
| **4-6-0 "Castle" 4073 Class** | 5045 Earl of Dudley |
| | 5046 Earl Cawdor |
| 5000 Launceston Castle | 5047 Earl of Dartmouth |
| 5001 Llandovery Castle | 5048 Earl of Devon |
| 5002 Ludlow Castle | 5049 Earl of Plymouth |
| 5003 Lulworth Castle | 5050 Earl of St. Germans |
| 5004 Llanstephan Castle | 5051 Earl Bathurst |
| 5005 Manorbier Castle | 5052 Earl of Radnor |
| 5006 Tregenna Castle | 5053 Earl Cairns |
| 5007 Rougemont Castle | 5054 Earl of Ducie |
| 5008 Raglan Castle | 5055 Earl of Eldon |
| 5009 Shrewsbury Castle | 5056 Earl of Powis |
| 5010 Restormel Castle | 5057 Earl Waldegrave |
| 5011 Tintagel Castle | 5058 Earl of Clancarty |
| 5012 Berry Pomeroy Castle | 5059 Earl St. Aldwyn |
| 5013 Abergavenny Castle | 5060 Earl of Berkeley |
| 5014 Goodrich Castle | 5061 Earl of Birkenhead |
| 5015 Kingswear Castle | 5062 Earl of Shaftesbury |
| 5016 Montgomery Castle | 5063 Earl Baldwin |
| 5017 St. Donats Castle | 5064 Bishop's Castle |
| 5018 St. Mawes Castle | 5065 Newport Castle |
| 5019 Treago Castle | 5066 Wardour Castle |
| 5020 Trematon Castle | 5067 St. Fagans Castle |
| 5021 Whittington Castle | 5068 Beverston Castle |
| 5022 Wigmore Castle | 5069 Isambard Kingdom Brunel |
| 5023 Brecon Castle | 5070 Sir Daniel Gooch |
| 5024 Carew Castle | 5071 Spitfire |
| 5025 Chirk Castle | 5072 Hurricane |
| 5026 Criccieth Castle | 5073 Blenheim |

**5074-5399**

5074 Hampden
5075 Wellington
5076 Gladiator
5077 Fairey Battle
5078 Beaufort
5079 Lysander
5080 Defiant
5081 Lockheed Hudson
5082 Swordfish
5083 Bath Abbey
5084 Reading Abbey
5085 Evesham Abbey
5086 Viscount Horne
5087 Tintern Abbey
5088 Llanthony Abbey
5089 Westminster Abbey
5090 Neath Abbey
5091 Cleeve Abbey
5092 Tresco Abbey
5093 Upton Castle
5094 Tretower Castle
5095 Barbury Castle
5096 Bridgwater Castle
5097 Sarum Castle
5098 Clifford Castle
5099 Compton Castle

| 2-8-0T | | | 4200 Cla |
|---|---|---|---|
| 5200 | 5217 | 5234 | 525| |
| 5201 | 5218 | 5235 | 5252 |
| 5202 | 5219 | 5236 | 5253 |
| 5203 | 5220 | 5237 | 5254 |
| 5204 | 5221 | 5238 | 5255 |
| 5205 | 5222 | 5239 | 5256 |
| 5206 | 5223 | 5240 | 5257 |
| 5207 | 5224 | 5241 | 5258 |
| 5208 | 5225 | 5242 | 5259 |
| 5209 | 5226 | 5243 | 5260 |
| 5210 | 5227 | 5244 | 526| |
| 5211 | 5228 | 5245 | 5262 |
| 5212 | 5229 | 5246 | 5263 |
| 5213 | 5230 | 5247 | 5264 |
| 5214 | 5231 | 5248 | |
| 5215 | 5232 | 5249 | |
| 5216 | 5233 | 5250 | |

| 2-6-0 | | | 4300 Cla |
|---|---|---|---|
| 5306 | 5327 | 5353 | 5379 |
| 5307 | 5328 | 5355 | 5380 |
| 5310 | 5330 | 5356 | 5381 |
| 5311 | 5331 | 5357 | 5382 |
| 5312 | 5332 | 5358 | 5384 |
| 5313 | 5333 | 5360 | 5385 |
| 5314 | 5334 | 5361 | 5386 |
| 5315 | 5335 | 5362 | 5388 |
| 5316 | 5336 | 5367 | 5390 |
| 5317 | 5337 | 5368 | 5391 |
| 5318 | 5338 | 5369 | 5392 |
| 5319 | 5339 | 5370 | 5393 |
| 5321 | 5341 | 5371 | 5394 |
| 5322 | 5344 | 5372 | 5395 |
| 5323 | 5345 | 5375 | 5396 |
| 5324 | 5347 | 5376 | 5397 |
| 5325 | 5350 | 5377 | 5398 |
| 5326 | 5351 | 5378 | 5399 |

| 2-6-2T | | | 5100 Class |
|---|---|---|---|
| 5101 | 5152 | 5168 | 5184 |
| 5102 | 5153 | 5169 | 5185 |
| 5103 | 5154 | 5170 | 5186 |
| 5104 | 5155 | 5171 | 5187 |
| 5105 | 5156 | 5172 | 5188 |
| 5106 | 5157 | 5173 | 5189 |
| 5107 | 5158 | 5174 | 5190 |
| 5108 | 5159 | 5175 | 5191 |
| 5109 | 5160 | 5176 | 5192 |
| 5110 | 5161 | 5177 | 5193 |
| 5112 | 5162 | 5178 | 5194 |
| 5113 | 5163 | 5179 | 5195 |
| 5140 | 5164 | 5180 | 5196 |
| 5148 | 5165 | 5181 | 5197 |
| 5150 | 5166 | 5182 | 5198 |
| 5151 | 5167 | 5183 | 5199 |

32

*Above:* 4000 Class 4-6-0 No. 4061 *Glastonbury Abbey.*

[R. H. G. Simpson

*Centre:* 6000 Class 4-6-0 No. 6000 *King George V.*

[G. R. Wheeler

*Below:* 2900 Class 4-6-0 No. 2920 *Saint David.*

[E. D. Bruton

4900 Class 4-6-0 No. 5985 *Mostyn Hall*.  [P. M. Alexander

6959 Class 4-6-0 No. 7914 *Lleweni Hall*.  [R. H. G. Sim

4300 Class 2-6-0 No. 5380.  [R. H. G. Sim

Class 4-6-0 No. 6854 *Roundhill Grange.*　　　　　　　　[E. W. Field

Class 4-6-0 No. 7804 *Baydon Manor*　　　　　　　　[F. W. Day

Class 2-6-0 No. 9304 (with side window cab).　　　　　　　　[C. G. Pearson

Top left: ROD Class 2-8-0 No. 3020. Top right: 4700 Class 2-8-0 No. 4702. Bottom left: 2800 Class 2-8-0 No. 2825. Bottom right: 2800 Class 2-8-0 No. 3833 (with side window cab). [G. R. Wheeler, S. Creer, C. H. S. Owen, P. Ransome-Wallis

Top left: Ex-Cam. R. 0-6-0 No. 855.    Top right: 9000 Class 4-4-0 No. 9013.
Bottom left:  2301 Class 0-6-0 No. 2538.   Bottom right:  2251 Class  0-6-0
No. 3208.          [F. W. Day, R. H. G. Simpson, P. Ransome-Wallis (2)

Top left: 1500 Class 0-6-0T No. 1502. Top right: 9400 Class
0-6-0T No. 8460. Bottom left: 8100 Class 2-6-2T No. 8109. Bottom
right: 3100 Class 2-6-2T No. 3100.
[Dr. G. D. Parkes, R. J. Buckley, T. E. Williams, P. Ransome-Wallis

Top left: 5101 Class 2-6-2T No. 5158. Top right: 4400 Class 2-6-2T No. 4406. Bottom left: 4575 Class 2-6-2T No. 4581. Bottom right: 4500 Class 2-6-2T No. 4530. [D. M. Rouse, A. Delicata, L. Elsey, R. S. Potts

## 6-0PT    5400 Class

| | | | |
|---|---|---|---|
| 00 | 5407 | 5414 | 5421 |
| 01 | 5408 | 5415 | 5422 |
| 02 | 5409 | 5416 | 5423 |
| 03 | 5410 | 5417 | 5424 |
| 04 | 5411 | 5418 | |
| 05 | 5412 | 5419 | |
| 06 | 5413 | 5420 | |

## 6-2T    4500 Class

| | | | |
|---|---|---|---|
| 00 | 5519 | 5538 | 5557 |
| 01 | 5520 | 5539 | 5558 |
| 02 | 5521 | 5540 | 5559 |
| 03 | 5522 | 5541 | 5560 |
| 04 | 5523 | 5542 | 5561 |
| 05 | 5524 | 5543 | 5562 |
| 06 | 5525 | 5544 | 5563 |
| 07 | 5526 | 5545 | 5564 |
| 08 | 5527 | 5546 | 5565 |
| 09 | 5528 | 5547 | 5566 |
| 10 | 5529 | 5548 | 5567 |
| 11 | 5530 | 5549 | 5568 |
| 12 | 5531 | 5550 | 5569 |
| 13 | 5532 | 5551 | 5570 |
| 14 | 5533 | 5552 | 5571 |
| 15 | 5534 | 5553 | 5572 |
| 16 | 5535 | 5554 | 5573 |
| 17 | 5536 | 5555 | 5574 |
| 18 | 5537 | 5556 | |

## 6-2T    5600 Class

| | | | |
|---|---|---|---|
| 00 | 5602 | 5604 | 5606 |
| 01 | 5603 | 5605 | 5607 |
| 5608 | 5631 | 5654 | 5677 |
| 5609 | 5632 | 5655 | 5678 |
| 5610 | 5633 | 5656 | 5679 |
| 5611 | 5634 | 5657 | 5680 |
| 5612 | 5635 | 5658 | 5681 |
| 5613 | 5636 | 5659 | 5682 |
| 5614 | 5637 | 5660 | 5683 |
| 5615 | 5638 | 5661 | 5684 |
| 5616 | 5639 | 5662 | 5685 |
| 5617 | 5640 | 5663 | 5686 |
| 5618 | 5641 | 5664 | 5687 |
| 5619 | 5642 | 5665 | 5688 |
| 5620 | 5643 | 5666 | 5689 |
| 5621 | 5644 | 5667 | 5690 |
| 5622 | 5645 | 5668 | 5691 |
| 5623 | 5646 | 5669 | 5692 |
| 5624 | 5647 | 5670 | 5693 |
| 5625 | 5648 | 5671 | 5694 |
| 5626 | 5649 | 5672 | 5695 |
| 5627 | 5650 | 5673 | 5696 |
| 5628 | 5651 | 5674 | 5697 |
| 5629 | 5652 | 5675 | 5698 |
| 5630 | 5653 | 5676 | 5699 |

## 0-6-0PT    5700 Class

| | | | |
|---|---|---|---|
| 5700 | 5721 | 5742 | 5763 |
| 5701 | 5722 | 5743 | 5764 |
| 5702 | 5723 | 5744 | 5765 |
| 5703 | 5724 | 5745 | 5766 |
| 5704 | 5725 | 5746 | 5767 |
| 5705 | 5726 | 5747 | 5768 |
| 5706 | 5727 | 5748 | 5769 |
| 5707 | 5728 | 5749 | 5770 |
| 5708 | 5729 | 5750 | 5771 |
| 5709 | 5730 | 5751 | 5772 |
| 5710 | 5731 | 5752 | 5773 |
| 5711 | 5732 | 5753 | 5774 |
| 5712 | 5733 | 5754 | 5775 |
| 5713 | 5734 | 5755 | 5776 |
| 5714 | 5735 | 5756 | 5777 |
| 5715 | 5736 | 5757 | 5778 |
| 5716 | 5737 | 5758 | 5779 |
| 5717 | 5738 | 5759 | 5780 |
| 5718 | 5739 | 5760 | 5781 |
| 5719 | 5740 | 5761 | 5782 |
| 5720 | 5741 | 5762 | 5783 |

**FACING PAGE**

Top to Bottom: "4200" Class 2-8-0 No. 4283; "5205" Class 2-8-0T No. 5223; "5205" Class 2-8-0T No. 5260 Nos.5255-64 only were built with raised running plate over cylinders); 7200 Class 2-8-2T No. 7228. [R.H.G. Simpson ?), P.C. Short, A. Delicata.

41

| 5784 | 5788 | 5792 | 5796 |
|------|------|------|------|
| 5785 | 5789 | 5793 | 5797 |
| 5786 | 5790 | 5794 | 5798 |
| 5787 | 5791 | 5795 | 5799 |

## 0-4-2T     1400 Class

| 5800 | 5805 | 5810 | 5815 |
|------|------|------|------|
| 5801 | 5806 | 5811 | 5816 |
| 5802 | 5807 | 5812 | 5817 |
| 5803 | 5808 | 5813 | 5818 |
| 5804 | 5809 | 5814 | 5819 |

## 4-6-0     4900 Class
### " Hall "

5900 Hinderton Hall
5901 Hazel Hall
5902 Howick Hall
5903 Keele Hall
5904 Kelham Hall
5905 Knowsley Hall
5906 Lawton Hall
5907 Marble Hall
5908 Moreton Hall
5909 Newton Hall
5910 Park Hall
5911 Preston Hall
5912 Queen's Hall
5913 Rushton Hall
5914 Ripon Hall
5915 Trentham Hall
5916 Trinity Hall
5917 Westminster Hall
5918 Walton Hall
5919 Worsley Hall
5920 Wycliffe Hall
5921 Bingley Hall
5922 Caxton Hall
5923 Colston Hall
5924 Dinton Hall
5925 Eastcote Hall
5926 Grotrian Hall
5927 Guild Hall
5928 Haddon Hall
5929 Hanham Hall
5930 Hannington Hall
5931 Hatherley Hall

5932 Haydon Hall
5933 Kingsway Hall
5934 Kneller Hall
5935 Norton Hall
5936 Oakley Hall
5937 Stanford Hall
5938 Stanley Hall
5939 Tangley Hall
5940 Whitbourne Hall
5941 Campion Hall
5942 Doldowlod Hall
5943 Elmdon Hall
5944 Ickenham Hall
5945 Leckhampton Hall
5946 Marwell Hall
5947 Saint Benet's Hall
5948 Siddington Hall
5949 Trematon Hall
5950 Wardley Hall
5951 Clyffe Hall
5952 Cogan Hall
5953 Dunley Hall
5954 Faendre Hall
5955 Garth Hall
5956 Horsley Hall
5957 Hutton Hall
5958 Knolton Hall
5959 Mawley Hall
5960 Saint Edmund Hall
5961 Toynbee Hall
5962 Wantage Hall
5963 Wimpole Hall
5964 Wolseley Hall
5965 Woollas Hall
5966 Ashford Hall
5967 Bickmarsh Hall
5968 Cory Hall
5969 Honington Hall
5970 Hengrave Hall
5971 Merevale Hall
5972 Olton Hall
5973 Rolleston Hall
5974 Wallsworth Hall
5975 Winslow Hall
5976 Ashwicke Hall
5977 Beckford Hall
5978 Bodinnick Hall

79 Cruckton Hall
80 Dingley Hall
81 Frensham Hall
82 Harrington Hall
83 Henley Hall
84 Linden Hall
85 Mostyn Hall
86 Arbury Hall
87 Brocket Hall
88 Bostock Hall
89 Cransley Hall
90 Dorford Hall
91 Gresham Hall
92 Horton Hall
93 Kirby Hall
94 Roydon Hall
95 Wick Hall
96 Mytton Hall
97 Sparkford Hall
98 Trevor Hall
99 Wollaton Hall

## 6-0 6000 Class "King"

00 King George V
01 King Edward VII
02 King William IV
03 King George IV
04 King George III
05 King George II
06 King George I
07 King William III
08 King James II
09 King Charles II
10 King Charles I
11 King James I
12 King Edward VI
13 King Henry VIII
14 King Henry VII
15 King Richard III
16 King Edward V
17 King Edward IV
18 King Henry VI
19 King Henry V
20 King Henry IV
6021 King Richard II
6022 King Edward III
6023 King Edward II
6024 King Edward I
6025 King Henry III
6026 King John
6027 King Richard I
6028 King George VI
6029 King Edward VIII

## 2-6-2T 6100 Class

| | | | |
|---|---|---|---|
| 6100 | 6118 | 6136 | 6153 |
| 6101 | 6119 | 6137 | 6154 |
| 6102 | 6120 | 6138 | 6155 |
| 6103 | 6121 | 6139 | 6156 |
| 6104 | 6122 | 6140 | 6157 |
| 6105 | 6123 | 6141 | 6158 |
| 6106 | 6124 | 6142 | 6159 |
| 6107 | 6125 | 6143 | 6160 |
| 6108 | 6126 | 6144 | 6161 |
| 6109 | 6127 | 6145 | 6162 |
| 6110 | 6128 | 6146 | 6163 |
| 6111 | 6129 | 6147 | 6164 |
| 6112 | 6130 | 6148 | 6165 |
| 6113 | 6131 | 6149 | 6166 |
| 6114 | 6132 | 6150 | 6167 |
| 6115 | 6133 | 6151 | 6168 |
| 6116 | 6134 | 6152 | 6169 |
| 6117 | 6135 | | |

## 2-6-0 4300 Class

| | | | |
|---|---|---|---|
| 6300 | 6313 | 6327 | 6340 |
| 6301 | 6314 | 6328 | 6341 |
| 6302 | 6316 | 6329 | 6342 |
| 6303 | 6317 | 6330 | 6343 |
| 6304 | 6318 | 6331 | 6344 |
| 6305 | 6319 | 6332 | 6345 |
| 6306 | 6320 | 6333 | 6346 |
| 6307 | 6321 | 6334 | 6347 |
| 6308 | 6322 | 6335 | 6348 |
| 6309 | 6323 | 6336 | 6349 |
| 6310 | 6324 | 6337 | 6350 |
| 6311 | 6325 | 6338 | 6351 |
| 6312 | 6326 | 6339 | 6352 |

| 6353 | 6365 | 6377 | 6389 |
| 6354 | 6366 | 6378 | 6390 |
| 6355 | 6367 | 6379 | 6391 |
| 6356 | 6368 | 6380 | 6392 |
| 6357 | 6369 | 6381 | 6393 |
| 6358 | 6370 | 6382 | 6394 |
| 6359 | 6371 | 6383 | 6395 |
| 6360 | 6372 | 6384 | 6396 |
| 6361 | 6373 | 6385 | 6397 |
| 6362 | 6374 | 6386 | 6398 |
| 6363 | 6375 | 6387 | 6399 |
| 6364 | 6376 | 6388 | |

## 0-6-0PT      6400 Class

| 6400 | 6410 | 6420 | 6430 |
| 6401 | 6411 | 6421 | 6431 |
| 6402 | 6412 | 6422 | 6432 |
| 6403 | 6413 | 6423 | 6433 |
| 6404 | 6414 | 6424 | 6434 |
| 6405 | 6415 | 6425 | 6435 |
| 6406 | 6416 | 6426 | 6436 |
| 6407 | 6417 | 6427 | 6437 |
| 6408 | 6418 | 6428 | 6438 |
| 6409 | 6419 | 6429 | 6439 |

## 0-6-2T      5600 Class

| 6600 | 6620 | 6640 | 6660 |
| 6601 | 6621 | 6641 | 6661 |
| 6602 | 6622 | 6642 | 6662 |
| 6603 | 6623 | 6643 | 6663 |
| 6604 | 6624 | 6644 | 6664 |
| 6605 | 6625 | 6645 | 6665 |
| 6606 | 6626 | 6646 | 6666 |
| 6607 | 6627 | 6647 | 6667 |
| 6608 | 6628 | 6648 | 6668 |
| 6609 | 6629 | 6649 | 6669 |
| 6610 | 6630 | 6650 | 6670 |
| 6611 | 6631 | 6651 | 6671 |
| 6612 | 6632 | 6652 | 6672 |
| 6613 | 6633 | 6653 | 6673 |
| 6614 | 6634 | 6654 | 6674 |
| 6615 | 6635 | 6655 | 6675 |
| 6616 | 6636 | 6656 | 6676 |
| 6617 | 6637 | 6657 | 6677 |
| 6618 | 6638 | 6658 | 6678 |
| 6619 | 6639 | 6659 | 6679 |

| 6680 | 6685 | 6690 | 6695 |
| 6681 | 6686 | 6691 | 6696 |
| 6682 | 6687 | 6692 | 6697 |
| 6683 | 6688 | 6693 | 6698 |
| 6684 | 6689 | 6694 | 6699 |

## 0-6-0PT      5700 Class

| 6700 | 6720 | 6740 | 6760 |
| 6701 | 6721 | 6741 | 6761 |
| 6702 | 6722 | 6742 | 6762 |
| 6703 | 6723 | 6743 | 6763 |
| 6704 | 6724 | 6744 | 6764 |
| 6705 | 6725 | 6745 | 6765 |
| 6706 | 6726 | 6746 | 6766 |
| 6707 | 6727 | 6747 | 6767 |
| 6708 | 6728 | 6748 | 6768 |
| 6709 | 6729 | 6749 | 6769 |
| 6710 | 6730 | 6750 | 6770 |
| 6711 | 6731 | 6751 | 6771 |
| 6712 | 6732 | 6752 | 6772 |
| 6713 | 6733 | 6753 | 6773 |
| 6714 | 6734 | 6754 | 6774 |
| 6715 | 6735 | 6755 | 6775 |
| 6716 | 6736 | 6756 | 6776 |
| 6717 | 6737 | 6757 | 6777 |
| 6718 | 6738 | 6758 | 6778 |
| 6719 | 6739 | 6759 | 6779 |

## 4-6-0      6800 Class
### "Grange"

6800 Arlington Grange
6801 Aylburton Grange
6802 Bampton Grange
6803 Bucklebury Grange
6804 Brockington Grange
6805 Broughton Grange
6806 Blackwell Grange
6807 Birchwood Grange
6808 Beenham Grange
6809 Burghclere Grange
6810 Blakemere Grange
6811 Cranbourne Grange
6812 Chesford Grange
6813 Eastbury Grange
6814 Enborne Grange

815 Frilford Grange
816 Frankton Grange
817 Gwenddwr Grange
818 Hardwick Grange
819 Highnam Grange
820 Kingstone Grange
821 Leaton Grange
822 Manton Grange
823 Oakley Grange
824 Ashley Grange
825 Llanvair Grange
826 Nannerth Grange
827 Llanfrechfa Grange
828 Trellech Grange
829 Burmington Grange
830 Buckenhill Grange
831 Bearley Grange
832 Brockton Grange
833 Calcot Grange
834 Dummer Grange
835 Eastham Grange
836 Estevarney Grange
837 Forthampton Grange
838 Goodmoor Grange
839 Hewell Grange
840 Hazeley Grange
841 Marlas Grange
842 Nunhold Grange
843 Poulton Grange
844 Penhydd Grange
845 Paviland Grange
846 Ruckley Grange
847 Tidmarsh Grange
848 Toddington Grange
849 Walton Grange
850 Cleeve Grange
851 Hurst Grange
852 Headbourne Grange
853 Morehampton Grange
854 Roundhill Grange
855 Saighton Grange
856 Stowe Grange
857 Tudor Grange
858 Woolston Grange
859 Yiewsley Grange
860 Aberporth Grange

6861 Crynant Grange
6862 Derwent Grange
6863 Dolhywel Grange
6864 Dymock Grange
6865 Hopton Grange
6866 Morfa Grange
6867 Peterston Grange
6868 Penrhos Grange
6869 Resolven Grange
6870 Bodicote Grange
6871 Bourton Grange
6872 Crawley Grange
6873 Caradoc Grange
6874 Haughton Grange
6875 Hindford Grange
6876 Kingsland Grange
6877 Llanfair Grange
6878 Longford Grange
6879 Overton Grange

## 4-6-0        4900 Class
### " Hall "

6900 Abney Hall
6901 Arley Hall
6902 Butlers Hall
6903 Belmont Hall
6904 Charfield Hall
6905 Claughton Hall
6906 Chicheley Hall
6907 Davenham Hall
6908 Downham Hall
6909 Frewin Hall
6910 Gossington Hall
6911 Holker Hall
6912 Helmster Hall
6913 Levens Hall
6914 Langton Hall
6915 Mursley Hall
6916 Misterton Hall
6917 Oldlands Hall
6918 Sandon Hall
6919 Tylney Hall
6920 Barningham Hall
6921 Borwick Hall
6922 Burton Hall
6923 Croxteth Hall

| | |
|---|---|
| 6924 Grantley Hall | 6967 Willesley Hall |
| 6925 Hackness Hall | 6968 Woodcock Hall |
| 6926 Holkham Hall | 6969 Wraysbury Hall |
| 6927 Lilford Hall | 6970 Whaddon Hall |
| 6928 Underley Hall | 6971 Athelhampton Hall |
| 6929 Whorlton Hall | 6972 Beningbrough Hall |
| 6930 Aldersey Hall | 6973 Bricklehampton Hall |
| 6931 Aldborough Hall | 6974 Bryngwyn Hall |
| 6932 Burwarton Hall | 6975 Capesthorne Hall |
| 6933 Birtles Hall | 6976 Graythwaite Hall |
| 6934 Beachamwell Hall | 6977 Grundisburgh Hall |
| 6935 Browsholme Hall | 6978 Haroldstone Hall |
| 6936 Breccles Hall | 6979 Helperly Hall |
| 6937 Conyngham Hall | 6980 Llanrumney Hall |
| 6938 Corndean Hall | 6981 Marbury Hall |
| 6939 Calveley Hall | 6982 Melmerby Hall |
| 6940 Didlington Hall | 6983 Otterington Hall |
| 6941 Fillongley Hall | 6984 Owsden Hall |
| 6942 Eshton Hall | 6985 Parwick Hall |
| 6943 Farnley Hall | 6986 Rydal Hall |
| 6944 Fledborough Hall | 6987 Shervington Hall |
| 6945 Glasfryn Hall | 6988 Swithland Hall |
| 6946 Heatherden Hall | 6989 Wightwick Hall |
| 6947 Helmingham Hall | 6990 Witherslack Hall |
| 6948 Holbrooke Hall | 6991 Acton Burnell Hall |
| 6949 Haberfield Hall | 6992 Arborfield Hall |
| 6950 Kingsthorpe Hall | 6993 Arthog Hall |
| 6951 Impney Hall | 6994 Baggrave Hall |
| 6952 Kimberley Hall | 6995 Benthall Hall |
| 6953 Leighton Hall | 6996 Blackwell Hall |
| 6954 Lotherton Hall | 6997 Bryn-Ivor Hall |
| 6955 Lydcott Hall | 6998 Burton Agnes Hall |
| 6956 Mottram Hall | 6999 Capel Dewi Hall |
| 6957 Norcliffe Hall | |
| 6958 Oxburgh Hall | |

**4-6-0**       4073 Cla

**" Castle "**

| |
|---|
| 7000 Viscount Portal |
| 7001 Sir James Milne |
| 7002 Devizes Castle |
| 7003 Elmley Castle |
| 7004 Eastnor Castle |
| 7005 Lamphey Castle |
| 7006 Lydford Castle |
| 7007 Great Western |
| 7008 Swansea Castle |

**4-6-0**       **6959 Class**

**" Modified Hall "**

| |
|---|
| 6959 Peatling Hall |
| 6960 Raveningham Hall |
| 6961 Stedham Hall |
| 6962 Soughton Hall |
| 6963 Throwley Hall |
| 6964 Thornbridge Hall |
| 6965 Thirlestaine Hall |
| 6966 Witchingham Hall |

| | |
|---|---|
| 09 | Athelney Castle |
| 10 | Avondale Castle |
| 11 | Banbury Castle |
| 12 | Barry Castle |
| 13 | Bristol Castle |
| 14 | Caerhays Castle |
| 15 | Carn Brea Castle |
| 16 | Chester Castle |
| 17 | G. J. Churchward |
| 18 | Drysllwyn Castle |
| 19 | Fowey Castle |
| 20 | Gloucester Castle |
| 21 | Haverfordwest Castle |
| 22 | Hereford Castle |
| 23 | Penrice Castle |
| 24 | Powis Castle |
| 25 | Sudeley Castle |
| 26 | Tenby Castle |
| 27 | Thornbury Castle |
| 28 | Cadbury Castle |
| 29 | Clun Castle |
| 30 | Cranbrook Castle |
| 31 | Cromwell's Castle |
| 32 | Denbigh Castle |
| 33 | Hartlebury Castle |
| 34 | Ince Castle |
| 35 | Ogmore Castle |
| 36 | Taunton Castle |
| 37 | Swindon |

## 8-2T     7200 Class

| | | | |
|---|---|---|---|
| 00 | 7214 | 7228 | 7242 |
| 01 | 7215 | 7229 | 7243 |
| 02 | 7216 | 7230 | 7244 |
| 03 | 7217 | 7231 | 7245 |
| 04 | 7218 | 7232 | 7246 |
| 05 | 7219 | 7233 | 7247 |
| 06 | 7220 | 7234 | 7248 |
| 07 | 7221 | 7235 | 7249 |
| 08 | 7222 | 7236 | 7250 |
| 09 | 7223 | 7237 | 7251 |
| 10 | 7224 | 7238 | 7252 |
| 11 | 7225 | 7239 | 7253 |
| 12 | 7226 | 7240 | |
| 13 | 7227 | 7241 | |

## 2-6-0     4300 Class

| | | | |
|---|---|---|---|
| 7300 | 7306 | 7312 | 7318 |
| 7301 | 7307 | 7313 | 7319 |
| 7302 | 7308 | 7314 | 7320 |
| 7303 | 7309 | 7315 | 7321 |
| 7304 | 7310 | 7316 | |
| 7305 | 7311 | 7317 | |

## 0-6-0PT     7400 Class

| | | | |
|---|---|---|---|
| 7400 | 7413 | 7426 | 7438 |
| 7401 | 7414 | 7427 | 7439 |
| 7402 | 7415 | 7428 | 7440 |
| 7403 | 7416 | 7429 | 7441 |
| 7404 | 7417 | 7430 | 7442 |
| 7405 | 7418 | 7431 | 7443 |
| 7406 | 7419 | 7432 | 7444 |
| 7407 | 7420 | 7433 | 7445 |
| 7408 | 7421 | 7434 | 7446 |
| 7409 | 7422 | 7435 | 7447 |
| 7410 | 7423 | 7436 | 7448 |
| 7411 | 7424 | 7437 | 7449 |
| 7412 | 7425 | | |

## 0-6-0PT     5700 Class

| | | | |
|---|---|---|---|
| 7700 | 7721 | 7742 | 7763 |
| 7701 | 7722 | 7743 | 7764 |
| 7702 | 7723 | 7744 | 7765 |
| 7703 | 7724 | 7745 | 7766 |
| 7704 | 7725 | 7746 | 7767 |
| 7705 | 7726 | 7747 | 7768 |
| 7706 | 7727 | 7748 | 7769 |
| 7707 | 7728 | 7749 | 7770 |
| 7708 | 7729 | 7750 | 7771 |
| 7709 | 7730 | 7751 | 7772 |
| 7710 | 7731 | 7752 | 7773 |
| 7711 | 7732 | 7753 | 7774 |
| 7712 | 7733 | 7754 | 7775 |
| 7713 | 7734 | 7755 | 7776 |
| 7714 | 7735 | 7756 | 7777 |
| 7715 | 7736 | 7757 | 7778 |
| 7716 | 7737 | 7758 | 7779 |
| 7717 | 7738 | 7759 | 7780 |
| 7718 | 7739 | 7760 | 7781 |
| 7719 | 7740 | 7761 | 7782 |
| 7720 | 7741 | 7762 | 7783 |

| | | | |
|---|---|---|---|
| 7784 | 7788 | 7792 | 7796 |
| 7785 | 7789 | 7793 | 7797 |
| 7786 | 7790 | 7794 | 7798 |
| 7787 | 7791 | 7795 | 7799 |

## 4-6-0      7800 Class
### " Manor "

7800 Torquay Manor
7801 Anthony Manor
7802 Bradley Manor
7803 Barcote Manor
7804 Baydon Manor
7805 Broome Manor
7806 Cockington Manor
7807 Compton Manor
7808 Cookham Manor
7809 Childrey Manor
7810 Draycott Manor
7811 Dunley Manor
7812 Erlestoke Manor
7813 Freshford Manor
7814 Fringford Manor
7815 Fritwell Manor
7816 Frilsham Manor
7817 Garsington Manor
7818 Granville Manor
7819 Hinton Manor
7820 Dinmore Manor
7821 Ditcheat Manor
7822 Foxcote Manor
7823 Hook Norton Manor
7824 Iford Manor
7825 Lechlade Manor
7826 Longworth Manor
7827 Lydham Manor
7828 Odney Manor
7829 Ramsbury Manor

## 4-6-0      6959 Class
### " Modified Hall "

7900 St. Peter's Hall
7901 Dodington Hall
7902 Eaton Mascot Hall
7903 Foremarke Hall
7904 Fountains Hall
7905 Fowey Hall
7906 Fron Hall
7907 Hart Hall
7908 Henshall Hall
7909 Heveningham Hall
7910 Hown Hall
7911 Lady Margaret Hall
7912 Little Linford Hall
7913 Little Wyrley Hall
7914 Lleweni Hall
7915 Mere Hall
7916 Mobberley Hall
7917 North Aston Hall
7918 Rhose Wood Hall
7919 Runter Hall
7920 Coney Hall
7921 Edstone Hall
7922 Salford Hall
7923 Speke Hall
7924 Thornycroft Hall
7925 Westol Hall
7926 Willey Hall
7927 Willington Hall
7928 Wolf Hall
7929 Wyke Hall

## 2-6-2T      8100 Class

| | | | |
|---|---|---|---|
| 8100 | 8103 | 8106 | 8108 |
| 8101 | 8104 | 8107 | 8109 |
| 8102 | 8105 | | |

## 0-6-0PT      9400 Class

| | | | |
|---|---|---|---|
| 8400 | 8414 | 8428 | 8442 |
| 8401 | 8415 | 8429 | 8443 |
| 8402 | 8416 | 8430 | 8444 |
| 8403 | 8417 | 8431 | 8445 |
| 8404 | 8418 | 8432 | 8446 |
| 8405 | 8419 | 8433 | 8447 |
| 8406 | 8420 | 8434 | 8448 |
| 8407 | 8421 | 8435 | 8449 |
| 8408 | 8422 | 8436 | 8450 |
| 8409 | 8423 | 8437 | 8451 |
| 8410 | 8424 | 8438 | 8452 |
| 8411 | 8425 | 8439 | 8453 |
| 8412 | 8426 | 8440 | 8454 |
| 8413 | 8427 | 8441 | 8455 |

| | | | | 2-6-0 | | 4300 Class | |
|---|---|---|---|---|---|---|---|
| 8456 | 8467 | 8478 | 8489 | 9300 | 9305 | 9310 | 9315 |
| 8457 | 8468 | 8479 | 8490 | 9301 | 9306 | 9311 | 9316 |
| 8458 | 8469 | 8480 | 8491 | 9302 | 9307 | 9312 | 9317 |
| 8459 | 8470 | 8481 | 8492 | 9303 | 9308 | 9313 | 9318 |
| 8460 | 8471 | 8482 | 8493 | 9304 | 9309 | 9314 | 9319 |
| 8461 | 8472 | 8483 | 8494 | | | | |
| 8462 | 8473 | 8484 | 8495 | **0-6-0PT** | | **9400 Class** | |
| 8463 | 8474 | 8485 | 8496 | 9400 | 9425 | 9450 | 9475 |
| 8464 | 8475 | 8486 | 8497 | 9401 | 9426 | 9451 | 9476 |
| 8465 | 8476 | 8487 | 8498 | 9402 | 9427 | 9452 | 9477 |
| 8466 | 8477 | 8488 | 8499 | 9403 | 9428 | 9453 | 9478 |

| **0-6-0PT** | | **5700 Class** | | | | | |
|---|---|---|---|---|---|---|---|
| 8700 | 8725 | 8750 | 8775 | 9404 | 9429 | 9454 | 9479 |
| 8701 | 8726 | 8751 | 8776 | 9405 | 9430 | 9455 | 9480 |
| 8702 | 8727 | 8752 | 8777 | 9406 | 9431 | 9456 | 9481 |
| 8703 | 8728 | 8753 | 8778 | 9407 | 9432 | 9457 | 9482 |
| 8704 | 8729 | 8754 | 8779 | 9408 | 9433 | 9458 | 9483 |
| 8705 | 8730 | 8755 | 8780 | 9409 | 9434 | 9459 | 9484 |
| 8706 | 8731 | 8756 | 8781 | 9410 | 9435 | 9460 | 9485 |
| 8707 | 8732 | 8757 | 8782 | 9411 | 9436 | 9461 | 9486 |
| 8708 | 8733 | 8758 | 8783 | 9412 | 9437 | 9462 | 9487 |
| 8709 | 8734 | 8759 | 8784 | 9413 | 9438 | 9463 | 9488 |
| 8710 | 8735 | 8760 | 8785 | 9414 | 9439 | 9464 | 9489 |
| 8711 | 8736 | 8761 | 8786 | 9415 | 9440 | 9465 | 9490 |
| 8712 | 8737 | 8762 | 8787 | 9416 | 9441 | 9466 | 9491 |
| 8713 | 8738 | 8763 | 8788 | 9417 | 9442 | 9467 | 9492 |
| 8714 | 8739 | 8764 | 8789 | 9418 | 9443 | 9468 | 9493 |
| 8715 | 8740 | 8765 | 8790 | 9419 | 9444 | 9469 | 9494 |
| 8716 | 8741 | 8766 | 8791 | 9420 | 9445 | 9470 | 9495 |
| 8717 | 8742 | 8767 | 8792 | 9421 | 9446 | 9471 | 9496 |
| 8718 | 8743 | 8768 | 8793 | 9422 | 9447 | 9472 | 9497 |
| 8719 | 8744 | 8769 | 8794 | 9423 | 9448 | 9473 | 9498 |
| 8720 | 8745 | 8770 | 8795 | 9424 | 9449 | 9474 | 9499 |
| 8721 | 8746 | 8771 | 8796 | | | | |
| 8722 | 8747 | 8772 | 8797 | **0-6-0PT** | | **5700 Class** | |
| 8723 | 8748 | 8773 | 8798 | 9600 | 9611 | 9622 | 9633 |
| 8724 | 8749 | 8774 | 8799 | 9601 | 9612 | 9623 | 9634 |

| **4-4-0** | | **9000 Class** | | | | | |
|---|---|---|---|---|---|---|---|
| | | | | 9602 | 9613 | 9624 | 9635 |
| 9000 | 9009 | 9016 | 9024 | 9603 | 9614 | 9625 | 9636 |
| 9001 | 9010 | 9017 | 9025 | 9604 | 9615 | 9626 | 9637 |
| 9002 | 9011 | 9018 | 9026 | 9605 | 9616 | 9627 | 9638 |
| 9003 | 9012 | 9019 | 9027 | 9606 | 9617 | 9628 | 9639 |
| 9004 | 9013 | 9020 | 9028 | 9607 | 9618 | 9629 | 9640 |
| 9005 | 9014 | 9021 | | 9608 | 9619 | 9630 | 9641 |
| 9008 | 9015 | 9022 | | 9609 | 9620 | 9631 | 9642 |
| | | 9023 | | 9610 | 9621 | 9632 | 9643 |

49

| | | | | | | | |
|---|---|---|---|---|---|---|---|
| 9644 | 9662 | 9680 | 9715 | 9733 | 9751 | 9769 | 9787 |
| 9645 | 9663 | 9681 | 9716 | 9734 | 9752 | 9770 | 9788 |
| 9646 | 9664 | 9682 | 9717 | 9735 | 9753 | 9771 | 9789 |
| 9647 | 9665 | 9700 | 9718 | 9736 | 9754 | 9772 | 9790 |
| 9648 | 9666 | 9701 | 9719 | 9737 | 9755 | 9773 | 9791 |
| 9649 | 9667 | 9702 | 9720 | 9738 | 9756 | 9774 | 9792 |
| 9650 | 9668 | 9703 | 9721 | 9739 | 9757 | 9775 | 9793 |
| 9651 | 9669 | 9704 | 9722 | 9740 | 9758 | 9776 | 9794 |
| 9652 | 9670 | 9705 | 9723 | 9741 | 9759 | 9777 | 9795 |
| 9653 | 9671 | 9706 | 9724 | 9742 | 9760 | 9778 | 9796 |
| 9654 | 9672 | 9707 | 9725 | 9743 | 9761 | 9779 | 9797 |
| 9655 | 9673 | 9708 | 9726 | 9744 | 9762 | 9780 | 9798 |
| 9656 | 9674 | 9709 | 9727 | 9745 | 9763 | 9781 | 9799 |
| 9657 | 9675 | 9710 | 9728 | 9746 | 9764 | 9782 | |
| 9658 | 9676 | 9711 | 9729 | 9747 | 9765 | 9783 | |
| 9659 | 9677 | 9712 | 9730 | 9748 | 9766 | 9784 | |
| 9660 | 9678 | 9713 | 9731 | 9749 | 9767 | 9785 | |
| 9661 | 9679 | 9714 | 9732 | 9750 | 9768 | 9786 | |

## STREAM-LINED DIESEL RAIL-CARS

| Car No. | Date | Engines | Total b.h.p. | Seats | Car No. | Date | Engines | Total b.h.p. | Seats |
|---|---|---|---|---|---|---|---|---|---|
| 1 | 1934 | 1 | 121 | 69 | 18§ | 1937 | 2 | 242 | 70 |
| 2-4* | 1934 | 2 | 242 | 44 | 19-21/3-32 | 1940 | 2 | 210 | 48 |
| 5-7 | 1935 | 2 | 242 | 70 | 33 | 1941 | 2 | 210 | 48 |
| 8 | 1936 | 2 | 242 | 70 | 34‡ | 1941 | 2 | 210 | — |
| 10-12† | 1936 | 2 | 242 | 63 | 35, 36‖ | 1941 | 4 | 420 | 104 |
| 13-16 | 1936 | 2 | 242 | 70 | 22, 38‖ | 1942 | 4 | 420 | 104 |
| 17‡ | 1936 | 2 | 242 | — | | | | | |

\* Buffet and lavatory facilities
† Lavatory facilities.
‡ Parcels cars.
§ Experimentally geared to haul trailer car, became prototype of subsequent designs.

Twin-coach units with buffet and lavatory facilities. Adjoining statistics apply per 2-car unit. When new, some of these units worked as 3-car rakes by the addition of an ordinary 70 ft. corridor coach.

| | | | | | | | | |
|---|---|---|---|---|---|---|---|---|
| 1 | 5 | 10 | 14 | 18 | 22 | 26 | 30 | 34 |
| 2 | 6 | 11 | 15 | 19 | 23 | 27 | 31 | 35 |
| 3 | 7 | 12 | 16 | 20 | 24 | 28 | 32 | 36 |
| 4 | 8 | 13 | 17 | 21 | 25 | 29 | 33 | 33 |

## SERVICE LOCOS
### Petrol
**0-4-0** : 23, 24, 26 and 27

**Total 4**

(Tractive Effort calculated to the nearest 5 lb.)  Su = Superheated.  SS = Some Superheated.

In the "Class" column, numbers in brackets refer to the lowest number in those classes which are not officially designated by a general class number.

| Class | Designer | Original Owning Co. (if other than G.W.) | Building or Rebuilding Date | Weight of Loco. (T. Cwt.) | Boiler Pressure | Cylinders | Driving Wheels | Tractive Effort at 85% B.P. | Power Class | Route Restriction Colour |
|---|---|---|---|---|---|---|---|---|---|---|
| **4-6-0** | | | | | | | | | | |
| 1000 | Hawksworth | — | 1945-7 | 76 17 | 280 Su. | (0) 18½ × 30 | 6' 3" | 32,580 | D | Red |
| 2900 | Churchward | — | 1903-13 | 72 17 | 225 Su. | (0) 18½ × 30 | 6' 8½" | 24,395 | C | Red |
| 4000 | Churchward | — | 1907-14 | 75 17 | 225 Su. | (4) 15 × 26 | 6' 8½" | 27,800 | D | Red |
| 4073 | Collett | — | 1923-50 | 72 10 | 225 Su. | (4) 16 × 26 | 6' 8½" | 31,625 | D | Red |
| 4900 | Churchward (1907) reb. Collett | — | 1924 | 75 0 | 225 Su. | (0) 18½ × 30 | 6' 0" | 27,275 | D | Red Double |
| 6000 | Collett | — | 1928-43 1927-30 | 89 0 | 250 Su. | (4) 16¼ × 28 | 6' 6" | 40,285 | Special | Red |
| 6800 | Collett | — | 1936-9 | 74 0 | 225 Su. | (0) 18½ × 30 | 5' 8" | 28,875 | D | Red |
| 6959 | Hawksworth | — | 1944-50 | 75 16 | 225 Su. | (0) 18½ × 30 | 6' 0" | 27,275 | D | Red |
| 7800 | Collett | — | 1938-50 | 68 18 | 225 Su. | (0) 18 × 30 | 5' 8" | 27,340 | D | Blue |
| **4-4-0** | | | | | | | | | | |
| 9000 | Dean (1895-7) reb. Collett | — | 1936-9 | 49 0 | 180 SS. | 18 × 26 | 5' 8" | 18,955 | B | Yellow |
| **2-8-0** | | | | | | | | | | |
| 2803 | Churchward Collett | — | 1903-19 1938-42 | 75 10 76 5 | 225 Su. | (0) 18½ × 30 | 4' 7½" | 35,380 | E | Blue |
| R.O.D. | Robinson (G.C.) | — | 1917-9 | 73 11 | 185 Su. | (0) 21 × 26 | 4' 8" | 32,200 | D | Blue |
| 4700 | Churchward | — | 1919-23 | 82 0 | 225 Su. | (0) 19 × 30 | 5' 8" | 30,460 | D | Red |

| Class | Designer | Original Owning Co. (if other than G.W.) | Building or Rebuilding Date | Weight of Loco | Boiler Pressure | Cylinders | Driving Wheels | Tractive Effort at 85% B.P. | Power Class | Route Restriction Colour |
|---|---|---|---|---|---|---|---|---|---|---|
| **2-6-0** 4300 | { Churchward<br>{ Collett | —<br>— | 1911–25<br>1932 | *T. Cwt.<br>{ 62 0<br>{ 64 0<br>{ 65 6 | 200 Su. | (O) 18½ × 30 | 5' 8" | 25,670 | D | { Blue<br>{ Red* |
| **2-4-0** (1334) | Dubs. | M.S.W.J. | 1894 | 35 5 | 165 | 17 × 24 | 5' 6" | 13,400 | A | — |
| **0-6-0** 2251 | Collett | — | 1930–48 | 43 8 | 200 Su. | 17½ × 24 | 5' 2" | 20,155 | B | Yellow |
| 2301 | Dean | — | 1884–99 | 36 16 | 180 Su. | { 17 × 24<br>{ 17½ × 24 | 5' 2" | { 17,120<br>{ 18,140 | A | — |
| (844) | Jones, reb. G.W. from 1924 | Cam | 1903–18 | 38 17 | 160 SS. | 18 × 26 | 5' 1¼" | 18,625 | A | Yellow |
| **2-8-2T** 7200 | Churchward (1913–30) reb. Collett | — | 1934–9 | 92 2 | 200 Su. | (O) 19 × 30 | 4' 7½" | 33,170 | E | Red |
| **2-8-0T** 4200 | Churchward | — | 1910–40 | { 81 12<br>{ 82 2 | 200 Su. | { (O)18½ × 30<br>{ (O)19 × 30 | 4' 7½" | { 31,450<br>{ 33,170 | E | Red |
| **2-6-2T** 3100 | Churchward (1907) reb. Collett | — | 1938–9 | 81 9 | 225 Su. | (O) 18½ × 30 | 5' 3" | 31,170 | E | Red |
| 3150 | Churchward | — | 1906–3 | 81 12 | 200 Su. | (O)18½ × 30 | 5' 8" | 25,670 | D | Red |
| 4400 | Churchward | — | 1904 | 56 13 | 180 Su. | (O)17 × 24 | 4' 1¼" | 21,440 | C | — |
| 4500 | { Churchward<br>{ Collett | — | 1906–24<br>1927–9 | 57 0<br>61 0 | 200 Su. | (O)17 × 24 | 4' 7½" | 21,250 | C | Yellow |

\* Nos. 9300-19

| Class | Builder / Rebuild | Railway | Years | Weight | Heating | Cylinders | Driving wheels | Tractive effort | Route | Colour |
|---|---|---|---|---|---|---|---|---|---|---|
| **5100** | Churchward (1905–6) reb. Collett | — | 1923–30 | 75 10 | 200 Su. | (0)18 × 30 | 5' 8" | 24,300 | D | Blue |
| **6100** | Collett | — | 1929–49 | 78 9 | 225 Su. | (0)18 × 30 | 5' 8" | 27,340 | D | Blue |
| **8100** | Collett reb. Churchward (1903–6) reb. Collett | — | 1938–9 | 76 11 | 225 Su. | (0)18 × 30 | 5' 6" | 28,165 | D | Blue |
| **(1205)\*** | Hawthorn Leslie | A.D. | 1920 | 65 0 | 160 | (0)19 × 26 | 4' 7" | 23,210 | C | Yellow |
| **(7)\*** | Davies & Metcalfe / Collett | V. of R. | 1902 / 1923 | 25 0 | 165 | (0)11 + 17 / (0)11¼ × 17 | 2' 6" | 9,615 / 10,510 | — | — |
| **0-6-2T** | | | | | | | | | | |
| **5600** | Collett | — | 1924–6 / 1927–8 | 68 12 / 69 7 | 200 Su. | 18 × 26 | 4' 7½" | 25,800 | D | Red |
| **(431)** | Dunbar, reb. G.W. from 1926 / Reb. G.W. from 1928 | B. & M. | 1915–20 | 59 5 | 175 Su. | 18 × 26 | 5' 0" | 20,885 | B | Blue |
| **(155)** | Ree. reb. G.W. 1928 | Car. | 1908 | 66 12 | 175 Su. | 18½ × 26 | 4' 6½" | 22,990 | C | Red |
| **(35)** | Hurry Riches / Hurry Riches reb. G.W. from 1926 | Rhym. | 1921 / 1907–21 | 66 10 / 62 10 | 175 Su. / 200 Su. | 18½ × 26 / 18½ × 26 | 4' 6" / 4' 6" | 24,520 / 28,015 | D / D | Red / Red |
| **(56)** | Hurry Riches / Hurry Riches reb. G.W. from 1929 | Rhym. | 1910–8 | 64 3 | 175 | 18 × 26 | 4' 4½" | 23,870 | C | Blue |
| **(82)** | Hurry Riches | Rhym. | 1910–8 | 63 0 | 175 Su. | 18 × 26 | 4' 4½" | 23,870 | C | Blue |
| **(77)** | Hurry Riches reb. G.W. 1926 | Rhym. | 1909 | 58 19 | 175 Su. | 18 × 26 | 5' 0" | 20,885 | B | Blue |
| **(204)** | Hurry Riches reb. G.W. from 1928 | Rhym. | 1909–21 | 63 0 | 175 Su. | 18½ × 26 | 5' 0" | 21,700 | B | Blue |
| | Hurry Riches | T.V. | 1924–31 | 61 0 | 175 Su. | 17½ × 26 | 4' 6½" | 21,730 | C | Blue |
| **(303)** | Cameron (1914–21) reb. G.W. (1907–10) | T.V. | 1924–48 | 65 14 | 175 Su. / 200 Su. | 18½ × 26 / 17½ × 26 | 5' 3" | 21,000 / 21,480 | C | Red |
| **0-6-0T** | | | | | | | | | | |
| **850** | Dean reb. Churchward | — | 1875–95 | 36 3 | 165 | 16 × 24 | 4' 1½" | 17,410 | — | — |

\*1' 11½" gauge.

## 0-6-0T

| Class | Designer | Original Owning Co. (if other than G.W.) | Building or Rebuilding Date | Weight of Loco. (T. Cwt.) | Boiler Pressure | Cylinders | Driving Wheels | Tractive Effort at 85% B.P. | Power Class | Route Restriction Colour |
|---|---|---|---|---|---|---|---|---|---|---|
| 1361 | Churchward | — | 1910 | 35 4 | 150 | (O)16 × 20 | 3' 8" | 14,835 | — | — |
| 1366 | Collett | — | 1934 | 35 15 | 165 | (O)16 × 20 | 3' 8" | 16,320 | — | — |
| 1500 | Hawksworth | — | 1949 | 58 4 | 200 | (O)17½ × 24 | 4' 7½" | 22,515 | C | Red |
| 1600 | Hawksworth | — | 1949–50 | 41 12 | 165 | (O)16½ × 24 | 4' 1½" | 18,515 | A | — |
| 2021 | Dean reb. Churchward | — | 1897–1905 | 39 15 | 165 | 16½ × 24 | 4' 1½" | 18,515 | A | — |
| 2181 | Dean, mod. Collett | — | 1939–40 | 46 12 | 165 | 16½ × 24 | 5' 2" | 14,780 | — | Yellow |
| 5400 | Collett | — | 1931–2 | 47 10 | 165 | 16½ × 24 | 4' 7½" | 22,515 | C | Yellow |
| 5700 | Collett | — | 1929–31 / 1933 | 50 15 / 49 0 | 200 | 17½ × 24 | 4' 7½" | 18,010 | — | Yellow / Blue* |
| 6400 & 7400 | Collett | — | 1933–49 / 1932–7 / 1936–50 | 45 2 / 45 9 | 180 | 16½ × 24 | 4' 7½" | — | A | Yellow |
| 9400 | Hawksworth | A.-D. | 1947–50 | 55 7 | 200 S.S. | (O)17½ × 24 | 4' 7½" | 22,515 | C | Red |
| (666) | Kerr Stuart | B.P.G.V. | 1917 | 50 0 | 160 | (O)15 × 24 | 4' 0½" | 19,650 | B | Blue |
| (2176) | Avonside | B.P.G.V. | 1906–8 | 38 5 | 170 | (O)15 × 22 | 3' 6" | 17,030 | A | — |
| (2198) | Avonside reb. G.W. | B.P.G.V. | 1907 | 38 5 | 165 | (O)15 × 22 | 3' 6" | 16,530 | A | — |
|  | Hudswell Clarke reb. G.W. | | 1910 | 37 15 | 165 | (O)15 × 22 | 3' 6" | 15,430 | | |
| (2162) | Hudswell Clarke | B.P.G.V. | 1912–9 | 44 4 / 44 6 | 160 | (O)16 × 24 | 3' 9" | 18,570 | A | Yellow |
| (681) | Hope reb. G.W. | Car. | 1920 | 45 6 | 165 | 18 × 24 | 4' 1½" | 22,000 | C | Yellow |
| (28) | M. Wardle reb. G.W. | C.M.D.P. | 1905 | 39 18 | 160 | (O)16 × 22 | 3' 6¾" | 18,235 | A | Yellow |

* Nos. 9700–10

# THE **ABC** OF

# RITISH RAILWAYS

# LOCOMOTIVES

## PART 2—Nos. 10000-39999

also S.R. Electric Train Units.

SUMMER
1953
EDITION

# MOTIVE POWER DEPOTS AND CODᴇ

## LONDON MIDLAND REGiON

| | | | | | |
|---|---|---|---|---|---|
| 1A | **Willesden** | 9D | Buxton | 19C | Canklow |
| 1B | Camden | 9E | Trafford Park | 20A | **Leeds (Holl** |
| 1C | Watford | 9F | Heaton Mersey | 20B | Stourton |
| 1D | Devons Road (Bow) | 9G | Northwich | 20C | Royston |
| 1E | Bletchley | 10A | **Springs Branch** | 20D | Normanton |
| 2A | **Rugby** | | **(Wigan)** | 20E | Manningham |
| 2B | Nuneaton | 10B | Preston | 20F | Skipton |
| 2C | Warwick | 10C | Patricroft | 20G | Hellifield |
| 2D | Coventry | 10D | Plodder Lane | 21A | **Saltley** |
| 2E | Northampton | 10E | Sutton Oak | 21B | Bournville |
| 3A | **Bescot** | 10F | Wigan (C.L.C.) | 21C | Bromsgrove |
| 3B | Bushbury | 11A | **Carnforth** | 21D | Stratford-on- |
| 3C | Walsall | 11B | Barrow | 22A | **Bristol** |
| 3D | Aston | 11C | Oxenholme | 22B | Gloucester |
| 3E | Monument Lane | 11D | Tebay | 24A | **Accrington** |
| 5A | **Crewe North** | 11E | Lancaster | 24B | Rose Grove |
| 5B | Crewe South | 12A | **Carlisle** | 24C | Lostock Hall |
| 5C | Stafford | | **(Upperby)** | 24D | Lower Darw |
| 5D | Stoke | 12C | Penrith | 24E | Blackpool |
| 5E | Alsager | 12D | Workington | 24F | Fleetwood |
| 5F | Uttoxeter | 12E | Moor Row | 25A | **Wakefield** |
| 6A | **Chester** | 14A | **Cricklewood** | 25B | Huddersfield |
| 6B | Mold Junction | 14B | Kentish Town | 25C | Goole |
| 6C | Birkenhead | 14C | St. Albans | 25D | Mirfield |
| 6D | Chester | 15A | **Wellingborough** | 25E | Sowerby Bri |
| | (Northgate) | 15B | Kettering | 25F | Low Moor |
| 6E | Wrexham | 15C | Leicester | 25G | Farnley Junc |
| 6F | Bidston | 15D | Bedford | 26A | **Newton H** |
| 6G | Llandudno | 16A | **Nottingham** | 26B | Agecroft |
| | Junction | 16C | Kirkby | 26C | Bolton |
| 6H | Bangor | 16D | Mansfield | 26D | Bury |
| 6J | Holyhead | 17A | **Derby** | 26E | Bacup |
| 6K | Rhyl | 17B | Burton | 26F | Lees |
| 8A | **Edge Hill** | 17C | Coalville | 26G | Belle Vue |
| 8B | Warrington | 17D | Rowsley | 27A | **Bank Hall** |
| 8C | Speke Junction | 18A | **Toton** | 27B | Aintree |
| 8D | Widnes | 18B | Westhouses | 27C | Southport |
| 8E | Brunswick (L'pool) | 18C | Hasland | 27D | Wigan |
| 9A | **Longsight** | 18D | Staveley | | (ex L & |
| 9B | Stockport | 19A | **Sheffield** | 27E | Walton |
| 9C | Macclesfield | 19B | Millhouses | | |

## EASTERN REGION

| | | | | | |
|---|---|---|---|---|---|
| 30A | **Stratford** | 31E | Bury St. Edmunds | 33B | Tilbury |
| 30B | Hertford East | 32A | **Norwich** | 33C | Shoeburynes |
| 30C | Bishops Stortford | 32B | Ipswich | 34A | **Kings Cros** |
| 30D | Southend | 32C | Lowestoft | 34B | Hornsey |
| | (Victoria) | 32D | Yarmouth | 34C | Hatfield |
| 30E | Colchester | | (South Town) | 34D | Hitchin |
| 30F | Parkeston | 32E | Yarmouth | 34E | Neasden |
| 31A | **Cambridge** | | (Vauxhall) | 35A | **New Engla** |
| 31B | March | 32F | Yarmouth (Beach) | 35B | Grantham |
| 31C | Kings Lynn | 32G | Melton Constable | 35C | Peterborougl |
| 31D | South Lynn | 33A | **Plaistow** | | (Spital) |

2

## EASTERN REGION—continued

| | | | | | |
|---|---|---|---|---|---|
| **Doncaster** | 37C | Bradford | 38A | 39B | Sheffield (Darnall) |
| Mexborough | 38A | **Colwick** | | 40A | **Lincoln** |
| Frodingham | 38B | Annesley | | 40B | Immingham |
| Barnsley | 38C | Leicester | | 40C | Louth |
| Retford | 38D | Staveley | | 40D | Tuxford |
| **Ardsley** | 38E | Woodford Halse | | 40E | Langwith Junction |
| Copley Hill | 39A | **Gorton** | | 40F | Boston |

## NORTH EASTERN REGION

| | | | | | |
|---|---|---|---|---|---|
| **York** | 51E | Stockton | | 52F | North Blyth |
| Leeds (Neville Hill) | 51F | West Auckland | | 53A | **Hull** |
| Selby | 51G | Haverton Hill | | | (Dairycoates) |
| Starbeck | 51H | Kirkby Stephen | | 53B | Hull |
| Scarborough | 51J | Northallerton | | | (Botanic Gardens) |
| Malton | 51K | Saltburn | | 53C | Hull (Springhead) |
| Whitby | 52A | **Gateshead** | | 53D | Bridlington |
| **Darlington** | 52B | Heaton | | 54A | **Sunderland** |
| Newport | 52C | Blaydon | | 54B | Tyne Dock |
| West Hartlepool | 52D | Tweedmouth | | 54C | Borough Gardens |
| Middlesbrough | 52E | Percy Main | | 54D | Consett |

## SCOTTISH REGION

| | | | | | |
|---|---|---|---|---|---|
| **Inverness** | 63E | Oban | | 65H | Helensburgh |
| Aviemore | 64A | **St. Margarets** | | 65 I | Balloch |
| Helmsdale | | **(Edinburgh)** | | 66A | **Polmadie** |
| Wick | 64B | Haymarket | | | **(Glasgow)** |
| Forres | 64C | Dalry Road | | 66B | Motherwell |
| **Kittybrewster** | 64D | Carstairs | | 66C | Hamilton |
| Aberdeen | 64E | Polmont | | 66D | Greenock |
| (Ferryhill) | 64F | Bathgate | | 67A | **Corkerhill** |
| Keith | 64G | Hawick | | | **(Glasgow)** |
| **Thornton** | 65A | **Eastfield** | | 67B | Hurlford |
| Dundee | | **(Glasgow)** | | 67C | Ayr |
| (Tay Bridge) | 65B | St. Rollox | | 67D | Ardrossan |
| Dunfermline | 65C | Parkhead | | 68A | **Carlisle** |
| (Upper) | 65D | Dawsholm | | | **(Kingmoor)** |
| **Perth South** | 65E | Kipps | | 68B | Dumfries |
| Stirling | 65F | Grangemouth | | 68C | Stranraer |
| Forfar | 65G | Yoker | | 68D | Beattock |
| Fort William | | | | 68E | Carlisle (Canal) |

## SOUTHERN REGION

| | | | | | |
|---|---|---|---|---|---|
| **Nine Elms** | 71J | Highbridge | | 74A | **Ashford (Kent)** |
| Feltham | 72A | **Exmouth** | | 74B | Ramsgate |
| Guildford | | **Junction** | | 74C | Dover |
| Basingstoke | 72B | Salisbury | | 74D | Tonbridge |
| Reading | 72C | Yeovil | | 74E | St. Leonards |
| **Eastleigh** | 72D | Plymouth | | 75A | **Brighton** |
| Bournemouth | 72E | Barnstaple Junction | | 75B | Redhill |
| Dorchester | 72F | Wadebridge | | 75C | Norwood Junction |
| Fratton | 73A | **Stewarts Lane** | | 75D | Horsham |
| Newport (I.O.W.) | 73B | Bricklayers Arms | | 75E | Three Bridges |
| Ryde (I.O.W.) | 73C | Hither Green | | 75F | Tunbridge Wells |
| Bath (S. & D.) | 73D | Gillingham (Kent) | | | West |
| Templecombe | 73E | Faversham | | 75G | Eastbourne |
| Southampton | | | | | |

## WESTERN REGION

| | | | | | |
|---|---|---|---|---|---|
| 81A | **Old Oak Common** | 84B | Oxley | 86J | Aberdare |
| 81B | Slough | 84C | Banbury | 86K | Abergavenny |
| 81C | Southall | 84D | Leamington Spa | 87A | **Neath** |
| 81D | Reading | 84E | Tyseley | 87B | Duffryn Yard |
| 81E | Didcot | 84F | Stourbridge | 87C | Danygraig |
| 81F | Oxford | 84G | Shrewsbury | 87D | Swansea East Dock |
| 82A | **Bristol (Bath Rd.)** | 84H | Wellington (Salop) | 87E | Landore |
| 82B | Bristol (St. Philip's Marsh) | 84J | Croes Newydd | 87F | Llanelly |
| | | 84K | Chester | 87G | Carmarthen |
| 82C | Swindon | 85A | **Worcester** | 87H | Neyland |
| 82D | Westbury | 85B | Gloucester | 87J | Goodwick |
| 82E | Yeovil | 85C | Hereford | 87K | Swansea (Vic |
| 82F | Weymouth | 85D | Kidderminster | 88A | **Cardiff (Cat** |
| 83A | **Newton Abbot** | 86A | **Newport (Ebbw. Jcn.)** | 88B | Cardiff East [ |
| 83B | Taunton | | | 88C | Barry |
| 83C | Exeter | 86B | Newport (Pill.) | 88D | Merthyr |
| 83D | Laira (Plymouth) | 86C | Cardiff (Canton) | 88E | Abercynon |
| 83E | St. Blazey | 86D | Llantrisant | 88F | Treherbert |
| 83F | Truro | 86E | Severn Tunnel Junction | 89A | **Oswestry** |
| 83G | Penzance | | | 89B | Brecon |
| 84A | **Wolverhampton (Stafford Road)** | 86F | Tondu | 89C | Machynlleth |
| | | 86G | Pontypool Road | | |
| | | 86H | Aberbeeg | | |

# SOUTHERN RAILWAY LOCOMOTIVE SUPERINTDENTS AND CHIEF MECHANICAL ENGINEERS CONSTITUENT COMPANIES

**LONDON & SOUTH WESTERN RAILWAY**

| | | | |
|---|---|---|---|
| J. Woods | ... | ... | 1835–1841 |
| J. V. Gooch | ... | ... | 1841–1850 |
| J. Beattie | ... | ... | 1850–1871 |
| W. G. Beattie | ... | ... | 1871–1878 |
| W. Adams | ... | ... | 1878–1895 |
| D. Drummond | ... | ... | 1895–1912 |
| R. W. Urie | ... | ... | 1912–1922 |

**LONDON, BRIGHTON AND SOUTH COAST RAILWAY**

| | | | |
|---|---|---|---|
| —. Statham | ... | ... | ? –1845 |
| J. Gray | ... | ... | 1845–1847 |
| S. Kirtley | ... | ... | 1847 |
| J. C. Craven | ... | ... | 1847–1869 |
| W. Stroudley | ... | ... | 1870–1889 |
| R. J. Billinton | ... | ... | 1890–1904 |
| D. Earle Marsh | ... | ... | 1905–1911 |
| L. B. Billinton | ... | ... | 1911–1922 |

**SOUTH EASTERN RAILW**

| | | | |
|---|---|---|---|
| B. Cubitt | ... | ... | ? |
| J. Cudworth | ... | ... | 1845 |
| A. M. Watkin | ... | ... | 1 |
| R. Mansell | ... | ... | 1877 |
| J. Stirling | ... | ... | 1878 |

**LONDON, CHATHAM DOVER RAILWAY**

| | | | |
|---|---|---|---|
| W. Cubitt | ... | ... | ? |
| W. Martley | ... | ... | 1860 |
| W. Kirtley | ... | ... | 1874 |

**SOUTH EASTERN AND CHATHAM RAILWAY**

| | | | |
|---|---|---|---|
| H. S. Wainwright | ... | ... | 1899 |
| R. E. L. Maunsell | ... | ... | 1913 |

**SOUTHERN RAILWAY**

| | | | |
|---|---|---|---|
| R. E. L. Maunsell | ... | ... | 1923 |
| O. V. Bulleid | ... | ... | 1937 |

# BRITISH RAILWAYS NON-STEAM LOCOMOTIVE CLASSES

## INTERNAL COMBUSTION LOCOMOTIVES

### +Co Diesel Electric

duced 1947: English Electric Co.
d H. A. Ivatt, main line passenger
sign for L.M.S.R.
ght: 121 tons 10 cwt.
ng Wheels: 3' 6".
41,400 lb.
e: English Electric Co. 16 cyls.
00 h.p.
rs: Six nose-suspended motors,
gle reduction gear drive.

| 0 | 10001 | **Total 2** |

### 4 Diesel Mechanical

, Ivatt and Fell design for L.M.S.R.
es: Four 500 h.p., 12-cylinder.
mission: Fell patent differential
ve and fluid couplings.
ht: 120 tons.
25,000 lb.
ng Wheels: 4' 3".

| 0 | **Total 1** |

### o+Co-1 Diesel Elec.

sh Electric Co. and Bulleid main
e passenger design for S.R.
e: English Co. 16 cyls. 1,750 h.p.
ht: 135 tons.
ng Wheels: 3' 7".
31,200 lb.

| 4 | 10202 | 10203 |

—Locos of this type are still
being delivered.

### +Bo Diesel Electric

luced 1950: N.B. Loco. Co.,
H. Co. and H. A. Ivatt, branch
design for L.M.S.R.
nt: 69 tons 16 cwt.
ng Wheels: 3' 6".
34,500 lb.
e: Davey Paxman 16 cyls. 827 h.p.
rs: Four nose-suspended motors,
e reduction gear drive.

| 0 | **Total 1** |

### 0 Diesel Mechanical

luced 1950: Bulleid S.R. design
shunting and transfer work.
nt: 49 tons 9 cwt.

Driving Wheels: 4' 6".
T.E.: 33,500 lb. (max. in lowgear).
Engine: Davey Paxman 12 cyls. 500 h.p.
Transmission: S.S.S. Powerflow three-speed gearbox and fluid coupling.

| 11001 | **Total 1** |

### 0-6-0 Diesel Mech. DMSI

Introduced 1952: 200 h.p. locomotives to replace ex-L.N.E.R. tram engines.
Weight: 29 tons 15 cwt.
Driving Wheels: 3' 3"
T.E.: 16,850 lb.
Engine: Gardner 8L3 type.

| 11100 | 11105 | 11109 | 11113 |
| 11101 | 11106 | 11110 | 11114 |
| 11102 | 11107 | 11111 | 11115 |
| 11103 | 11108 | 11112 | |

N.B.—Locos of this type are still being delivered.

### 0-4-0 Diesel Mechanical

Introduced 1950: Hibberd & Co. for North Eastern Region.
Weight: 11 tons
Engine: English National Gas type DA 4, 4-cyls., 52 h.p. at 1,250 r.p.m. Transmission spur type gear box with roller chains; three forward and three reverse gears.

| 11104 (Service Loco) | **Total 1** |

### 0-4-0 Diesel Mechanical

To be introduced 1953: 153 h.p. locomotives for E.R. and S.R.

| 11500 | 11501 | 11502 | 11503 |
| | | | **Total 4** |

### 0-6-0 Diesel Electric

Introduced 1936: English Electric-Hawthorn Leslie design for L.M.S.R.
Weight: ⎰51 tons.* ⎱47 tons.†
Driving Wheels: 4' 0½".
T.E.: 30,000 lb.
Engine: English Electric 6 cyls. 350 h.p.
Motors: Two nose-suspended motors, single reduction gear drive.

| 12000* | 12001* | 12002† | **Total 3** |

## 0-6-0    Diesel Electric

Introduced 1939: English Electric and Stanier design for L.M.S.R., development of previous design with jack-shaft drive.
Weight: 54 tons 16 cwt.
Driving Wheels: 4′ 3″
T.E.: 33,000 lb.
Engine: English Electric, 6 cyls. 350 h.p.
Motors: Single motor; jackshaft drive.

| | | | |
|---|---|---|---|
| 12003 | 12011 | 12019 | 12027 |
| 12004 | 12012 | 12020 | 12028 |
| 12005 | 12013 | 12021 | 12029 |
| 12006 | 12014 | 12022 | 12030 |
| 12007 | 12015 | 12023 | 12031 |
| 12008 | 12016 | 12024 | 12032 |
| 12009 | 12017 | 12025 | |
| 12010 | 12018 | 12026 | |

**Total 30**

## 0-6-0    Diesel Electric

Introduced 1945: English Electric and Fairburn design for L.M.S.R., development of previous design with double reduction gear drive.
Weight: 50 tons.
Driving Wheels: 4′ 0½″.
T.E.: 33,000 lb.
Engine: English Electric, 6 cyls. 350 h.p.
Engine: Two nose-suspended motors double reduction gear drive.

| | | | |
|---|---|---|---|
| 12033 | 12050 | 12067 | 12084 |
| 12034 | 12051 | 12068 | 12085 |
| 12035 | 12052 | 12069 | 12086 |
| 12036 | 12053 | 12070 | 12087 |
| 12037 | 12054 | 12071 | 12088 |
| 12038 | 12055 | 12072 | 12089 |
| 12039 | 12056 | 12073 | 12090 |
| 12040 | 12057 | 12074 | 12091 |
| 12041 | 12058 | 12075 | 12092 |
| 12042 | 12059 | 12076 | 12093 |
| 12043 | 12060 | 12077 | 12094 |
| 12044 | 12061 | 12078 | 12095 |
| 12045 | 12062 | 12079 | 12096 |
| 12046 | 12063 | 12080 | 12097 |
| 12047 | 12064 | 12081 | 12098 |
| 12048 | 12065 | 12082 | 12099 |
| 12049 | 12066 | 12083 | 12100 |

| | | | |
|---|---|---|---|
| 12101 | 12111 | 12121 | 12 |
| 12102 | 12112 | 12122 | 12 |
| 12103 | 12113 | 12123 | 12 |
| 12104 | 12114 | 12124 | 12 |
| 12105 | 12115 | 12125 | 12 |
| 12106 | 12116 | 12126 | 12 |
| 12107 | 12117 | 12127 | 12 |
| 12108 | 12118 | 12128 | 12 |
| 12109 | 12119 | 12129 | To |
| 12110 | 12120 | 12130 | 1 |

## 0-6-0    Diesel Electri

Introduced 1953.
Weight :
Driving Wheels : 4′ 6″.
T.E. :

| | | | |
|---|---|---|---|
| 13000 | 13021 | 13042 | 13 |
| 13001 | 13022 | 13043 | 13 |
| 13002 | 13023 | 13044 | 13 |
| 13003 | 13024 | 13045 | 13 |
| 13004 | 13025 | 13046 | 13 |
| 13005 | 13026 | 13047 | 13 |
| 13006 | 13027 | 13048 | 13 |
| 13007 | 13028 | 13049 | 13 |
| 13008 | 13029 | 13050 | 13 |
| 13009 | 13030 | 13051 | 13 |
| 13010 | 13031 | 13052 | 13 |
| 13011 | 13032 | 13053 | 13 |
| 13012 | 13033 | 13054 | 13 |
| 13013 | 13034 | 13055 | 13 |
| 13014 | 13035 | 13056 | 13 |
| 13015 | 13036 | 13057 | 13 |
| 13016 | 13037 | 13058 | 13 |
| 13017 | 13038 | 13059 | 13 |
| 13018 | 13039 | 13060 | 13 |
| 13019 | 13040 | 13061 | |
| 13020 | 13041 | 13062 | |

**N.B.—Locos of this class are being delivered.**

## 0-6-0 Diesel Electric DE

Introduced 1944: English Electric Thompson design for L.N. (L.N.E.R. version of L.M.S. series).
Weight: 51 tons.
Driving Wheels: 4′ 0″.

: 32,000 lb.
ne: English Electric, 6 cyls. 350 h.p.
ors: Two nose-suspended motors,
ouble reduction gear.

000 | 15001 | 15002 | 15003
**Total 4**

**-0 Diesel Electric DES 2**

oduced 1949: Brush design for E.R.
ght: 51 tons.
ing Wheels: 4′ 0″.
: 32,000 lb.
ne: Petter 4 cyls. 360 h.p.
04
**Total 1**

**-0 Petrol Class Y11**

oduced 1921: Motor, Rail and
am Car Co., design (purchased by
B.R. and L.N.E.R.).
ght: 8 tons.
ing Wheels: 3′ 1″.
e: 4 cyls. 40 h.p. petrol.
e: Chains and two-speed gear box.
98          15099          **Total 2**

**-0          Diesel Electric**

duced 1936: Hawthorn Leslie and
glish Electric design for G.W.R.
W.R. version of L.M.S.R. Nos.
00/1).
ht: 51 tons 10 cwt.
ng Wheels: 4′ 1″.
30,000 lb.
ue: English Electric 6 cyls. 350 h.p.
rs: Two nose-suspended motors,
gle reduction gear drive.
0          **Total 1**

**0          Diesel Electric**

duced 1948: English Electric and
wksworth design for Western
gion (W.R. version of L.M.S
033 series).
ht: 46 tons 9 cwt.
ng Wheels: 4′ 0¼″.
33,500 lb.
e: English Electric 6 cyls. 350 h.p.
rs: Two nose-suspended motors,
gle reduction gear drive.
1 | 15103 | 15105
2 | 15104 | 15106     **Total 6**

## 0-6-0    Diesel Electric

Introduced 1949: Brush design for
W.R.

15107                          **Total 1**

## 0-6-0    Diesel Electric

Introduced 1937: English Electric and
Bulleid design for S.R.
Weight: 55 tons 5 cwt.
Driving Wheels: 4′ 6″.
T.E.: 30,000 lb.
Engine: English Electric 6 cyls. 350 h.p.
Motors: Two nose-suspended motors,
single reduction gear drive.

15201    15202    15203    **Total 3**

## 0-6-0    Diesel Electric

Introduced 1949: English Electric and
Bulleid design for S.R. (S.R. version
of L.M.S.R. 12033 series, but designed
for higher speeds).
Weight: 49 tons.
Driving Wheels: 4′ 6″.
T.E.: 24,000 lb.
Engine: English Electric 6 cyls. 350 h.p.
Motors: Two nose-suspended motors,
double reduction gear drive.

| 15211 | 15218 | 15225 | 15232 |
| 15212 | 15219 | 15226 | 15233 |
| 15213 | 15220 | 15227 | 15234 |
| 15214 | 15221 | 15228 | 15235 |
| 15215 | 15222 | 15229 | 15236 |
| 15216 | 15223 | 15230 | |
| 15217 | 15224 | 15231 | |

**Total 26**

## A-1-A+A-1-A
## Gas Turbine

Introduced 1949: Brown Boveri
(Switzerland) design for W.R.
Weight: 115 tons.
Driving Wheels: 4′ 0¼″.
T.E.: 31,500 lb. at 21 m.p.h.
Engine: 2,500 h.p. gas turbine.
Motors: Four independently mounted
motors with spring drive.

18000                          **Total 1**

## Co + Co     Gas Turbine

Metropolitan-Vickers and Hawksworth
   design for G.W.R.
Weight: 129 tons 10 cwt.
Driving Wheels: 3' 8".

T.E.: maximum 60.000 lb. Continu
   rating : 30,000.lb
Motors: Six nose-suspended mo
   with single reduction gear drive

18100        Tota

# ELECTRIC LOCOMOTIVES

## Co + Co     Class CC

*Introduced 1941: Raworth & Bulleid
   design for S.R.
†Introduced 1948: Later design with
   detail differences.
Weight: { 99 tons 14 cwt.*
       { 104 tons 14 cwt.†
Driving Wheels: 3' 7".
T.E.: { 40,000 lb.*
    { 45,000 lb.†
Voltage: 660 D.C.
Current Collection: Overhead and third
   rail, with flywheel-driven generator
   for gaps in third rail.

| | | |
|---|---|---|
| 20001* | 20002* | 20003† |
| | | Total 3 |

## Bo + Bo     Class EMI

*Introduced 1941: Metropolitan-Vickers
   and Gresley design for L.N.E.R.
Remainder. Introduced 1950.
Production design with detail altera-
tions.
Weight: 87 tons 18 cwt.
Driving Wheels: 4' 2".
T.E.: 45,000 lb.    Voltage: 1,500 D.C.
Current Collection : overhead.

| | | | |
|---|---|---|---|
| 26000* | 26015 | 26030 | 26045 |
| 26001 | 26016 | 26031 | 26046 |
| 26002 | 26017 | 26032 | 26047 |
| 26003 | 26018 | 26033 | 26048 |
| 26004 | 26019 | 26034 | 26049 |
| 26005 | 26020 | 26035 | 26050 |
| 26006 | 26021 | 26036 | 26051 |
| 26007 | 26022 | 26037 | 26052 |
| 26008 | 26023 | 26038 | 26053 |
| 26009 | 26024 | 26039 | 26054 |
| 26010 | 26025 | 26040 | 26055 |
| 26011 | 26026 | 26041 | 26056 |
| 26012 | 26027 | 26042 | 26057 |
| 26013 | 26028 | 26043 | Total |
| 26014 | 26029 | 26044 | 58 |

## Bo + Bo     Class E

Built 1902: Brush & Thomson-Hou
   shunting design for N.E.R.
Weight: 46 tons.
Voltage: 600 D.C.    T.E.: 25,000

| | | |
|---|---|---|
| 26500 | 26501 | Tot |

## Bo + Bo     Class E

EBI Introduced 1946: L.N.E.R. re
   of N.E.R. Raven freight d
   (Introduced 1914) for banking
   on Manchester-Wath line.
Weight: 74 tons 8 cwt.
Driving Wheels: 4' 0".
T.E.: 37,600 lb.    Voltage: 1,500
Current collection: overhead.

26510        Tota

## Co + Co

Under construction: Metropol
   Vickers and L.N.E.R. design, dev
   ment of E.M.I. with six axles
   higher speed range.
Weight: 102 tons.
Driving Wheels: 4' 2".
T.E.: 45,000 lb.    Voltage: 1,500
Current Collection: Overhead.

| | | | |
|---|---|---|---|
| 27000 | 27007 | 27014 | 27 |
| 27001 | 27008 | 27015 | 27 |
| 27002 | 27009 | 27016 | 27 |
| 27003 | 27010 | 27017 | 2 |
| 27004 | 27011 | 27018 | 2 |
| 27005 | 27012 | 27019 | 2 |
| 27006 | 27013 | 27020 | |

NOTE: Locomotives of this
   are still being delivered

# UMMARY OF SOUTHERN REGION STEAM LOCOMOTIVE CLASSES

## IN ALPHABETICAL ORDER
### WITH HISTORICAL NOTES AND DIMENSIONS

**-6-0T** OP **Class A1 & A1X**

A1 Introduced 1872: Stroudley L.B.S.C. "Terrier," later fitted with Marsh boiler, retaining original type smokebox.

A1X Introduced 1911: Rebuild of A1 with Marsh boiler and extended smokebox.

A1X Loco. with increased cylinder diameter.

B. *Western Region No. 5 is also of this class.*

Weight: $\left\{ \begin{array}{l} 27 \text{ tons } 10 \text{ cwt.*} \\ 28 \text{ tons } 5 \text{ cwt.†‡} \end{array} \right.$

essure: 150 lb. Cyls. $\left\{ \begin{array}{l} 12'' \times 20''† \\ 14\frac{3}{16}'' \times 20''‡ \end{array} \right.$

riving Wheels: 4' 0".

E.: $\left\{ \begin{array}{l} 7,650 \text{ lb.*†} \\ 10,695 \text{ lb.‡} \end{array} \right.$

DS680

DS377 DS515, 32640/6/55/9/61 /2/70/7/8.

32636

**Totals: A1 1**
**A1X 12**

**-4-0T** OF **Class B4**

ntroduced 1891: Adams L.S.W. design for dock shunting.
ntroduced 1908: Drummond K14 locos., with smaller boiler and detail alterations.

Adams locos. fitted with Drummond boiler.

Drummond loco. fitted with Adams boiler.

Weight: $\left\{ \begin{array}{l} 33 \text{ tons } 9 \text{ cwt.*‡} \\ 32 \text{ tons } 18 \text{ cwt.†§} \end{array} \right.$

essure: 140 lb. Cyls. (O): 16" × 22".

riving Wheels: 3' 9¾".

E.: 14,650 lb.

30086/7/9/93/4/6, 30102.

30082/3     ‡30088     §30084

**Total 11**

---

**4-6-2** 6MT **Class BB**
(see Class WC & BB)

**0-6-0** 3F **Class C**
Introduced 1900: Wainwright S.E.C. design.
Weight: Loco. 43 tons 16 cwt.
Pressure: 160 lb. Cyls.: 18½" × 26"
Driving Wheels: 5' 2".
T.E.: 19,520 lb.

31004/18/33/7/8/54/9/61 /3/8/71/ 86/90, 31102/12/3/50/91, 31218 /9/21/3/5/7/9/34/42–5/52/3/5/6 /60/7/8/70–2/7/80/7/91/3/4/7/8, 31317,     31461/80/1/6/95/8, 31508/10/3/72/3/5/6/8–85/8–90 /2/3, 31681–4/6–95, 31711–25.

**Total 104**

**0-6-0** 3F **Class C2X**
C2X Introduced 1908: Marsh rebuild of R. J. Billinton L.B.S.C. C.2 with larger C3-type boiler, extended smokebox, etc.
Weight: Loco. 45 tons 5 cwt.
Pressure: 170 lb.
Cyls.: 17½" × 26".
Driving Wheels: 5' 0".
T.E.: 19,175 lb.

32434/7/8/40–51, 32521–9/32/4– 41/3–54.

**Total 45**

**0-4-0T** OF **Class C14**
Introduced 1923: Urie rebuild as shunting locos. of Drummond L.S.W. motor-train 2-2-0T (originally introduced 1906).
Weight: 25 tons 15 cwt.
Pressure: 150 lb.
Cyls.: (O) 14" × 14".
Driving Wheels: 3' 0".
T.E.: 9,720 lb.
Walschaerts gear.

DS77, 30588/9.     **Total 3**

9

## Classes D–E1/R

### 4-4-0 {1P D / 2P D1} Classes D & D1

*D Introduced 1901: Wainwright S.E.C. design, with round-top fire box, some later fitted with extended smokebox.

†D1 Introduced 1921: Maunsell rebuild of Class D, with superheated Belpaire boiler, and long-travel piston valves.

Weights: { 50 tons.* / 52 tons 4 cwt.†
Pressure: { 175 lb.* / 180 lb. Su.†
Cyls.: 19″ × 26″.
Driving Wheels: 6′ 8″.
T.E.: { 17,450 lb.* / 17,950 lb.†

*31075, 31488/93/6, 31549/74/ 7/86/91, 31728/9/33/4/7/44/6.

†31145, 31246/7, 31470/87/9/92/ 4, 31505/9/45, 31727/35/9/41/ 3/9.

Total: Class D 16
Class D1 17

### 0-4-4T 1P Class D3

Introduced 1892: R. J. Billinton L.B.S.C. design, later reboilered by Marsh and fitted from 1934 for push-and-pull working.

Weight: 52 tons.
Pressure: 170 lb.  Cyls.: 17½″ × 26″.
Driving Wheels: 5′ 6″.
T.E.: 17,435 lb.

32372/6/80/4/5/90.

Total 6

### 4-4-0 3P Class D15

Introduced 1912: Drummond L.S.W. design, superheated by Urie from 1915.

Weight: Loco. 61 tons 11 cwt.
Pressure: 180 lb. Su.
Cyls.: 20″ × 26″.
Driving Wheels: 6′ 7″.
T.E.: 20,140 lb.
Walschaerts gear, P.V.

30464/5/7/71.

Total 4

### 4-4-0 {1P E / 2P E1} Classes E & E1

*E Introduced 1905: Wainwright S.E.C. design with Belpaire boiler.

‡E1 Introduced 1919 : Maunsell rebuild of E. with larger superheated Belpaire boiler and long-travel piston valves.

Weight: Loco. { 52 tons 5 cwt.* / 53 tons 9 cwt.‡
Pressure: 180 lb.
Cyls.: 19″ × 26″.
T.E.: 18,410 lb.
Driving Wheels: 6′ 6″.

*31166, 31315.

‡31019/67, 31165, 3149
31504/6/7.

Total: Class E
Class E1

### 0-6-0T 2F Class E

Introduced 1874: Stroudley L.B.S. design, reboilered by Marsh.

Weight: 44 tons 3 cwt.
Pressure: 170 lb.  Cyls.: 17″ × 24″.
Driving Wheels: 4′ 6″.
T.E.: 18,560 lb.

32113/8/9/51      32606/89/9
(W) 1–4.

Total 1

### 0-6-2T 2MT Class E1/

Introduced 1927: Maunsell rebuild Stroudley E1, with radial trailing axl and larger bunker for passenge service in West of England.

Weight: 50 tons 5 cwt.
Pressure: 170 lb.  Cyls.: 17″ × 24″.
Driving Wheels: 4′ 6″.
T.E.: 18,560 lb.

32094–6, 32124/35, 32608/10/9
–7.

Total 1

10

## 0-6-0T     3F     Class E2

Introduced 1913: L. B. Billinton
L.B.S.C. design.
Introduced 1915: Later locos. with
tanks extended further forward.
Weight: { 52 tons 15 cwt.*
{ 53 tons 10 cwt.†
Pressure: 170 lb.   Cyls.: 17½" × 26"
Driving Wheels: 4' 6".
T.E.: 21,305 lb.

32100-4.
32105-9.

Total 10

## 0-6-2T     3F     Class E3

Introduced 1894: R. J. Billinton
L.B.S.C. design, development of
Stroudley " West Brighton " (intro-
duced 1891), reboilered and fitted
with extended smokebox, 1918 on-
wards: cylinder diameter reduced
from 18" by S.R.
Weight: 56 tons 10 cwt.
Pressure: { 160 lb.
{ 170 lb.*
Cyls.: 17½" × 26".
Driving Wheels: 4' 6".
T.E.: { 20,055 lb.
{ 21,305 lb.*

*32165-70.
32453-6/8-62

Total 15

## 0-6-2T     2MT

### Classes E4 & E4X

*E4 Introduced 1910: R. J. Billinton
L.B.S.C. design, development of E3
with larger wheels, reboilered with
Marsh boiler and extended smokebox,
cylinder diameter reduced from 18"
by S.R.
†E4X Introduced 1909: E4 reboilered
with larger 12 4-4-2T type boiler.
Weights: { 57 tons 10 cwt.*
{ 59 tons 5 cwt.†
Pressure: 170 lb.   Cyls.: 17½" × 26"
Driving Wheels: 5' 0"
T E.: 19,175 lb.

### Classes E2–E6 & E6X

*32463-5/7-76/9-82/4-8/90-9,
32500-20/56-66/77-82.
†32466/77/8/89.

Totals:   E4   70
        E4X   4

## 0-6-2T     2MT

### Classes E5 & E5X

*‡E5 Introduced 1902: R. J. Billinton
L.B.S.C. design, development of E4
with larger wheels and firebox,
cylinder diameter reduced from 18"
by S.R.
†E5X Introduced 1911: E5 reboilered
with larger C3-type boiler.
Weights: { 60 tons.*
{ 64 tons 5 cwt.†
{ 160 lb.‡
Pressure: { 175 lb.‡
{ 170 lb.†
Cyls.: 17½" × 26".
Driving Wheels: 5' 6".
T.E.: { 16,410 lb.*
{ 17,945 lb.‡
{ 17,435 lb.†
*‡32399, 32568/71/3/83/5/7/8/
91-3.
†32401, 32570/6/86.

Totals: E5   11
        E5X 4

## 0-6-2T     4F

### Classes E6 & E6X

*‡E6 Introduced 1904: R. J. Billinton
L.B.S.C. design, development of E5
with smaller wheels.
†E6X Introduced 1911: E6 reboilered
with larger C3-type boiler.
Weights: { 61 tons.*
{ 63 tons.†
{ 160 lb.*
Pressure: { 175 lb.‡
{ 170 lb.†
Cyls.: 18" × 26".
Driving Wheels: 4' 6".
T.E.: { 21,215 lb.*
{ 23,205 lb.‡
{ 22,540 lb.†
*‡32408-10/2-8.
†32407/11.

Totals   E6   10
        E6X   2

11

## 0-6-0T  3F  Class G6

*Introduced 189?; Adams L.S.W. design, later additions by Drummond, but with Adams type boiler.
†Introduced 1925: Fitted with Drummond type boiler.
Weight: 47 tons 13 cwt.
Pressure: 160 lb.  Cyls.: 17½″ × 24″.
Driving Wheels: 4′ 10″.
T.E.: 17,235 lb.

*30162, 30238/58/60/6/70/7, 30349, DS3152
†30160, 30274.

Total 11

## 4-8-0T  7F  Class G16

Introduced 1921: Urie L.S.W. "Hump" loco.
Weight: 95 tons 2 cwt.
Pressure: 180 lb. Su.
Cyls.: (O) 22″ × 28″
Driving Wheels: 5′ 1″
T.E.: 33,990 lb.
Walschaerts gear, P.V.

30492–5

Total 4

## 0-4-4T  1P  Class H

Introduced 1904. Wainwright S.E.C. design.
*Introduced 1949. Fitted for push-and-pull working.
Weight: 54 tons 8 cwt.
Pressure: 160 lb.  Cyls.: 18″ × 26″.
Driving Wheels: 5′ 6″
T.E.: 17,360 lb.

31005,   31177/93, 31259/61/3/5 /6/9/74/6/8,   31305-11/20/1/4/ 6-9,   31500/3/21/30/1/3/40/ 2-4/50-3.
*31158/61/2/4/84/93,  31239/79/ 95, 31319/22, 31512/7—20/2/ 3/48/54.

Total 59

## 4-4-2  4P  Class H2

Introduced 1911: Marsh L.B.S.C. design, superheated development of H1 with larger cylinders.
Weight: Loco. 68 tons 5 cwt.
Pressure: 200 lb. Su.
Cyls.: (O) 21″ × 26″.
Driving Wheels: 6′ 7½″.
T.E.: 24,520 lb.
P.V.

32421/2/4-6.

Total 5

## 4-6-0  4MT  Class H15

*Introduced 1914: Urie L.S.W. design fitted with "Maunsell" superheater from 1927, replacing earlier types (30490 built saturated).
†Introduced 1915: Urie rebuild with two outside cylinders of Drummond E14, 4 cyl. 4–6–0 introduced 1907, retaining original boiler retubed and fitted with superheater.
‡Introduced 1924:   Maunsell locos with N15 type boiler and smaller tenders.
§Introduced 1924: Maunsell rebuild of Drummond F13 4-cyl. 4–6–0 introduced 1905, with detail differences from rebuild of E14.
¶Introduced 1927: Urie loco. (built 1914 saturated) rebuilt with later N15 class boiler, with smaller firebox.

Weight: Loco. $\begin{cases} 81 \text{ tons } 5 \text{ cwt.}^* \\ 82 \text{ tons } 1 \text{ cwt.}† \\ 79 \text{ tons } 19 \text{ cwt.}‡¶ \\ 80 \text{ tons } 11 \text{ cwt.}§ \end{cases}$
Pressure: $\begin{cases} 180 \text{ lb. Su.}^{*}‡¶ \\ 175 \text{ lb. Su.}^{*}§ \end{cases}$
Cyls.: 21″ × 28″
Driving Wheels: 6′ 0″.
T.E.: $\begin{cases} 26,240 \text{ lb.}^{*}‡¶ \\ 25,510 \text{ lb.}†§ \end{cases}$
Walschaerts gear, P.V
*30482-90
†30335
‡30473-8, 30521-4
§30330-4
¶30491

Total 26

12

## -2T 5F Class H16

duced 1921: Urie L.S.W. design
heavy freight traffic.
ght: 96 tons 8 cwt.
ure: 180 lb. Su.
: (O) 21″ × 28″.
ing Wheels: 5′ 7″.
28,200 lb.
chaerts valve gear, P.V.

6–20                        **Total 5**

## -0 4MT Class K

duced 1913: L. B. Billinton
B.S.C. design.
ght: Loco. 63 tons 15 cwt.
ure: 180 lb. Su.
: (O) 21″ × 26″.
ing Wheels: 5′ 6″.
26,580 lb.

37–53                       **Total 17**

## -0 2P Class L

duced 1914: Wainwright S.E.C.
sign, with detail alterations by
aunsell.
ght: Loco. 57 tons 9 cwt.
ure: 160 lb. Su.
: 20½″ × 26″.
ing Wheels: 6′ 8″.
18,575 lb.

60–81                       **Total 22**

## -0 2P Class L1

duced 1926: Post-grouping devel-
ment of L, with long-travel valves
e window cab and detail alterations
ght: Loco. 57 tons 16 cwt.
ure: 180 lb. Su.
: 19½″ × 26″.
ng Wheels: 6′ 8″.
18,910 lb.

53–9/82–9                   **Total 15**

## 4-4-0 2P Class L12

Introduced 1904: Drummond L.S.W.
design, development of T9 with larger
boiler, superheated from 1915.
Weight: Loco. 55 tons 5 cwt.
Pressure: 175 lb. Su.
Cyls.: 19″ × 26″.
Driving Wheels: 6′ 7″.
T.E.: 17,675 lb.

30434

**Total 1**

## 4-6-0 6P Class LN

*Introduced 1926: Maunsell design,
cylinders and tender modified by
Bulleid from 1938, and fitted with
multiple-jet blastpipes and large
chimney.
†Introduced 1929: Loco. fitted experi-
mentally with smaller driving wheels.
‡Introduced 1929: Loco. fitted experi-
mentally with longer boiler.
Weights: Loco. $\begin{cases} 83 \text{ tons } 10 \text{ cwt.}^{*\dagger} \\ 84 \text{ tons } 16 \text{ cwt.}^{\ddagger} \end{cases}$
Pressure: 220 lb. Su.
Cyls.: (4) 16½″ × 26″.*
Driving Wheels: $\begin{cases} 6′ 7″ ^{*\ddagger} \\ 6′ 3″ ^{\dagger} \end{cases}$
T.E.: $\begin{cases} 33,510 \text{ lb.}^{*\ddagger} \\ 35\,300 \text{ lb.}^{\dagger} \end{cases}$
Walschaerts gear, P.V.

*30850–8/61–5.
†30859        ‡30860

**Total 16**

## 0-4-4T 2P Class M7

*Introduced 1897: Drummond L.S.W.
M7 design.
†Introduced 1903: Drummond X14
design, with increased front overhang, steam reverser and detail
alterations, now classified M7 (30254
originally M7).

13

## Classes M7–N15

‡Introduced 1925. X14 design fitted for push-and-pull working.

Weights: $\begin{cases} 60 \text{ tons } 4 \text{ cwt.*} \\ 60 \text{ tons } 3 \text{ cwt.†} \\ 62 \text{ tons } 0 \text{ cwt.‡} \end{cases}$

Pressure: 175 lb.
Cyls.: 18½″ × 26″.
Driving Wheels: 5′ 7″.
T.E.: 19.755 lb.

*30022–6/31–44, 30112, 30241–53/5/6, 30318–24/56/7, 30667–71/3–6.
†30030,    30123/4/7/30/2/3, 30254, 30374–8, 30479.
‡30021/7/8/9/45–60,30104–11/25/8/9/31, 30328/79, 30480/1.

Total 103

## 4-6-2   8P   Class MN

*Introduced 1941: Bulleid design.
†Introduced 1951: Modified with single blastpipe and chimney.
Weight: Loco. 94 tons 15 cwt.
Pressure: 280 lb.
Cyl.: (3) 18″ × 24″.
Driving Wheels: 6′ 2″.
T.E.: 37,515 lb.
Bulleid valve gear, P.V.

*35001–18/20–30
†35019

Total 30

## 2-6-0 4MT Classes N & N1

*N Introduced 1917: Maunsell S.E.C. mixed traffic design.
†N1 Introduced 1922: 3-cylinder development of N.
Weight: Loco. $\begin{cases} 61 \text{ tons } 4 \text{ cwt.*} \\ 64 \text{ tons } 5 \text{ cwt.†} \end{cases}$
Pressure: 200 lb.
Cyls.: $\begin{cases} (O) \ 19″ \times 28″* \\ (3) \ 16″ \times 28″† \end{cases}$
Driving Wheels: 5′ 6″

T.E.: $\begin{cases} 26,035 \text{ lb.*} \\ 27,695 \text{ lb.†} \end{cases}$
Walschaerts gear, P.V.

*31400–14, 31810–21/3–75
†31822/76–80

Totals: Class N
         Class N

## 4-6-0   5P   Class N

*Introduced 1918: Urie L.S.W. de...
†Introduced 1928: Urie Locos. mo... with cylinders of reduced diam...
‡Introduced 1925: Maunsell L... with long-travel valves, incr... boiler pressure, smaller fireb... and tenders from Drummond ... 4-6-0's.
§Introduced 1925: Later locos. ... detail alterations and incr... weight.
‖Introduced 1925: Locos. with r... fied cabs to suit Eastern Section ... new bogie tenders.
¶Introduced 1926: Locos. with ... alterations and six-wheeled te... for Central Section.

Weight: Loco. $\begin{cases} 80 \text{ tons } 7 \text{ cwt.*†} \\ 79 \text{ tons } 18 \text{ cwt.‡} \\ 80 \text{ tons } 19 \text{ cwt.§} \\ 81 \text{ tons } 17 \text{ cwt.¶} \end{cases}$
Pressure: $\begin{cases} 180 \text{ lb. Su.*†} \\ 200 \text{ lb. Su.‡‖¶} \end{cases}$
Cyls.: $\begin{cases} (O) \ 22″ \times 28″* \\ (O) \ 21″ \times 28″† \\ (O) \ 20½″ \times 28″‡§‖¶ \end{cases}$
Driving Wheels: 6′ 7″
T.E.: $\begin{cases} 26,245 \text{ lb.*} \\ 23.915 \text{ lb.†} \\ 25,320 \text{ lb.§‡‖¶} \end{cases}$
Walschaerts gear, P.V.

NOTE: Nos. 30736/7/41/52/5 are f... with multiple jet blastpipe ... large diameter chimney.

*30755            †30736–53...
‡30453–7          §30448–52...
‖30763–92         ¶30793–30...
                   Tota...

## 6-0   4P   Class N15X

roduced 1934: Maunsell rebuild of
. B. Billinton L.B.S.C. Class
4-6-4T (introduced 1914).
eight: Loco. 73 tons 2 cwt.
ssure: 180 lb. Su.
s.: (O) 21″ × 28″.
iving Wheels: 6′ 9″.
.: 23,325 lb.
lschaerts gear, P.V.

327–33                          **Total 7**

## 6-0   IF   Class O1

troduced 1903: Wainwright rebuild
ith domed boiler and new cab of
tirling S.E.R. Class O 0–6–0 (intro-
uced 1878).
troduced 1903: Locos. with smaller
riving wheels.
ight: Loco. 41 tons 1 cwt.
ssure: 150 lb. Cyls.: 18″ × 26″.
ving Wheels: $\begin{cases} 5′ 2″* \\ 5′ 1″† \end{cases}$
.: $\begin{cases} 17,325 \text{ lb.*} \\ 17,610 \text{ lb.†} \end{cases}$

064/5,      31258,      31370,
31425/30/4
048

                                **Total 8**

## 4-4T   IP   Class O2

troduced 1889: Adams L.S.W.
esign.
troduced 1923: Fitted with West-
ghouse brake for I.O.W., bunkers
nlarged from 1932.
ted with Drummond-type boiler.
ted for push-and-pull working.
ight: $\begin{cases} 46 \text{ tons 18 cwt.*†} \\ 48 \text{ tons 8 cwt.†} \end{cases}$
ssure: 160 lb. Cyls.: 17½″ × 24″.
ving Wheels: 4′ 10″.
: 17,235 lb.

177/9/92/3/9,    30200/12/6/
24/9/30/2/6.
(W)14–34 †§ (W)35/6.
0203/21/3/33.
30182/3, 30207/25.

                                **Total 44**

## 0-6-0T   0F   Class P

Introduced 1909: Wainwright S.E.C.
design for push-and-pull work, now
used for shunting.
Weight: 28 tons 10 cwt.
Pressure: 160 lb. Cyls.: 12″ × 18″.
Driving Wheels: 3′ 9⅝″.

31027, 31178, 31323/5, 31555–8.

                                **Total 8**

## 0-6-0   4F   Class Q

Introduced 1938: Maunsell design, later
fitted with multiple-jet blastpipe and
large chimney.
Weight: Loco. 49 tons 10 cwt.
Pressure: 200 lb. Su.
Cyls.: 19″ × 26″.
Driving Wheels: 5′ 1″.
T.E.: 26,160 lb.
P.V.

30530–49                        **Total 20**

## 0-6-0   5F   Class QI

Introduced 1942: Bulleid " Austerity "
design.
Weight: Loco. 51 tons 5 cwt.
Pressure: 230 lb. Su.
Cyls.: 19″ × 26″.
Driving Wheels: 5′ 1″.
T.E.: 30,080 lb.
P.V.

33001–40                        **Total 40**

## 0-4-4T   IP   Classes R & RI

*R Introduced 1891: Kirtley L.C.D.
design, since rebuilt with H. class
boiler.
†RI Introduced 1900: Locos. built for
S.E.C. with enlarged bunkers, since
rebuilt with H class boiler

## Classes R & RI–U & UI

‡Fitted for push-and-pull working.
Weight: $\begin{cases} 48 \text{ tons } 15 \text{ cwt.}^* \\ 52 \text{ tons } 3 \text{ cwt.}† \end{cases}$
Pressure: 160 lb. Cyls.: $17\frac{1}{2}'' \times 24''$.
Driving Wheels: 5′ 6″.
T.E.: 15,145 lb.

*31661.
†31698.
*‡31660/2/3/6/71.
†‡31703/4.

Total: Class R 6
Class RI 3

### 0-6-0T    2F    Class RI

*Introduced 1888: Stirling S.E. design, later rebuilt with domed boiler.
†Introduced 1938: Fitted with Urie type short chimney for Whitstable branch, and fitted with or retaining original Stirling-type cab.
‡ Introduced 1952. Rebuilt with domed boiler but retaining Stirling Cab.
Weight: $\begin{cases} 46 \text{ tons } 15 \text{ cwt.}^* \\ 46 \text{ tons } 8 \text{ cwt.}†‡ \end{cases}$
Pressure: 160 lb. Cyls.: $18'' \times 26''$.
Driving Wheels: $\begin{cases} 5' \ 2''^* \\ 5' \ 1''†‡ \end{cases}$
T.E.: $\begin{cases} 18,480 \text{ lb.}^* \\ 18,780 \text{ lb.}†‡ \end{cases}$

*31047, 31128/54/74, 31335/7/40
†31010, 31107/47, 31339.
‡31069

Total 12

### 4-4-0    2P    Class SII

Introduced 1903: Drummond L.S.W. design, development of T9 with larger boiler and smaller wheels for West of England, superheated from 1920.
Weight: Loco. 53 tons, 15 cwt.
Pressure: 175 lb. Su.
Cyls.: $19'' \times 26''$.
Driving Wheels: 6′ 0″.
T.E.: 19,390 lb.

30400

Total 1

### 4-6-0    6F    Class S15

*Introduced 1920: Urie L.S.W. design, development of N15 for mixed traffic work.

---

†Introduced 1927: Post-grouping loco with higher pressure, smaller gra modified footplating and other de differences. 30833-7 with 6-wh tenders for Central Section.
‡Introduced 1936: Later locos. w detail differences and reduced weig
Weight Loco. $\begin{cases} 79 \text{ tons } 16 \text{ cwt.}^* \\ 80 \text{ tons } 14 \text{ cwt.}† \\ 79 \text{ tons } 5 \text{ cwt.}‡ \end{cases}$
Pressure: $\begin{cases} 180 \text{ lb. Su.}^* \\ 200 \text{ lb. Su.}†‡ \end{cases}$
Cyls.: $\begin{cases} (O) \ 21'' \times 28''^* \\ (O) \ 20\frac{1}{2}'' \times 28''†‡ \end{cases}$
Driving Wheels: 5′ 7″
T.E.: $\begin{cases} 28,200 \text{ lb.}^* \\ 29,855 \text{ lb.}†‡ \end{cases}$
Walschaerts gear, P.V.

*30496–30515    †30823–37
‡30838–47

Total

### 4-4-0    2P    Class T

*Introduced 1899: Drummond L.S. design, fitted with superheater a larger cylinders by Urie from 1922.
†Introduced 1899: Locos. with de differences (originally fitted with fi box watertubes).
‡Introduced 1900: Locos. with wid cab and splashers, and witho coupling rod splashers (origina fitted with firebox watertubes.)
Weight: Loco. $\begin{cases} 51 \text{ tons } 18 \text{ cwt.}^* \\ 51 \text{ tons } 16 \text{ cwt.}† \\ 51 \text{ tons } 7 \text{ cwt.}‡ \end{cases}$
Pressure: 175 lb. Su.
Cyls.: $19'' \times 26''$.
Driving Wheels: 6′ 7″.
T.E.: 17,675 lb.

*30117/20, 30282–5/7–9
†30702/5–12/5/7–9/21/4/6–30/2
‡30300/1/4/10/3/37/8

Total 3

### 2-6-0    4MT    Classes U & U

*U Introduced 1928: Rebuild Maunsell S.E.C. Class K ("River 2-6-4T (introduced 1917).
†U Introduced 1928: Locos. built Class U, with smaller splashers ar detail alterations.

Top to bottom:
Gas Turbine
Electric A-1-A+
A-1-A No. 18000;
Diesel Electric
Co+Co-1 No.
10202; Diesel
Electric 0-6-0
No. 12029, Die-
sel Mechanical
0-6-0 No. 11001.
P. Ransome-
Wallis, A. T. H.
Sayler, G. Clarke,
E. Morrison

Top left: Class O2 0-4-4T No. 32 Bonchurch (I.O.W.). Top right: Class O2 0-4-4T No. 30200. Bottom left: Class M7 0-4-4T No. 30132 (originally Class X14). Bottom right: Class M7 0-4-4T No. 30250.

[E. D. Bruton, P. H. Wells, H. C. Casserley, G. R. Wheeler

Top left: Class B4 0-4-0T No. 30089. Top right: Class USA 0-6-0T No. 30072. Bottom left: Class G6 0-6-0T No. DS 3152. Bottom right: Class C14 0-4-0T No. 30589. [G. R. Wheeler (3), P. Ransome-Wallis

This page. To bottom: Class N 2-6 31832; Class U Nos. 31621 and (rebuilt from Cl 2-6-4T); Class UI No. 31907.
[P. H. Wells, F. W R. M. Casserley, P. Herbert

Facing page. T bottom: Class S15 No. 30513; Class 4-6-0s Nos. 3045 Bedivere, 30789 Si (with later type ca bogie tender) and Sir Ector de Maris six-wheel tender).
[P. Ransome-Wallis, Earley, G. R. W R. E. Vincent

acing page. *Top to bottom:* Class S15 4-6-0 No. 30834 (1927 batch); Class H15 4-6-0s Nos. 30485 (Urie design), 30331 (rebuilt from Drummond, Class F13 4-6-0) and 30474 (Maunsell design).
. Elsey, D. Kelk, G. R. Wheeler, R. E. Vincent

is page. *Top to bottom:* Class S11 4-4-0 . 30400; Class T9 4-4-0 . 30288; Class D15 -0 No. 30464; Class D -0 No. 31746.
. R. Wheeler (2), R. E. cent, Dr. G. D. Parkes

Top to bottom: C
H2 4-4-2 No. 32
Beachy Head;    C
N15X 4-6-0 No. 32
Stroudley;    Clas
4-4-0s Nos.   30
Blundells (with h
sided   tender)
30919 Harrow (
multiple-jet blast
and   large diam
chimney).
[A. T. H. Tayler, C
Wheeler (3).

Introduced 1928: 3-cylinder development of Class U (prototype 1890, rebuilt from 2-6-4T, originally built 1925).

Weight: Loco. { 63 tons*
62 tons 6 cwt.†
65 tons 6 cwt.‡

Pressure: 200 lb. Su.
Cyls.: { (O) 19" × 28"*†
(3) 16" × 28"‡
Driving Wheels: 6' 0".
T.E.: { 23,865 lb.*†
25,385 lb.‡
Walschaerts gear, P.V.

31790-31809    †31610-39
‡31890-31910

Total: Class U 50
Class UI 21

## 0-6-0T    3F    Class USA

Introduced 1942: U.S. Army Transportation Corps design, purchased by S.R. 1946, and fitted with modified cab and bunker and other detail alterations.
Weight: 46 tons 10 cwt.
Pressure: 210 lb.
Cyls.: (O) 16½" × 24".
Driving Wheels: 4' 6".
T.E.: 21,600 lb.
Walschaerts gear, P.V.

30061-74    Total 14

## 4-4-0    5P    Class V

Introduced 1930: Maunsell design. Introduced 1938: Fitted with multiple jet blastpipe and larger chimney by Bulleid.
Weight: Loco. 67 tons 2 cwt.
Pressure: 220 lb. Su.
Cyls.: (3) 16½" × 26".
Driving Wheels: 6' 7".
T.E.: 25,135 lb.
Walschaerts gear, P.V.

30902-6/8/10-2/6/22/3/5-8/32/5/6.
30900/1/7/9/13-5/7-21/4/29-31/3/4/7-9.

Total 40

## 2-6-4T    5F    Class W

Introduced 1931: Maunsell design, developed from Class N1 2-6-0.
Weight: 90 tons 14 cwt.
Pressure: 200 lb. Su.
Cyls.: (3) 16½" × 28".
Driving Wheels: 5' 6".
T.E.: 29,450 lb.
Walschaerts gear, P.V.

31911-25    Total 15

## 4-6-2    6MT

### Classes WC & BB

*Introduced 1945: Bulleid " West Country " Class.
†Introduced 1946: Bulleid " Battle of Britain " Class.
‡Introduced 1948: Locos. with larger tenders.
Weight: Loco. 86 tons 0 cwt.
Pressure: 280 lb. Su.
Cyls.: (3) 16⅜" × 24".
Driving Wheels: 6' 2".
T.E.: 31,050 lb.
Bulleid valve gear, P.V.

*34001-48    †34049-70
†‡34071-90, 34109/10
*‡34091-34108

Total 110

## 0-8-0T    7F    Class Z

Introduced 1929: Maunsell design for heavy shunting.
Weight: 71 tons 12 cwt.
Pressure: 180 lb. Cyls.: (3) 16" × 18".
Driving Wheels: 4' 8".
T.E.: 29,375 lb.
Walschaerts gear, P.V.

30950-7    Total 8

## 0-6-0    4F    Class 700

Introduced 1897: Drummond L.S.W. design, superheated from 1921.
Weight: Loco. 46 tons 14 cwt.
Pressure: 180 lb. Su.
Cyls.: 19" × 26".
Driving Wheels: 5' 1".
T.E.: 23,540 lb.

30306-8/9/15-7/25-7/39/46/50/2/5/68, 30687-30701.

Total 30

**0-6-2T** IMT **Class 757**

Introduced 1907: Hawthorn Leslie
design for P.D.S.W.J.
Weight: 49 tons 19 cwt.
Pressure: 170 lb.
Cyls.: (O) 16″ × 24″.
Driving Wheels: 4′ 0″.
T.E.: 18,495 lb.

30757–8 **Total 2**

**2-4-0WT** OF **Class 0298**

Introduced 1874: Beattie L.S.W.
design, rebuilt by Adams (1884-92),
Urie (1921-2) and Maunsell (1931-5)
Weight: 37 tons 16 cwt.
Pressure: 160 lb.
Cyls.: (O) 16½″ × 20″.
Driving Wheels: 5′ 7″.
T.E.: 11,050 lb.

30585–7 **Total 3**

**0-6-0** IF **Class 0395**

*Introduced 1881: Adams L.S.W.
design.
†Introduced 1885: Adams " 496 "
class with longer front overhang.
‡Introduced 1928: Reboilered with
ex-S.E.C. Class M3 4-4-0 boiler.
§Fitted with Drummond type boiler.
Weight: Loco. { 37 tons 12 cwt.*
{ 38 tons 14 cwt.†
Pressure: { 140 lb.*
{ 150 lb.†

Driving Wheels: 5′ 1″.
T.E.: { 15,535 lb.*
{ 16,645 lb†.
*30568–72/4/5/7/8
†30566/79            *‡30573
* §30567  ††30580  † §30564

**Total I**

**4-4-2T** IP **Class 041**

Introduced 1882: Adams L.S.V
design later reboilered.
Weight: 55 tons 2 cwt.
Pressure: 160 lb.
Cyls.: (O) 17½″ × 24″.
Driving Wheels: 5′ 7″.
T.E.: 14,920 lb.

30582–4 **Total**

**0-4-0ST** OF **Class 045**

Introduced 1890: Hawthorn Les
design for Southampton Docks Co
absorbed by L.S.W., 1892.
Weight: 21 tons 2 cwt.
Pressure: 120 lb
Cyls.: (O) 12″ × 20″.
Driving Wheels: 3′ 2″.
T.E.: 7,730 lb.

30458 **Total**

# BRITISH RAILWAYS' LOCOMOTIVES
## Nos. 30021-30323, W1-36

**Named Engines are indicated by an Asterisk (*)**

| No. | Class | No. | Class | No. | Class | No. | Class |
|---|---|---|---|---|---|---|---|
| 21 | M7 | 30060 | M7 | 30125 | M7 | 30248 | M7 |
| 22 | M7 | 30061 | U.S.A. | 30127 | M7 | 30249 | M7 |
| 23 | M7 | 30062 | U.S.A. | 30128 | M7 | 30250 | M7 |
| 24 | M7 | 30063 | U.S.A. | 30129 | M7 | 30251 | M7 |
| 25 | M7 | 30064 | U.S.A. | 30130 | M7 | 30252 | M7 |
| 26 | M7 | 30065 | U.S.A. | 30131 | M7 | 30253 | M7 |
| 27 | M7 | 30066 | U.S.A. | 30132 | M7 | 30254 | M7 |
| 28 | M7 | 30067 | U.S.A. | 30133 | M7 | 30255 | M7 |
| 29 | M7 | 30068 | U.S.A. | 30160 | G6 | 30256 | M7 |
| 30 | M7 | 30069 | U.S.A. | 30162 | G6 | 30258 | G6 |
| 31 | M7 | 30070 | U.S.A. | 30177 | O2 | 30260 | G6 |
| 32 | M7 | 30071 | U.S.A. | 30179 | O2 | 30266 | G6 |
| 33 | M7 | 30072 | U.S.A. | 30182 | O2 | 30270 | G6 |
| 34 | M7 | 30073 | U.S.A. | 30183 | O2 | 30274 | G6 |
| 35 | M7 | 30074 | U.S.A. | 30192 | O2 | 30277 | G6 |
| 36 | M7 | 30082 | B4 | 30193 | O2 | 30282 | T9 |
| 37 | M7 | 30083 | B4 | 30199 | O2 | 30283 | T9 |
| 38 | M7 | 30084 | B4 | 30200 | O2 | 30284 | T9 |
| 39 | M7 | 30086* | B4 | 30203 | O2 | 30285 | T9 |
| 40 | M7 | 30087 | B4 | 30207 | O2 | 30287 | T9 |
| 41 | M7 | 30088 | B4 | 30212 | O2 | 30288 | T9 |
| 42 | M7 | 30089 | B4 | 30216 | O2 | 30289 | T9 |
| 43 | M7 | 30093 | B4 | 30221 | O2 | 30300 | T9 |
| 44 | M7 | 30094 | B4 | 30223 | O2 | 30301 | T9 |
| 45 | M7 | 30096 | B4 | 30224 | O2 | 30304 | T9 |
| 46 | M7 | 30102 | B4 | 30225 | O2 | 30306 | 700 |
| 47 | M7 | 30104 | M7 | 30229 | O2 | 30308 | 700 |
| 48 | M7 | 30105 | M7 | 30230 | O2 | 30309 | 700 |
| 49 | M7 | 30106 | M7 | 30232 | O2 | 30310 | T9 |
| 50 | M7 | 30107 | M7 | 30233 | O2 | 30313 | T9 |
| 51 | M7 | 30108 | M7 | 30236 | O2 | 30315 | 700 |
| 52 | M7 | 30109 | M7 | 30238 | G6 | 30316 | 700 |
| 53 | M7 | 30110 | M7 | 30241 | M7 | 30317 | 700 |
| 54 | M7 | 30111 | M7 | 30242 | M7 | 30318 | M7 |
| 55 | M7 | 30112 | M7 | 30243 | M7 | 30319 | M7 |
| 56 | M7 | 30117 | T9 | 30244 | M7 | 30320 | M7 |
| 57 | M7 | 30120 | T9 | 30245 | M7 | 30321 | M7 |
| 58 | M7 | 30123 | M7 | 30246 | M7 | 30322 | M7 |
| 59 | M7 | 30124 | M7 | 30247 | M7 | 30323 | M7 |

| No. | Class | No. | Class | No. | Class | No. | Clas |
|---|---|---|---|---|---|---|---|
| 30324 | M7 | 30467 | D15 | 30514 | S15 | 30578 | 039 |
| 30325 | 700 | 30471 | D15 | 30515 | S15 | 30579 | 039 |
| 30326 | 700 | 30473 | H15 | 30516 | H16 | 30580 | 039 |
| 30327 | 700 | 30474 | H15 | 30517 | H16 | 30582 | 041 |
| 30328 | M7 | 30475 | H15 | 30518 | H16 | 30583 | 041 |
| 30330 | H15 | 30476 | H15 | 30519 | H16 | 30584 | 041 |
| 30331 | H15 | 30477 | H15 | 30520 | H16 | 30585 | 029 |
| 30332 | H15 | 30478 | H15 | 30521 | H15 | 30586 | 029 |
| 30333 | H15 | 30479 | M7 | 30522 | H15 | 30587 | 029 |
| 30334 | H15 | 30480 | M7 | 30523 | H15 | 30588 | C |
| 30335 | H15 | 30481 | M7 | 30524 | H15 | 30589 | C |
| 30337 | T9 | 30482 | H15 | 30530 | Q | 30667 | M |
| 30338 | T9 | 30483 | H15 | 30531 | Q | 30668 | N |
| 30339 | 700 | 30484 | H15 | 30532 | Q | 30669 | N |
| 30346 | 700 | 30485 | H15 | 30533 | Q | 30670 | N |
| 30349 | G6 | 30486 | H15 | 30534 | Q | 30671 | N |
| 30350 | 700 | 30487 | H15 | 30535 | Q | 30673 | N |
| 30352 | 700 | 30488 | H15 | 30536 | Q | 30674 | N |
| 30355 | 700 | 30489 | H15 | 30537 | Q | 30675 | N |
| 30356 | M7 | 30490 | H15 | 30538 | Q | 30676 | N |
| 30357 | M7 | 30491 | H15 | 30539 | Q | 30687 | 7 |
| 30368 | 700 | 30492 | G16 | 30540 | Q | 30688 | 7 |
| 30374 | M7 | 30493 | G16 | 30541 | Q | 30689 | 7 |
| 30375 | M7 | 30494 | G16 | 30542 | Q | 30690 | 7 |
| 30376 | M7 | 30495 | G16 | 30543 | Q | 30691 | 7 |
| 30377 | M7 | 30496 | S15 | 30544 | Q | 30692 | 7 |
| 30378 | M7 | 30497 | S15 | 30545 | Q | 30693 | 7 |
| 30379 | M7 | 30498 | S15 | 30546 | Q | 30694 | 7 |
| 30400 | S11 | 30499 | S15 | 30547 | Q | 30695 | 7 |
| 30434 | L12 | 30500 | S15 | 30548 | Q | 30696 | 7 |
| 30448* | N15 | 30501 | S15 | 30549 | Q | 30697 | 7 |
| 30449* | N15 | 30502 | S15 | 30564 | 0395 | 30698 | 7 |
| 30450* | N15 | 30503 | S15 | 30566 | 0395 | 30699 | 7 |
| 30451* | N15 | 30504 | S15 | 30567 | 0395 | 30700 | 7 |
| 30452* | N15 | 30505 | S15 | 30568 | 0395 | 30701 | 7 |
| 30453* | N15 | 30506 | S15 | 30569 | 0395 | 30702 | |
| 30454* | N15 | 30507 | S15 | 30570 | 0395 | 30705 | |
| 30455* | N15 | 30508 | S15 | 30571 | 0395 | 30706 | |
| 30456* | N15 | 30509 | S15 | 30572 | 0395 | 30707 | |
| 30457* | N15 | 30510 | S15 | 30573 | 0395 | 30708 | |
| 30458* | 0458 | 30511 | S15 | 30574 | 0395 | 30709 | |
| 30464 | D15 | 30512 | S15 | 30575 | 0395 | 30710 | |
| 30465 | D15 | 30513 | S15 | 30577 | 0395 | 30711 | |

| No. | Class | No. | Class | No. | Class | No. | Class |
|---|---|---|---|---|---|---|---|
| 30712 | T9 | 30772* | N15 | 30831 | S15 | 30910* | V |
| 30715 | T9 | 30773* | N15 | 30832 | S15 | 30911* | V |
| 30717 | T9 | 30774* | N15 | 30833 | S15 | 30912* | V |
| 30718 | T9 | 30775* | N15 | 30834 | S15 | 30913* | V |
| 30719 | T9 | 30776* | N15 | 30835 | S15 | 30914* | V |
| 30721 | T9 | 30777* | N15 | 30836 | S15 | 30915* | V |
| 30724 | T9 | 30778* | N15 | 30837 | S15 | 30916* | V |
| 30726 | T9 | 30779* | N15 | 30838 | S15 | 30917* | V |
| 30727 | T9 | 30780* | N15 | 30839 | S15 | 30918* | V |
| 30728 | T9 | 30781* | N15 | 30840 | S15 | 30919* | V |
| 30729 | T9 | 30782* | N15 | 30841 | S15 | 30920* | V |
| 30730 | T9 | 30783* | N15 | 30842 | S15 | 30921* | V |
| 30732 | T9 | 30784* | N15 | 30843 | S15 | 30922* | V |
| 30736* | N15 | 30785* | N15 | 30844 | S15 | 30923* | V |
| 30737* | N15 | 30786* | N15 | 30845 | S15 | 30924* | V |
| 30738* | N15 | 30787* | N15 | 30846 | S15 | 30925* | V |
| 30739* | N15 | 30788* | N15 | 30847 | S15 | 30926* | V |
| 30740* | N15 | 30789* | N15 | 30850* | LN | 30927* | V |
| 30741* | N15 | 30790* | N15 | 30851* | LN | 30928* | V |
| 30742* | N15 | 30791* | N15 | 30852* | LN | 30929* | V |
| 30743* | N15 | 30792* | N15 | 30853* | LN | 30930* | V |
| 30744* | N15 | 30793* | N15 | 30854* | LN | 30931* | V |
| 30745* | N15 | 30794* | N15 | 30855* | LN | 30932* | V |
| 30746* | N15 | 30795* | N15 | 30856* | LN | 30933* | V |
| 30747* | N15 | 30796* | N15 | 30857* | LN | 30934* | V |
| 30748* | N15 | 30797* | N15 | 30858* | LN | 30935* | V |
| 30749* | N15 | 30798* | N15 | 30859* | LN | 30936* | V |
| 30750* | N15 | 30799* | N15 | 30860* | LN | 30937* | V |
| 30751* | N15 | 30800* | N15 | 30861* | LN | 30938* | V |
| 30752* | N15 | 30801* | N15 | 30862* | LN | 30939* | V |
| 30753* | N15 | 30802* | N15 | 30863* | LN | 30950 | Z |
| 30755* | N15 | 30803* | N15 | 30864* | LN | 30951 | Z |
| 30757* | 757 | 30804* | N15 | 30865* | LN | 30952 | Z |
| 30758* | 757 | 30805* | N15 | 30900* | V | 30953 | Z |
| 30763* | N15 | 30806* | N15 | 30901* | V | 30954 | Z |
| 30764* | N15 | 30823 | S15 | 30902* | V | 30955 | Z |
| 30765* | N15 | 30824 | S15 | 30903* | V | 30956 | Z |
| 30766* | N15 | 30825 | S15 | 30904* | V | 30957 | Z |
| 30767* | N15 | 30826 | S15 | 30905* | V | 31004 | C |
| 30768* | N15 | 30827 | S15 | 30906* | V | 31005 | H |
| 30769* | N15 | 30828 | S15 | 30907* | V | 31010 | R1 |
| 30770* | N15 | 30829 | S15 | 30908* | V | 31018 | C |
| 30771* | N15 | 30830 | S15 | 30909* | V | 31019 | E1 |

| No. | Class | No. | Class | No. | Class | No. | Cl |
|-----|-------|-----|-------|-----|-------|-----|----|
| 31027 | P | 31223 | C | 31306 | H | 31470 | |
| 31033 | C | 31225 | C | 31307 | H | 31480 | |
| 31037 | C | 31227 | C | 31308 | H | 31481 | |
| 31038 | C | 31229 | C | 31309 | H | 31486 | |
| 31047 | RI | 31234 | C | 31310 | H | 31487 | |
| 31048 | OI | 31239 | H | 31311 | H | 31488 | |
| 31054 | C | 31242 | C | 31315 | E | 31489 | |
| 31059 | C | 31243 | C | 31317 | C | 31492 | |
| 31061 | C | 31244 | C | 31319 | H | 31493 | |
| 31063 | C | 31245 | C | 31320 | H | 31494 | |
| 31064 | OI | 31246 | DI | 31321 | H | 31495 | |
| 31065 | OI | 31247 | DI | 31322 | H | 31496 | |
| 31067 | EI | 31252 | C | 31323 | P | 31497 | |
| 31068 | C | 31253 | C | 31324 | H | 31498 | |
| 31069 | RI | 31255 | C | 31325 | P | 31500 | |
| 31071 | C | 31256 | C | 31326 | H | 31503 | |
| 31075 | D | 31258 | OI | 31327 | H | 31504 | |
| 31086 | C | 31259 | H | 31328 | H | 31505 | |
| 31090 | C | 31260 | C | 31329 | H | 31506 | |
| 31102 | C | 31261 | H | 31335 | RI | 31507 | |
| 31107 | RI | 31263 | H | 31337 | RI | 31508 | |
| 31112 | C | 31265 | H | 31339 | RI | 31509 | |
| 31113 | C | 31266 | H | 31340 | RI | 31510 | |
| 31128 | RI | 31267 | C | 31370 | OI | 31512 | |
| 31145 | DI | 31268 | C | 31400 | N | 31513 | |
| 31147 | RI | 31269 | H | 31401 | N | 31517 | |
| 31150 | C | 31270 | C | 31402 | N | 31518 | |
| 31154 | RI | 31271 | C | 31403 | N | 31519 | |
| 31158 | H | 31272 | C | 31404 | N | 31520 | |
| 31161 | H | 31274 | H | 31405 | N | 31521 | |
| 31162 | H | 31276 | H | 31406 | N | 31522 | |
| 31164 | H | 31277 | C | 31407 | N | 31523 | |
| 31165 | EI | 31278 | H | 31408 | N | 31530 | |
| 31166 | E | 31279 | H | 31409 | N | 31531 | |
| 31174 | RI | 31280 | C | 31410 | N | 31533 | |
| 31177 | H | 31287 | C | 31411 | N | 31540 | |
| 31178 | P | 31291 | C | 31412 | N | 31542 | |
| 31184 | H | 31293 | C | 31413 | N | 31543 | |
| 31191 | C | 31294 | C | 31414 | N | 31544 | |
| 31193 | H | 31295 | H | 31425 | OI | 31545 | |
| 31218 | C | 31297 | C | 31430 | OI | 31548 | |
| 31219 | C | 31298 | C | 31434 | OI | 31549 | |
| 31221 | C | 31305 | H | 31461 | C | 31550 | |

| No. | Class | No. | Class | No. | Class | No. | Class |
|---|---|---|---|---|---|---|---|
| 31551 | H | 31624 | U | 31715 | C | 31772 | L |
| 31552 | H | 31625 | U | 31716 | C | 31773 | L |
| 31553 | H | 31626 | U | 31717 | C | 31774 | L |
| 31554 | H | 31627 | U | 31718 | C | 31775 | L |
| 31555 | P | 31628 | U | 31719 | C | 31776 | L |
| 31556 | P | 31629 | U | 31720 | C | 31777 | L |
| 31557 | P | 31630 | U | 31721 | C | 31778 | L |
| 31558 | P | 31631 | U | 31722 | C | 31779 | L |
| 31572 | C | 31632 | U | 31723 | C | 31780 | L |
| 31573 | C | 31633 | U | 31724 | C | 31781 | L |
| 31574 | D | 31634 | U | 31725 | C | 31782 | LI |
| 31575 | C | 31635 | U | 31727 | DI | 31783 | LI |
| 31576 | C | 31636 | U | 31728 | D | 31784 | LI |
| 31577 | D | 31637 | U | 31729 | D | 31785 | LI |
| 31578 | C | 31638 | U | 31733 | D | 31786 | LI |
| 31579 | C | 31639 | U | 31734 | D | 31787 | LI |
| 31580 | C | 31660 | R | 31735 | DI | 31788 | LI |
| 31581 | C | 31661 | R | 31737 | D | 31789 | LI |
| 31582 | C | 31662 | R | 31739 | DI | 31790 | U |
| 31583 | C | 31663 | R | 31741 | DI | 31791 | U |
| 31584 | C | 31666 | R | 31743 | DI | 31792 | U |
| 31585 | C | 31671 | R | 31744 | D | 31793 | U |
| 31586 | D | 31681 | C | 31746 | D | 31794 | U |
| 31588 | C | 31682 | C | 31749 | DI | 31795 | U |
| 31589 | C | 31683 | C | 31753 | LI | 31796 | U |
| 31590 | C | 31684 | C | 31754 | LI | 31797 | U |
| 31591 | D | 31686 | C | 31755 | LI | 31798 | U |
| 31592 | C | 31687 | C | 31756 | LI | 31799 | U |
| 31593 | C | 31688 | C | 31757 | LI | 31800 | U |
| 31610 | U | 31689 | C | 31758 | LI | 31801 | U |
| 31611 | U | 31690 | C | 31759 | LI | 31802 | U |
| 31612 | U | 31691 | C | 31760 | L | 31803 | U |
| 31613 | U | 31692 | C | 31761 | L | 31804 | U |
| 31614 | U | 31693 | C | 31762 | L | 31805 | U |
| 31615 | U | 31694 | C | 31763 | L | 31806 | U |
| 31616 | U | 31695 | C | 31764 | L | 31807 | U |
| 31617 | U | 31698 | RI | 31765 | L | 31808 | U |
| 31618 | U | 31703 | RI | 31766 | L | 31809 | U |
| 31619 | U | 31704 | RI | 31767 | L | 31810 | N |
| 31620 | U | 31711 | C | 31768 | L | 31811 | N |
| 31621 | U | 31712 | C | 31769 | L | 31812 | N |
| 31622 | U | 31713 | C | 31770 | L | 31813 | N |
| 31623 | U | 31714 | C | 31771 | L | 31814 | N |

| No. | Class | No. | Class | No. | Class | No. | Cl |
|---|---|---|---|---|---|---|---|
| 31815 | N | 31858 | N | 31910 | UI | 32329* | NI |
| 31816 | N | 31859 | N | 31911 | W | 32330* | NI |
| 31817 | N | 31860 | N | 31912 | W | 32331* | NI |
| 31818 | N | 31861 | N | 31913 | W | 32332* | NI |
| 31819 | N | 31862 | N | 31914 | W | 32333* | NI |
| 31820 | N | 31863 | N | 31915 | W | 32337 | |
| 31821 | N | 31864 | N | 31916 | W | 32338 | |
| 31822 | NI | 31865 | N | 31917 | W | 32339 | |
| 31823 | N | 31866 | N | 31918 | W | 32340 | |
| 31824 | N | 31867 | N | 31919 | W | 32341 | |
| 31825 | N | 31868 | N | 31920 | W | 32342 | |
| 31826 | N | 31869 | N | 31921 | W | 32343 | |
| 31827 | N | 31870 | N | 31922 | W | 32344 | |
| 31828 | N | 31871 | N | 31923 | W | 32345 | |
| 31829 | N | 31872 | N | 31924 | W | 32346 | |
| 31830 | N | 31873 | N | 31925 | W | 32347 | |
| 31831 | N | 31874 | N | 32094 | EI/R | 32348 | |
| 31832 | N | 31875 | N | 32095 | EI/R | 32349 | |
| 31833 | N | 31876 | NI | 32096 | EI/R | 32350 | |
| 31834 | N | 31877 | NI | 32100 | E2 | 32351 | |
| 31835 | N | 31878 | NI | 32101 | E2 | 32352 | |
| 31836 | N | 31879 | NI | 32102 | E2 | 32353 | |
| 31837 | N | 31880 | NI | 32103 | E2 | 32372 | |
| 31838 | N | 31890 | UI | 32104 | E2 | 32376 | |
| 31839 | N | 31891 | UI | 32105 | E2 | 32380 | |
| 31840 | N | 31892 | UI | 32106 | E2 | 32384 | |
| 31841 | N | 31893 | UI | 32107 | E2 | 32385 | |
| 31842 | N | 31894 | UI | 32108 | E2 | 32390 | |
| 31843 | N | 31895 | UI | 32109 | E2 | 32399 | |
| 31844 | N | 31896 | UI | 32113 | EI | 32401 | E |
| 31845 | N | 31897 | UI | 32124 | EI/R | 32407 | E |
| 31846 | N | 31898 | UI | 32135 | EI/R | 32408 | |
| 31847 | N | 31899 | UI | 32138 | EI | 32409 | |
| 31848 | N | 31900 | UI | 32139 | EI | 32410 | |
| 31849 | N | 31901 | UI | 32151 | EI | 32411 | E |
| 31850 | N | 31902 | UI | 32165 | E3 | 32412 | |
| 31851 | N | 31903 | UI | 32166 | E3 | 32413 | |
| 31852 | N | 31904 | UI | 32167 | E3 | 32414 | |
| 31853 | N | 31905 | UI | 32168 | E3 | 32415 | |
| 31854 | N | 31906 | UI | 32169 | E3 | 32416 | |
| 31855 | N | 31907 | UI | 32170 | E3 | 32417 | |
| 31856 | N | 31908 | UI | 32327* | NI5X | 32418 | |
| 31857 | N | 31909 | UI | 32328* | NI5X | 32421* | |

Class L
No. 31781.
G. Pearson

Class E
No. 31315.
Casserley

Class LI
31759.
Wheeler

Class DI
31739.
Buckley

[M. W. Ea

Class LN 4-6-0 No. 30856 *Lord St. Vincent.*

[C.

Class MN 4-6-2 No. 35018 *British India Line* (with self-weighing tender).

[F.

Class WC 4-6-2 No. 34034 *Honiton.*

bottom: Class
6-0 No. 33007;
Q 0-6-0 No.
; Class C2X
No. 32440;
K 2-6-0 No.

. Pearson, A. F.
D. Kelk, F. W.

Top left: Class C 0-6-0 No. 31271.  Top right: Class O1 0-6-0 No. 31048.
Bottom left: Class 700 0-6-0 No. 30317.  Bottom right: Class 0395 0-6-0
No. 30577.
[C. G. Pearson, D. J. Borthwick, P. C. Short, A. B. Crompton

*Top left:* Class G16 4-8-0T No. 30494. *Top right:* Class W 2-6-4T No. 31924.
*Bottom left:* Class H16 4-6-2T No. 30516. *Bottom right:* Class Z 0-8-0T No.30953.
[E. D. Bruton, P. Ransome-Wallis, F. W. Day, H. C. Casserley

Top left: Class E1/R 0-6-2T No. 32697    Top right: Class E6 0-6-2T No. 32416.    Bottom left: Class E4 0-6-2T No. 32494.    Bottom right:
Class E5X 0-6-2T No. 32586.                                                      F. W. Day (2), R. E. Vincent, R. J. Buckley

Top left: Class E1 0-6-0T No. 1 Medina.  Top right: Class E2 0-6-0T No. 32103.
Bottom left: Class H 0-4-4T No. 31184.  Bottom right: Class D3 0-4-4T No.
32384.

[H. C. Casserley, (2) P. C. Short, E. R. Wethersett]

Top left: Diesel 0-6-0 No. DS1173. Top right: Class R1 0-6-0T No. 31339. Bottom left: Class A1X 0-6-0T No. 32640. Bottom right: Class P 0-6-0T No. 31323.

[G. R. Wheeler, F. J. Saunders, P. Ransome-Wallis (2)]

| No. | Class | No. | Class | No. | Class | No. | Class |
|---|---|---|---|---|---|---|---|
| 2* | H2 | 32478 | E4X | 32522 | C2X | 32573 | E5 |
| 4* | H2 | 32479 | E4 | 32523 | C2X | 32576 | E5X |
| 5* | H2 | 32480 | E4 | 32524 | C2X | 32577 | E4 |
| 6* | H2 | 32481 | E4 | 32525 | C2X | 32578 | E4 |
| 4 | C2X | 32482 | E4 | 32526 | C2X | 32579 | E4 |
| 7 | C2X | 32484 | E4 | 32527 | C2X | 32580 | E4 |
| 8 | C2X | 32485 | E4 | 32528 | C2X | 32581 | E4 |
| 0 | C2X | 32486 | E4 | 32529 | C2X | 32582 | E4 |
| 1 | C2X | 32487 | E4 | 32532 | C2X | 32583 | E5 |
| 2 | C2X | 32488 | E4 | 32534 | C2X | 32585 | E5 |
| 3 | C2X | 32489 | E4X | 32535 | C2X | 32586 | E5X |
| 4 | C2X | 32490 | E4 | 32536 | C2X | 32587 | E5 |
| 5 | C2X | 32491 | E4 | 32537 | C2X | 32588 | E5 |
| 6 | C2X | 32492 | E4 | 32538 | C2X | 32591 | E5 |
| 7 | C2X | 32493 | E4 | 32539 | C2X | 32592 | E5 |
| 8 | C2X | 32494 | E4 | 32540 | C2X | 32593 | E5 |
| 9 | C2X | 32495 | E4 | 32541 | C2X | 32606 | E1 |
| 0 | C2X | 32496 | E4 | 32543 | C2X | 32608 | E1/R |
| 1 | C2X | 32497 | E4 | 32544 | C2X | 32610 | E1/R |
| 3 | E3 | 32498 | E4 | 32545 | C2X | 32636 | A1X |
| 4 | E3 | 32499 | E4 | 32546 | C2X | 32640 | A1X |
| 5 | E3 | 32500 | E4 | 32547 | C2X | 32646 | A1X |
| 6 | E3 | 32501 | E4 | 32548 | C2X | 32655 | A1X |
| 8 | E3 | 32502 | E4 | 32549 | C2X | 32659 | A1X |
| 9 | E3 | 32503 | E4 | 32550 | C2X | 32661 | A1X |
| 0 | E3 | 32504 | E4 | 32551 | C2X | 32662 | A1X |
| 1 | E3 | 32505 | E4 | 32552 | C2X | 32670 | A1X |
| 2 | E3 | 32506 | E4 | 32553 | C2X | 32677 | A1X |
| 3 | E4 | 32507 | E4 | 32554 | C2X | 32678 | A1X |
| 4 | E4 | 32508 | E4 | 32556 | E4 | 32689 | E1 |
| 5 | E4 | 32509 | E4 | 32557 | E4 | 32694 | E1 |
| 6 | E4X | 32510 | E4 | 32558 | E4 | 32695 | E1/R |
| 7 | E4 | 32511 | E4 | 32559 | E4 | 32696 | E1/R |
| 8 | E4 | 32512 | E4 | 32560 | E4 | 32697 | E1/R |
| 9 | E4 | 32513 | E4 | 32561 | E4 | 33001 | Q1 |
| 0 | E4 | 32514 | E4 | 32562 | E4 | 33002 | Q1 |
| 1 | E4 | 32515 | E4 | 32563 | E4 | 33003 | Q1 |
| 2 | E4 | 32516 | E4 | 32564 | E4 | 33004 | Q1 |
| 3 | E4 | 32517 | E4 | 32565 | E4 | 33005 | Q1 |
| 4 | E4 | 32518 | E4 | 32566 | E4 | 33006 | Q1 |
| 5 | E4 | 32519 | E4 | 32568 | E5 | 33007 | Q1 |
| 6 | E4 | 32520 | E4 | 32570 | E5X | 33008 | Q1 |
| 7 | E4X | 32521 | C2X | 32571 | E5 | 33009 | Q1 |

| No. | Class | No. | Class | No. | Class | No. |
|---|---|---|---|---|---|---|
| 33010 | QI | 34013* | WC | 34056* | BB | 34099* |
| 33011 | QI | 34014* | WC | 34057* | BB | 34100* |
| 33012 | QI | 34015* | WC | 34058* | BB | 34101* |
| 33013 | QI | 34016* | WC | 34059* | BB | 34102* |
| 33014 | QI | 34017* | WC | 34060* | BB | 34103* |
| 33015 | QI | 34018* | WC | 34061* | BB | 34104* |
| 33016 | QI | 34019* | WC | 34062* | BB | 34105* |
| 33017 | QI | 34020* | WC | 34063* | BB | 34106* |
| 33018 | QI | 34021* | WC | 34064* | BB | 34107* |
| 33019 | QI | 34022* | WC | 34065* | BB | 34108* |
| 33020 | QI | 34023* | WC | 34066* | BB | 34109* |
| 33021 | QI | 34024* | WC | 34067* | BB | 34110* |
| 33022 | QI | 34025* | WC | 34068* | BB | 35001* |
| 33023 | QI | 34026* | WC | 34069* | BB | 35002* |
| 33024 | QI | 34027* | WC | 34070* | BB | 35003* |
| 33025 | QI | 34028* | WC | 34071* | BB | 35004* |
| 33026 | QI | 34029* | WC | 34072* | BB | 35005* |
| 33027 | QI | 34030* | WC | 34073* | BB | 35006* |
| 33028 | QI | 34031* | WC | 34074* | BB | 35007* |
| 33029 | QI | 34032* | WC | 34075* | BB | 35008* |
| 33030 | QI | 34033* | WC | 34076* | BB | 35009* |
| 33031 | QI | 34034* | WC | 34077* | BB | 35010* |
| 33032 | QI | 34035* | WC | 34078* | BB | 35011* |
| 33033 | QI | 34036* | WC | 34079* | BB | 35012* |
| 33034 | QI | 34037* | WC | 34080* | BB | 35013* |
| 33035 | QI | 34038* | WC | 34081* | BB | 35014* |
| 33036 | QI | 34039* | WC | 34082* | BB | 35015* |
| 33037 | QI | 34040* | WC | 34083* | BB | 35016* |
| 33038 | QI | 34041* | WC | 34084* | BB | 35017* |
| 33039 | QI | 34042* | WC | 34085* | BB | 35018* |
| 33040 | QI | 34043* | WC | 34086* | BB | 35019* |
| 34001* | WC | 34044* | WC | 34087* | BB | 35020* |
| 34002* | WC | 34045* | WC | 34088* | BB | 35021* |
| 34003* | WC | 34046* | WC | 34089* | BB | 35022* |
| 34004* | WC | 34047* | WC | 34090* | BB | 35023* |
| 34005* | WC | 34048* | WC | 34091* | WC | 35024* |
| 34006* | WC | 34049* | BB | 34092* | WC | 35025* |
| 34007* | WC | 34050* | BB | 34093* | WC | 35026* |
| 34008* | WC | 34051* | BB | 34094* | WC | 35027* |
| 34009* | WC | 34052* | BB | 34095* | WC | 35028* |
| 34010* | WC | 34053* | BB | 34096* | WC | 35029* |
| 34011* | WC | 34054* | BB | 34097* | WC | 35030* |
| 34012* | WC | 34055* | BB | 34098* | WC | |

## ISLE OF WIGHT LOCOMOTIVES

| | | | | | | | |
|---|---|---|---|---|---|---|---|
| 1* | E1 | W17* | O2 | W24* | O2 | W31* | O2 |
| 2* | E1 | W18* | O2 | W25* | O2 | W32* | O2 |
| 3* | E1 | W19* | O2 | W26* | O2 | W33* | O2 |
| 4* | E1 | W20* | O2 | W27* | O2 | W34* | O2 |
| 14* | O2 | W21* | O2 | W28* | O2 | W35* | O2 |
| 15* | O2 | W22* | O2 | W29* | O2 | W36* | O2 |
| 16* | O2 | W23* | O2 | W30* | O2 | | |

## OUTHERN REGION SERVICE LOCOMOTIVES

| No. | Old No. | Class | Station |
|---|---|---|---|
| DS 74 | — | Bo-Bo | Durnsford Road Power Station |
| DS 75 | — | Bo | W'loo & City |
| DS 77 | 0745 | C14 | Redbridge Sleeper Depot |
| DS 377 | 2635 | AIX | Brighton Wks. |
| DS 515 | L.B.S.C. 650 I.W.9 | AIX | Lancing Carr. Wks. |
| DS 600 | — | 0–4–0 D.esel | Eastleigh Carr. Wks. |
| DS 680 | L.B.S.C. 654 SEC. 751. | A 1 | Lancing Carr. Works |
| S 1173 | 2217 | 0–6–0 Diesel | Engineer's Dt. |
| S 3152 | 30272 | G 6 | Meldon Q. |

Electric          † Repainted 1947 in Stroudley livery

43

# BRITISH RAILWAYS' LOCOMOTIVE

## Nos. 26000-35030

### NAMED ENGINES

#### CLASS EM1 BO-BO ELECTRIC

26000   Tommy

#### CLASS B4 0–4–0T

30086   Havre

#### CLASS N15 " KING ARTHUR " 4–6–0

| | | | |
|---|---|---|---|
| 30448 | Sir Tristram | 30453 | King Arthur |
| 30449 | Sir Torre | 30454 | Queen Guinevere |
| 30450 | Sir Kay | 30455 | Sir Launcelot |
| 30451 | Sir Lamorak | 30456 | Sir Galahad |
| 30452 | Sir Meliagrance | 30457 | Sir Bedivere |

#### CLASS 0458 0–4–0ST

30458   Ironside

#### CLASS N15 " KING ARTHUR " 4–6–0

| | | | |
|---|---|---|---|
| 30736 | Excalibur | 30746 | Pendragon |
| 30737 | King Uther | 30747 | Elaine |
| 30738 | King Pellinore | 30748 | Vivien |
| 30739 | King Leodegrance | 30749 | Iseult |
| 30740 | Merlin | 30750 | Morgan le Fay |
| 30741 | Joyous Gard | 30751 | Etarre |
| 30742 | Camelot | 30752 | Linette |
| 30743 | Lyonnesse | 30753 | Melisande |
| 30744 | Maid of Astolat | 30755 | The Red Knight |
| 30745 | Tintagel | | |

#### CLASS 757 0–6–2T

30757   Earl of Mount Edgcumbe   |   30758   Lord St. Levan

## CLASS N15 " KING ARTHUR " 4–6–0

| | | | |
|---|---|---|---|
| '63 | Sir Bors de Ganis | 30785 | Sir Mador de la Porte |
| '64 | Sir Gawin | 30786 | Sir Lionel |
| '65 | Sir Gareth | 30787 | Sir Menadeuke |
| '66 | Sir Geraint | 30788 | Sir Urre of the Mount |
| '67 | Sir Valence | 30789 | Sir Guy |
| '68 | Sir Balin | 30790 | Sir Villiars |
| '69 | Sir Balan | 30791 | Sir Uwaine |
| '70 | Sir Prianius | 30792 | Sir Hervis de Revel |
| '71 | Sir Sagramore | 30793 | Sir Ontzlake |
| '72 | Sir Percivale | 30794 | Sir Ector de Maris |
| '73 | Sir Lavaine | 30795 | Sir Dinadan |
| '74 | Sir Gaheris | 30796 | Sir Dodinas le Savage |
| '75 | Sir Agravaine | 30797 | Sir Blamor de Ganis |
| '76 | Sir Galagars | 30798 | Sir Hectimere |
| '77 | Sir Lamiel | 30799 | Sir Ironside |
| '78 | Sir Pelleas | 30800 | Sir Meleaus de Lile |
| '79 | Sir Colgrevance | 30801 | Sir Meliot de Logres |
| '80 | Sir Persant | 30802 | Sir Durnore |
| '81 | Sir Aglovale | 30803 | Sir Harry le Fise Lake |
| '82 | Sir Brian | 30804 | Sir Cador of Cornwall |
| '83 | Sir Gillemere | 30805 | Sir Constantine |
| '84 | Sir Nerovens | 30806 | Sir Galleron |

## CLASS LN " LORD NELSON " 4–6–0

| | | | |
|---|---|---|---|
| 350 | Lord Nelson | 30858 | Lord Duncan |
| 351 | Sir Francis Drake | 30859 | Lord Hood |
| 352 | Sir Walter Raleigh | 30860 | Lord Hawke |
| 853 | Sir Richard Grenville | 30861 | Lord Anson |
| 854 | Howard of Effingham | 30862 | Lord Collingwood |
| 855 | Robert Blake | 30863 | Lord Rodney |
| 856 | Lord St. Vincent | 30864 | Sir Martin Frobisher |
| 857 | Lord Howe | 30865 | Sir John Hawkins |

## CLASS V " SCHOOLS " 4–4–0

| | | | |
|---|---|---|---|
| 900 | Eton | 30903 | Charterhouse |
| 901 | Winchester | 30904 | Lancing |
| 902 | Wellington | 30905 | Tonbridge |

## NAMED LOCOMOTIVES (cont.)

| | | | |
|---|---|---|---|
| 30906 | Sherborne | 30923 | Bradfield |
| 30907 | Dulwich | 30924 | Haileybury |
| 30908 | Westminster | 30925 | Cheltenham |
| 30909 | St. Paul's | 30926 | Repton |
| 30910 | Merchant Taylors | 30927 | Clifton |
| 30911 | Dover | 30928 | Stowe |
| 30912 | Downside | 30929 | Malvern |
| 30913 | Christ's Hospital | 30930 | Radley |
| 30914 | Eastbourne | 30931 | King's Wimbledon |
| 30915 | Brighton | 30932 | Blundells |
| 30916 | Whitgift | 30933 | King's Canterbury |
| 30917 | Ardingly | 30934 | St. Lawrence |
| 30918 | Hurstpierpoint | 30935 | Sevenoaks |
| 30919 | Harrow | 30936 | Cranleigh |
| 30920 | Rugby | 30937 | Epsom |
| 30921 | Shrewsbury | 30938 | St. Olave's |
| 30922 | Marlborough | 30939 | Leatherhead |

## CLASS N15X " REMEMBRANCE " 4-6-0

| | | | |
|---|---|---|---|
| 32327 | Trevithick | 32331 | Beattie |
| 32328 | Hackworth | 32332 | Stroudley |
| 32329 | Stephenson | 32333 | Remembrance |
| 32330 | Cudworth | | |

## CLASS H2 4-4-2

| | | | |
|---|---|---|---|
| 32421 | South Foreland | 32425 | Trevose Head |
| 32422 | North Foreland | 32426 | St. Alban's Head |
| 32424 | Beachy Head | | |

## CLASSES WC & BB 4-6-2
'WEST COUNTRY " and " BATTLE OF BRITAIN "

| | | | |
|---|---|---|---|
| 34001 | Exeter | 34005 | Barnstaple |
| 34002 | Salisbury | 34006 | Bude |
| 34003 | Plymouth | 34007 | Wadebridge |
| 34004 | Yeovil | 34008 | Padstow |

| | | | |
|---|---|---|---|
| 9 | Lyme Regis | 34053 | Sir Keith Park |
| 0 | Sidmouth | 34054 | Lord Beaverbrook |
| 1 | Tavistock | 34055 | Fighter Pilot |
| 2 | Launceston | 34056 | Croydon |
| 3 | Okehampton | 34057 | Biggin Hil. |
| 4 | Budleigh Salterton | 34058 | Sir Frederick Pile |
| 5 | Exmouth | 34059 | Sir Archibald Sinclair |
| 6 | Bodmin | 34060 | 25 Squadron |
| 7 | Ilfracombe | 34061 | 73 Squadron |
| 8 | Axminster | 34062 | 17 Squadron |
| 9 | Bideford | 34063 | 229 Squadron |
| 0 | Seaton | 34064 | Fighter Command |
| 1 | Dartmoor | 34065 | Hurricane |
| 2 | Exmoor | 34066 | Spitfire |
| 3 | Blackmore Vale | 34067 | Tangmere |
| 4 | Tamar Valley | 34068 | Kenley |
| 5 | Whimple | 34069 | Hawkinge |
| 6 | Yes Tor | 34070 | Manston |
| 7 | Taw Valley | 34071 | 601 Squadron |
| 8 | Eddystone | 34072 | 257 Squadron |
| 9 | Lundy | 34073 | 249 Squadron |
| 0 | Watersmeet | 34074 | 46 Squadron |
| 1 | Torrington | 34075 | 264 Squadron |
| 2 | Camelford | 34076 | 41 Squadron |
| 3 | Chard | 34077 | 603 Squadron |
| 4 | Honiton | 34078 | 222 Squadron |
| 5 | Shaftesbury | 34079 | 141 Squadron |
| 6 | Westward Ho | 34080 | 74 Squadron |
| 7 | Clovelly | 34081 | 92 Squadron |
| 8 | Lynton | 34082 | 615 Squadron |
| 9 | Boscastle | 34083 | 605 Squadron |
| 0 | Crewkerne | 34084 | 253 Squadron |
| 1 | Wilton | 34085 | 501 Squadron |
| 2 | Dorchester | 34086 | 219 Squadron |
| 3 | Combe Martin | 34087 | 45 Squadron |
| 4 | Woolacombe | 34088 | 213 Squadron |
| 5 | Ottery St. Mary | 34089 | 602 Squadron |
| 6 | Braunton | 34090 | Sir Eustace Missenden, Southern Railway |
| 7 | Callington | | |
| 8 | Crediton | 34091 | Weymouth |
| 9 | Anti-Aircraft Command | 34092 | City of Wells |
| 0 | Royal Observer Corps | 34093 | Saunton |
| 1 | Winston Churchill | 34094 | Mortehoe |
| 2 | Lord Dowding | 34095 | Brentor |

## NAMED LOCOMOTIVES (cont.)

| | | | |
|---|---|---|---|
| 34096 | Trevone | 34104 | Bere Alston |
| 34097 | Holsworthy | 34105 | Swanage |
| 34098 | Templecombe | 34106 | Lydford |
| 34099 | Lynmouth | 34107 | Blandford Forum |
| 34100 | Appledore | 34108 | Wincanton |
| 34101 | Hartland | 34109 | Sir Trafford |
| 34102 | Lapford | | Leigh-Ma |
| 34103 | Calstock | 34110 | 66 Squadron |

### CLASS MN " MERCHANT NAVY " 4-6-2

| | | | |
|---|---|---|---|
| 35001 | Channel Packet | 35015 | Rotterdam Lloyd |
| 35002 | Union Castle | 35016 | Elders Fyffes |
| 35003 | Royal Mail | 35017 | Belgian Marine |
| 35004 | Cunard White Star | 35018 | British India Line |
| 35005 | Canadian Pacific | 35019 | French Line CGT |
| 35006 | Peninsular & Oriental S.N. Co. | 35020 | Bibby Line |
| | | 35021 | New Zealand Line |
| 35007 | Aberdeen Commonwealth | 35022 | Holland-America L |
| | | 35023 | Holland-Afrika Line |
| 35008 | Orient Line | 35024 | East Asiatic Compa |
| 35009 | Shaw Savill | 35025 | Brocklebank Line |
| 35010 | Blue Star | 35026 | Lamport & Holt Li |
| 35011 | General Steam Navigation | 35027 | Port Line |
| | | 35028 | Clan Line |
| 35012 | United States Line | 35029 | Ellerman Lines |
| 35013 | Blue Funnel | 35030 | Elder Dempster Lir |
| 35014 | Nederland Line | | |

### CLASS E1 0-6-0T

| | | | |
|---|---|---|---|
| W 1 | Medina | W 3 | Ryde |
| W 2 | Yarmouth | W 4 | Wroxall |

### CLASS O2 0-4-4T

| | | | | | |
|---|---|---|---|---|---|
| W14 | Fishbourne | W22 | Brading | W30 | Shorwel |
| W15 | Cowes | W23 | Totland | W31 | Chale |
| W16 | Ventnor | W24 | Calbourne | W32 | Bonchur |
| W17 | Seaview | W25 | Godshill | W33 | Bembrid |
| W18 | Ningwood | W26 | Whitwell | W34 | Newpor |
| W19 | Osborne | W27 | Merstone | W35 | Freshwa |
| W20 | Shanklin | W28 | Ashey | W36 | Carisbro |
| W21 | Sandown | W29 | Alverstone | | |

# NUMERICAL LIST OF SOUTHERN REGION ELECTRIC MOTOR UNITS

*(Number to be seen on front of each set)*

## TWO-CAR MOTOR UNITS
*(South London and Wimbledon-West Croydon services)*

| | | |
|---|---|---|
| 301 | 1806 | 1810 |
| 303 | 1808 | 1811 |
| 304 | 1809 | 1812 |
| 305 | | |

## TWO-CAR NON-CORRIDOR MOTOR UNITS
### (2-NOL.)

| | | | |
|---|---|---|---|
| 3* | 1833* | 1853 | 1873 |
| 4* | 1834* | 1854 | 1874 |
| 5* | 1835* | 1856 | 1875 |
| 6* | 1836* | 1857 | 1876 |
| 7* | 1837* | 1858 | 1877 |
| 8* | 1839* | 1859 | 1878 |
| 9* | 1840* | 1860 | 1879 |
| 0* | 1841* | 1861 | 1880 |
| 1* | 1842* | 1862 | 1881 |
| 2* | 1843* | 1863 | 1882 |
| 3* | 1844* | 1864 | 1883† |
| 4* | 1845* | 1865 | 1884† |
| 5* | 1846* | 1866 | 1885† |
| 6* | 1847* | 1867 | 1886† |
| 7* | 1848* | 1868 | 1887† |
| 9* | 1849 | 1869 | 1888† |
| 0* | 1850 | 1870 | 1889† |
| 1* | 1851 | 1871 | 1890† |
| 2* | 1852 | 1872 | |

With 1st and 3rd class compartments.

With electro-pneumatic control gear.

## TWO-CAR MOTOR LAVATORY UNITS
### (2-BIL.)

| | | | |
|---|---|---|---|
| 1† | 2003† | 2005† | 2007† |
| 2† | 2004† | 2006† | 2008† |

| | | | |
|---|---|---|---|
| 2009† | 2045 | 2080 | 2116 |
| 2010† | 2046 | 2081 | 2117 |
| 2011 | 2047 | 2082 | 2118 |
| 2012 | 2048 | 2083 | 2120 |
| 2013 | 2049 | 2084 | 2121 |
| 2015 | 2050 | 2085 | 2122 |
| 2016 | 2051 | 2086 | 2123 |
| 2017 | 2052 | 2087 | 2124 |
| 2018 | 2053 | 2088* | 2125 |
| 2019 | 2054 | 2089 | 2126 |
| 2020 | 2055 | 2090 | 2127 |
| 2021 | 2056† | 2091 | 2128 |
| 2022 | 2057 | 2092 | 2129 |
| 2023 | 2058 | 2093 | 2130 |
| 2024 | 2059 | 2094 | 2132 |
| 2025 | 2060 | 2095 | 2134 |
| 2026 | 2061 | 2096 | 2135 |
| 2027 | 2062 | 2097 | 2136 |
| 2028 | 2063 | 2098 | 2137 |
| 2029 | 2064 | 2099 | 2138 |
| 2030 | 2065 | 2100 | 2139 |
| 2031 | 2066 | 2101 | 2140 |
| 2032 | 2067 | 2103 | 2141 |
| 2033 | 2068 | 2104 | 2142 |
| 2034 | 2069 | 2105 | 2143 |
| 2035 | 2070 | 2106 | 2144 |
| 2036 | 2071 | 2107 | 2145 |
| 2037 | 2072 | 2108 | 2146 |
| 2038 | 2073 | 2109 | 2147 |
| 2039 | 2074 | 2110 | 2148 |
| 2040 | 2075 | 2111 | 2149 |
| 2041 | 2076 | 2112 | 2150 |
| 2042 | 2077 | 2113 | 2151 |
| 2043 | 2078 | 2114 | 2152 |
| 2044 | 2079 | 2115 | |

†88 3rd seats instead of 84 and all-electric control gear.

*BIL Motor Coach and HAL trailer.

# TWO-CAR MOTOR LAVATORY UNITS

*(with one corridor and one non-corridor coach).*

## (2-HAL.)

| | | | |
|---|---|---|---|
| 2601 | 2626 | 2652 | 2677 |
| 2602 | 2627 | 2653 | 2678 |
| 2603 | 2628 | 2654 | 2679 |
| 2604 | 2629 | 2655 | 2680 |
| 2605 | 2630 | 2656 | 2681 |
| 2606 | 2631 | 2657 | 2682 |
| 2607 | 2632 | 2658 | 2683 |
| 2608 | 2633 | 2659 | 2684 |
| 2609 | 2634 | 2660 | 2685 |
| 2610 | 2635 | 2661 | 2686 |
| 2611 | 2636 | 2662 | 2687 |
| 2612 | 2637 | 2663 | 2688 |
| 2613 | 2638 | 2664 | 2689 |
| 2614 | 2639 | 2665 | 2690 |
| 2615 | 2640 | 2666 | 2691 |
| 2616 | 2641 | 2667 | 2692 |
| 2617 | 2642 | 2668 | 2693 |
| 2618 | 2643 | 2669 | 2694 |
| 2619 | 2644 | 2670 | 2695 |
| 2620 | 2645 | 2671 | 2696 |
| 2621 | 2647 | 2672 | 2697 |
| 2622 | 2648 | 2673 | 2698 |
| 2623 | 2649 | 2674 | 2699 |
| 2624 | 2650 | 2675 | |
| 2625 | 2651 | 2676 | |

# FOUR-CAR MOTOR LAVATORY UNITS

*(with three non-corridor 3rd and one 3rd/1st corridor coach).*

## (4-LAV.)

| | | | |
|---|---|---|---|
| 2921 | 2928 | 2935 | 2942 |
| 2922 | 2929 | 2936 | 2943 |
| 2923 | 2930 | 2937 | 2944 |
| 2924 | 2931 | 2938 | 2945 |
| 2925 | 2932 | 2939 | 2946 |
| 2926* | 2933 | 2940 | 2947 |
| 2927 | 2934 | 2941 | 2948 |

| | | | |
|---|---|---|---|
| 2949 | 2951 | 2953 | 29 |
| 2950 | 2952 | 2954† | |

*One motor coach electro-pneumatic control g
†With electro-pneumatic co gear.

# SIX-CAR MOTOR CORRID UNITS *(with Pullman Car*

## (6-PUL.)

| | | | |
|---|---|---|---|
| 3001 | 3007 | 3013 | 301 |
| 3002 | 3008 | 3014 | 302 |
| 3003 | 3009 | 3015 | 304 |
| 3004 | 3010 | 3016 | 304 |
| 3005 | 3011 | 3017 | 304 |
| 3006 | 3012 | 3018 | |

*Ex-" 6-CIT " Units.

# SIX-CAR MOTOR CORRID UNITS *(with Pantry Car)*

## (6-PAN.)

| | | | |
|---|---|---|---|
| 3021 | 3026 | 3030 | 303 |
| 3022 | 3027 | 3031 | 303 |
| 3023 | 3028 | 3032 | 303 |
| 3024 | 3029 | 3033 | 303 |
| 3025 | | | |

# FIVE-CAR PULLMAN MOT UNITS

*(For "Brighton Belle" Servic*

## (5-BEL.)

| | | |
|---|---|---|
| 3051 | 3052 | 3053 |

# FOUR-CAR KITCHEN CORRIDOR MOTOR UNI

## (4-RES.)

| | | | |
|---|---|---|---|
| 3054 | 3059 | 3065 | 306 |
| 3055 | 3061 | 3066 | 307 |
| 3056 | 3062 | 3067 | 307 |
| 3057 | 3064 | 3068 | 307 |

## FOUR-CAR BUFFET CORRIDOR MOTOR UNITS

### (4-BUF.)

| | | | |
|---|---|---|---|
| '3 | 3077 | 3080 | 3083 |
| 4 | 3078 | 3081 | 3084 |
| '5 | 3079 | 3082 | 3085 |
| 6 | | | |

## FOUR-CAR CORRIDOR MOTOR UNITS

### (4-COR.)

| | | | |
|---|---|---|---|
| 1 | 3116 | 3131 | 3145 |
| 2 | 3117 | 3132 | 3146 |
| 3 | 3118 | 3133 | 3147 |
| 4 | 3119 | 3134 | 3148 |
| 5 | 3120 | 3135 | 3149 |
| 6 | 3121 | 3136 | 3150 |
| 7 | 3122 | 3137 | 3151 |
| 8 | 3123 | 3138 | 3152 |
| 9 | 3124 | 3139 | 3153 |
| 0 | 3125 | 3140 | 3154 |
| 1 | 3126 | 3141 | 3155 |
| 2 | 3127 | 3142 | 3156 |
| 3 | 3128 | 3143 | 3157 |
| 4 | 3129 | 3144 | 3158 |
| 5 | 3130 | | |

## FOUR-CAR DOUBLE DECK SUBURBAN UNITS

### (4-DD.)

| | |
|---|---|
| 4001 | 4002 |

## FOUR-CAR NON CORRIDOR SUBURBAN UNITS

### (4-SUB.)

| | | | |
|---|---|---|---|
| 01 | 4108 | 4115 | 4122 |
| 02 | 4109 | 4116 | 4123 |
| 03 | 4110 | 4117 | 4124 |
| 04 | 4111 | 4118 | 4125 |
| 05 | 4112 | 4119 | 4126 |
| 06 | 4113 | 4120 | 4127 |
| 07 | 4114 | 4121 | 4128 |

| | | | |
|---|---|---|---|
| 4129 | 4175 | 4221 | 4289 |
| 4130 | 4176 | 4223 | 4290 |
| 4131 | 4177 | 4224 | 4291 |
| 4132 | 4178 | 4225 | 4292 |
| 4133 | 4179 | 4226 | 4293 |
| 4135 | 4180 | 4227 | 4294 |
| 4136 | 4181 | 4228 | 4295 |
| 4137 | 4182 | 4229 | 4296 |
| 4138 | 4183 | 4230 | 4297 |
| 4139 | 4185 | 4231 | 4298 |
| 4140 | 4186 | 4232 | 4299 |
| 4141 | 4187 | 4234 | 4300 |
| 4142 | 4188 | 4235 | 4301 |
| 4143 | 4189 | 4236 | 4302 |
| 4144 | 4190 | 4237 | 4303 |
| 4145 | 4191 | 4238 | 4304 |
| 4146 | 4192 | 4239 | 4305 |
| 4147 | 4193 | 4240 | 4306 |
| 4148 | 4194 | 4241 | 4307 |
| 4149 | 4195 | 4242 | 4308 |
| 4150 | 4196 | 4243 | 4309 |
| 4151 | 4197 | 4244 | 4310 |
| 4152 | 4198 | 4245 | 4311 |
| 4153 | 4199 | 4246 | 4312 |
| 4154 | 4200 | 4247 | 4313 |
| 4155 | 4201 | 4248 | 4314 |
| 4156 | 4202 | 4249 | 4315 |
| 4157 | 4203 | 4250 | 4316 |
| 4158 | 4204 | 4251 | 4317 |
| 4159 | 4205 | 4252 | 4318 |
| 4160 | 4206 | 4253 | 4319 |
| 4161 | 4207 | 4254 | 4320 |
| 4162 | 4208 | 4255 | 4321 |
| 4163 | 4209 | 4277 | 4322 |
| 4164 | 4210 | 4278 | 4323 |
| 4165 | 4211 | 4279 | 4324 |
| 4166 | 4212 | 4280 | 4325 |
| 4167 | 4213 | 4281 | 4326 |
| 4168 | 4214 | 4282 | 4327 |
| 4169 | 4215 | 4283 | 4328 |
| 4170 | 4216 | 4284 | 4329 |
| 4171 | 4217 | 4285 | 4330 |
| 4172 | 4218 | 4286 | 4331 |
| 4173 | 4219 | 4287 | 4332 |
| 4174 | 4220 | 4288 | 4333 |

| | | | | | | | |
|---|---|---|---|---|---|---|---|
| 4334 | 4376 | 4535 | 4603 | 4657 | 4686 | 4714 | 47 |
| 4335 | 4377 | 4536 | 4604 | 4658 | 4687 | 4715 | 47 |
| 4336 | 4378 | 4537 | 4605 | 4659 | 4688 | 4716 | 47 |
| 4337 | 4379 | 4538 | 4606 | 4660 | 4689 | 4717 | 47 |
| 4338 | 4380 | 4539 | 4607 | 4661 | 4690 | 4718 | 47 |
| 4339 | 4381 | 4540 | 4621 | 4662 | 4691 | 4719 | 47 |
| 4340 | 4382 | 4541 | 4622 | 4663 | 4692 | 4720 | 47 |
| 4341 | 4383 | 4542 | 4623 | 4664 | 4693 | 4721 | 47 |
| 4342 | 4384 | 4543 | 4624 | 4665 | 4694 | 4722 | 47 |
| 4343 | 4385 | 4544 | 4625 | 4666 | 4695 | 4723 | 47 |
| 4344 | 4386 | 4545 | 4626 | 4667 | 4696 | 4724 | 47 |
| 4345 | 4387 | 4546 | 4627 | 4668 | 4697 | 4725 | 47 |
| 4346 | 4408 | 4547 | 4628 | 4669 | 4698 | 4726 | 47 |
| 4347 | 4409 | 4548 | 4629 | 4670 | 4699 | 4727 | 50 |
| 4348 | 4411 | 4549 | 4630 | 4671 | 4700 | 4728 | 50 |
| 4349 | 4412 | 4550 | 4631 | 4672 | 4701 | 4729 | 50 |
| 4351 | 4416 | 4551 | 4632 | 4673 | 4702 | 4730 | 50 |
| 4352 | 4420 | 4552 | 4633 | 4674 | 4703 | 4731 | 50 |
| 4353 | 4424 | 4553 | 4634 | 4675 | 4704 | 4732 | 50 |
| 4354 | 4425 | 4554 | 4635 | 4676 | 4705 | 4733 | 50 |
| 4355 | 4426 | 4555 | 4636 | 4677 | 4706 | 4734 | 50 |
| 4356 | 4427 | 4556 | 4637 | 4678 | 4707 | 4735 | 50 |
| 4357 | 4428 | 4557 | 4638 | 4679 | 4708 | 4736 | 50 |
| 4358 | 4429 | 4558 | 4639 | 4680 | 4709 | 4737 | 50 |
| 4359 | 4503 | 4559 | 4640 | 4681 | 4710 | 4738 | 50 |
| 4360 | 4505 | 4560 | 4641 | 4682 | 4711 | 4739 | 50 |
| 4361 | 4510 | 4561 | 4642 | 4683 | 4712 | 4740 | 50 |
| 4362 | 4515 | 4564 | 4643 | 4684 | 4713 | 4741 | 50 |
| 4363 | 4517 | 4565 | 4644 | 4685 | | | |
| 4364 | 4518 | 4566 | 4645 | | | | |
| 4365 | 4519 | 4567 | 4646 | | | | |
| 4366 | 4520 | 4571 | 4647 | | | | |
| 4367 | 4526 | 4572 | 4648 | | | | |
| 4368 | 4527 | 4573 | 4649 | | | | |
| 4369 | 4528 | 4579 | 4650 | | | | |
| 4370 | 4529 | 4580 | 4651 | | | | |
| 4371 | 4530 | 4586 | 4652 | | | | |
| 4372 | 4531 | 4590 | 4653 | | | | |
| 4373 | 4532 | 4594 | 4654 | | | | |
| 4374 | 4533 | 4601 | 4655 | | | | |
| 4375 | 4534 | 4602 | 4656 | | | | |

**WATERLOO AND CITY LINE**

MOTOR COACH NOS.

| | | | |
|---|---|---|---|
| 51 | 54 | 57 | 60 |
| 52 | 55 | 58 | 61 |
| 53 | 56 | 59 | 62 |

# FOUR-CAR SUBURBAN (4 SUB) UNITS
## Make-up, Seating Capacity, etc.

| Unit Nos. | Type | Motor Coaches | Trailer Coaches | Seating Capacity |
|---|---|---|---|---|
| 01–10 | All-Steel Built 1942 | 9 compt. | 1 10 compt.<br>1 11 compt. | 468 |
| 11–20 | All-Steel Built 1946 | 8 compt. | 1 9 compt.<br>1 10 compt. | 420 |
| 21–29 | All-Steel Built 1946 | Semi-Saloon | 1 Semi-Saloon<br>1 9 compt. | 382 |
| 30 | All-Steel Built 1946 | Semi-Saloon<br>Lightweight<br>Motors | 1 Semi-Saloon<br>1 9 compt. | 382 |
| 31–71 | Original L.S.W.R. Units | 1 8 compt.<br>1 7 compt. | 10 compt. | 350 |
| 72–94 | L.S.W.R. Stock converted S.R. | 1 8 compt.<br>1 7 compt. | 10 compt. | 350 |
| 95–134 | Original L.S.W.R. Units | 7½ compt. | 1 11 compt.<br>1 9 compt.<br>(with saloon) | 352 or 354 |
| 35–50 | L.S.W.R. Stock converted S.R. | 1 8 compt.<br>1 7 compt. | 1 11 compt.<br>1 10 compt. | 360 |
| 51/2 | L.B.S.C. Stock converted S.R. | 1 7 compt.<br>1 8 compt. | 10 compt. | 350 |
| 53/5 | L.S.W.R. Stock converted S.R. | 1 7 compt.<br>1 8 compt. | 10 compt. | 350 |
| 54 | L.B.S.C., L.S.W. and S.E.C.R. Stock converted S.R. | 1 L.B.S.C.<br>7 compt.<br>1 L.S.W.<br>7½ compt. | 1 L.B.S.C.<br>10 compt.<br>1 S.E.C.R.<br>8 compt. | 340 |
| 77–99 | All-Steel Built 1949 | Saloon ; Light-weight Motors | 1 Saloon<br>1 10 compt. | 386 |
| 00–19<br>21–25 | Augmented W-Section Built 1925 | 7 compt. | 1 9 compt. *<br>1 All-Steel<br>10 compt. | 350 |
| 20 | Augmented W-Section Built 1925 | 7 compt. | 1 10 compt.<br>1 All-Steel<br>9 compt. | 350 |
| 26–54 | Augmented E-Section Built 1925/6 | 8 compt. | 1 9 compt.<br>1 All-Steel<br>10 compt. | 370 |
| 55–63 | All-Steel Built 1947/8 | 8 compt. | 10 compt. | 432 |

* No. 4313 has a 9 compt. all steel trailer.

| No. | Description | Motor coach | | Trailer | Seats |
|---|---|---|---|---|---|
| 4364–4376 | All-Steel Built 1947/8 | 8 compt. | 1 | 9 compt. | 420 |
| | | | 1 | 10 compt. | |
| 4377 | All-Steel Built 1947 | 8 compt. | 1 | 9 compt. | 402 |
| | | | 1 | Saloon | |
| 4378–4387 | All-Steel Built 1948 | Saloon | 1 | Saloon | 386 |
| | | | 1. | 10 compt. | |
| 4408–4409 | Augmented L.S.W.R. Stock converted S.R. | 8 compt. | 1 | 9 compt. | 370 |
| | | | 1 | All-Steel 10 compt. | |
| 4411/2/ 20–3 | Augmented L.S.W.R. Stock converted S.R. | 7½ compt. | 1 | 9 compt. | 360 |
| | | | 1 | All-Steel 10 compt. | |
| 4416 | L.S.W.R. Stock converted S.R. | 7½ compt. | 2 | 9 compt. | 350 |
| 4424–4429 | Augmented L.S.W.R. Stock converted S.R. | 8 compt. Electro-pneumatic Control | 1 | 9 compt. | 370 |
| | | | 1 | All-Steel 10 compt. | |
| 4503/5/ 10/5 4580/6 | Augmented S.E.C.R. Stock converted S.R. | 8 compt. (No. 4515, No.1 L.B.S.C. motor) | 1 | 9 compt. | 370 |
| | | | 1 | All-Steel 10 compt. | |
| 4517–79 4581–5 4584 | Augmented L.S.W.R. and L.B.S.C. converted S.R.† | 1 8 compt. 1 7 compt † | 1 | 10 compt. | 368 or 370 |
| | | | 1 | All Steel 9 compt. or 10 compt.† | |
| 4590 | Augmented L.B.S.C.R. Stock converted S.R. | 1 L.B.S.C.R. 7 compt. 1 Saloon | 1 | L.B.S.C.R. 9 compt. | 350 |
| | | | 1 | All-Steel 9 compt. | |
| 4601– 4607 | All-Steel bodies on original underframes Rebuilt 1949/50 | Saloon | 2 | 10 compt. | 404 |
| 4621– 4666 | | Saloon | 1 | Saloon | 386 |
| | | | 1 | 10 compt. | |
| 4667– 4754 | New all-steel bodies (1951/2) on original underframes. | Saloon | 1 | Saloon | 385 |
| | | | 1 | 10 compt.* | |
| 5001–15 | | Saloon | 1 | Saloon | 386 |
| | | | 1 | 10 compt.* | |

* Except Nos. 4688/96, 4723/8/33/9, 5005 which have 9 compt. trailers.    † Except 4518—2 L.S.W.R. motors, 1 10-compt. L.S.W.R. trailer and 1 9-compt. S.E.C.R. trailer ;  4520—2 8-compt. L.B.S.C. motors, 1 9-compt. S.E.C.R. trailer, and 1 10-compt. all-steel trailer ;  4526—1 8-compt. L.S.W.R. motor, 1 7-compt. L.B.S.C. motor, 1 L.S.W.R. 10-compt. trailer and 1 L.S.W.R. 9-compt. trailer ;  4551— 1 L.B.S.C. 7-compt. and 1 8-compt. motor, 1 all-steel 10-compt. and 1 L.S.W. 10-compt. trailer ;  4567—1 L.B.S.C. 7-compt. and 1 8-compt. motor, 1 L.B.S.C. 10-compt. trailer, 1 L.S.W.R. 9-compt. trailer ;  4573—1 L.B.S.C. 8-compt. and 1 L.S.W.R. 7-compt. motor, 1 L.S.W.R. 10-compt. and 1 L.S.W.R. 9-compt. trailer

# THE **ABC** OF

# BRITISH RAILWAYS

# LOCOMOTIVES

**PART 3—Nos. 40000-59999**
and L.M.R. Electric Motor Coaches

SUMMER
1953
EDITION

# FOREWORD

THIS booklet lists all British Railways locomotives numbe
between 40000 and 59999 and London Midland electric mo
coaches. This series of numbers includes all London Midl.
Region and Scottish (ex-L.M.S.) Region steam locos.

1. At the head of each class will be found a list of any import
sub-divisions of the class, usually in order of introduction. E
sub-division is given a reference mark, by which its relev
dimensions (if differing from those of other sub-divisions) and
locomotives it comprises (if known) may be identified.

2. The lists of dimensions at the head of each class show lo
motives fitted with two inside cylinders unless otherwise stat
e.g. (O) = two outside cylinders.

3. Superheated locos. are denoted by the letters " Su " a
the boiler pressure. " SS " denotes that some are superheated

4. The date on which the first locomotive of a class was b
is denoted by " Introduced."

5. Where locomotives have been renumbered other than by
addition of 40000 to their former L.M.S. numbers, the details
former L.M.S. numbers are given.

6. The numbers of locomotives in service have been checked
**February 21st, 1953.**

## CHIEF MECHANICAL ENGINEERS

### BRITISH RAILWAYS (L.M. Region)

H.G. Ivatt ... 1948–1951

### L.M.S.

| | | | | |
|---|---|---|---|---|
| George Hughes ... | ... | 1923–1925 | Sir William Stanier ... | 1932– |
| Sir Henry Fowler | ... | 1925–1931 | Charles E. Fairburn ... | 1944– |
| E.H.J. Lemon | | | H. G. Ivatt ... ... | 1945– |
| (Sir Ernest Lemon) | 1931–1932 | | | |

## LOCOMOTIVE SUPERINTENDENTS AND C.M.E.'S—L.M.S. CONSTITUENT COMPANIES

| CALEDONIAN RAILWAY | | | Dugald Drummond | ... | 1882– |
|---|---|---|---|---|---|
| Robert Sinclair | | | Hugh Smellie ... | ... | 18⁹ |
| (First loco. engineer)* | 1847–1856 | | J. Lambie ... ... | ... | 1890– |
| Benjamin Connor | ... | 1856–1876 | J. F. McIntosh ... | ... | 1895– |
| George Brittain ... | ... | 1876–1882 | William Pickersgill | ... | 1914– |

* Exclusive of previous service with constituent company.

# LOCOMOTIVE SUPERINTENDENTS
## AND C.M.E.'S (continued)

### FURNESS RAILWAY

| Mason | ... | ... | ... | 1890–1897 |
|---|---|---|---|---|
| F. Pettigrew | | ... | ... | 1897–1918 |
| J. Rutherford | ... | ... | | 1918–1923 |

### GLASGOW AND SOUTH WESTERN RLY.

| rick Stirling | | ... | ... | 1853–1866 |
|---|---|---|---|---|
| nes Stirling | | ... | ... | 1866–1878 |
| gh Smellie | | ... | ... | 1878–1890 |
| nes Manson | | ... | ... | 1890–1912 |
| ter Drummond | | ... | ... | 1912–1918 |
| H. Whitelegg | ... | ... | | 1918–1923 |

### HIGHLAND RAILWAY

| lliam Stroudley | | | | |
|---|---|---|---|---|
| (First loco. engineer) | ... | ... | | 1866–1869 |
| vid Jones | | ... | ... | 1869–1896 |
| ter Drummond | | ... | ... | 1896–1911 |
| G. Smith | | ... | ... | 1912–1915 |
| Cumming | | ... | ... | 1915–1923 |

### L. & Y.R.

John Hawkshaw (Consultant),*
Hurst and Jenkins successively to 1868

| Hurst | ... | ... | ... | 1868–1876 |
|---|---|---|---|---|
| Barton Wright | | ... | ... | 1876–1886 |
| hn A. F. Aspinall | | ... | ... | 1886–1899 |
| A. Hoy | ... | | ... | 1899–1904 |
| orge Hughes | | ... | ... | 1904–1921 |

e L. & Y. amalgamated with L.N.W.R. in 1921.

### L.N.W.R.

ancis Trevithick and
J. E. McConnell, first
loco. engineers, 1846
with Alexander Allan
largely responsible for
design at Crewe.*

| hn Ramsbottom | | ... | ... | 1857–1871 |
|---|---|---|---|---|
| ancis William Webb | | ... | ... | 1871–1903 |
| eorge Whale | | ... | ... | 1903–1909 |
| harles John | | | | |
| Bowen-Cooke | .. | ... | | 1909–1920 |
| apt. Hewitt Pearson | | | | |
| Montague Beames | | ... | | 1920–1921 |
| eorge Hughes | | ... | | 1922 |

### L.T. & S.R.

| homas Whitelegg | | ... | | 1880–1910 |
|---|---|---|---|---|
| obert Harben | | | | |
| Whitelegg | | ... | ... | 1910–1912 |

.T. & S.R. absorbed by M.R., control
locos. transferred to Derby as from
ug., 1912.)

### MARYPORT & CARLISLE

| Hugh Smellie | ... | ... | 1870–1878 |
|---|---|---|---|
| J. Campbell | ... | ... | 1878– |
| William Coulthard | ... | * | –1904 |
| J. B. Adamson | ... | ... | 1904–1923 |

### MIDLAND RAILWAY

| Matthew Kirtley | | | |
|---|---|---|---|
| (First loco. engineer) | ... | | 1844–1873 |
| Samuel Waite Johnson | ... | | 1873–1903 |
| Richard Mountford Deeley | | | 1903–1909 |
| Henry Fowler | ... | ... | 1909–1923 |

### SOMERSET AND DORSET JOINT RAILWAY

Until leased by Mid. and L. & S.W. (as from 1st Nov., 1875) locomotives were bought from outside builders, principally George England of Hatcham Iron Works, S.E. After the above date, Derby and its various Loco. Supts. and C.M.E.'s have acted for S. & D.J., aided by a resident Loco. Supt. stationed at Highbridge works.

### NORTH STAFFORDSHIRE RAILWAY

| L. Clare | ... | ... | ... | 1876–1882 |
|---|---|---|---|---|
| L. Longbottom | ... | ... | | 1882–1902 |
| J. H. Adams | ... | ... | | 1902–1915 |
| J. A. Hookham | ... | ... | | 1915–1923 |

W. Angus was Loco. Supt. at Stoke prior to 1876. No earlier records can be traced.

### WIRRAL

| Eric G. Barker | ... | ... | 1892–1902 |
|---|---|---|---|
| T. B. Hunter | ... | ... | 1903–1923 |

Barker of the Wirral Railway is noteworthy for originating the 4-4-4 tank type in this country (1896).

### NORTH LONDON RAILWAY

(Worked by L. & N.W. by agreement dated Dec., 1908.)

| William Adams | ... | ... | 1853–1873 |
|---|---|---|---|
| J. C. Park | ... | ... | 1873–1893 |
| Henry J. Pryce | ... | ... | 1893–1908 |

---

* Date of actual entry into office not known.

# BRITISH RAILWAYS LOCOMOTI

## SHEDS AND SHED CODES

### LONDON MIDLAND REGION

| | | | | | |
|---|---|---|---|---|---|
| 1A | **Willesden** | 9A | **Longsight** | 19A | **Sheffield** |
| 1B | Camden | 9B | Stockport (Edgeley) | 19B | Millhouses |
| 1C | Watford | 9C | Macclesfield | 19C | Canklow |
| 1D | Devons Road (Bow) | 9D | Buxton | | |
| 1E | Bletchley | 9E | Trafford Park | 20A | **Leeds (Holb** |
| | Leighton Buzzard | 9F | Heaton Mersey | 20B | Stourton |
| | Newport Pagnell | 9G | Northwich | 20C | Royston |
| 2A | **Rugby** | 10A | **Springs Branch** | 20D | Normanton |
| | Market | | **(Wigan)** | 20E | Manningham |
| | Harborough | 10B | Preston | | Ilkley |
| | Seaton | 10C | Patricroft | | Ilkley (ex-L. |
| 2B | Nuneaton | 10D | Plodder Lane | 20F | Skipton |
| 2C | Warwick | | (Bolton) | | Keighley |
| 2D | Coventry | 10E | Sutton Oak | 20G | Hellifield |
| 2E | Northampton | | | | Ingleton |
| 3A | **Bescot** | 11A | **Carnforth** | | |
| 3B | Bushbury | 11B | Barrow | 21A | **Saltley** |
| 3C | Walsall | | Coniston | 21B | Bournville |
| 3D | Aston | 11C | Oxenholme | | Redditch |
| 3E | Monument Lane | 11D | Tebay | 21C | Bromsgrove |
| 5A | **Crewe North** | 11E | Lancaster | | |
| | Whitchurch | 12A | **Carlisle(Upperby)** | 22A | **Bristol** |
| | Whitchurch | 12C | Penrith | 22B | Gloucester |
| | (ex-G.W.) | 12D | Workington | | Tewkesbury |
| 5B | Crewe South | 12E | Moor Row | | Dursley |
| | Crewe | 14A | **Cricklewood** | | |
| | (Gresty Lane) | 14B | Kentish Town | 24A | **Accrington** |
| 5C | Stafford | 14C | St. Albans | 24B | Rose Grove |
| | Coalport | 15A | **Wellingborough** | 24C | Lostock Hall |
| 5D | Stoke | 15B | Kettering | 24D | Lower Darwe |
| 5E | Alsager | 15C | Leicester | 24E | Blackpool |
| 5F | Uttoxeter | 15D | Bedford | | Blackpool N |
| 6A | **Chester** | 16A | **Nottingham** | 24F | Fleetwood |
| 6B | Mold Junction | | Southwell | 25A | **Wakefield** |
| 6C | Birkenhead | | Lincoln (Midland) | 25B | Huddersfield |
| 6D | Chester (Northgate) | 16C | Kirkby | 25C | Goole |
| 6E | Wrexham | 16D | Mansfield | 25D | Mirfield |
| 6F | Bidston | 17A | **Derby** | 25E | Sowerby Bridg |
| 6G | Llandudno Junction | 17B | Burton | 25F | Low Moor |
| 6H | Bangor | | Overseal | 25G | Farnley Juncti |
| 6J | Holyhead | 17C | Coalville | 26A | **Newton Hea** |
| 6K | Rhyl | 17D | Rowsley | 26B | Agecroft |
| | Denbigh | | Cromford | 26C | Bolton |
| 8A | **Edge Hill** | | Middleton | 26D | Bury |
| 8B | Warrington | | Sheep Pasture | 26E | Bacup |
| 8C | Speke Junction | 18A | **Toton** | 26F | Lees |
| 8D | Widnes | 18B | Westhouses | 26G | Belle Vue |
| | Widnes (C.L.C.) | 18C | Hasland | | |
| 8E | Brunswick | | Clay Cross | 27A | **Bank Hall** |
| | (Liverpool) | 18D | Staveley | 27B | Aintree |
| | Warrington | | Sheepbridge | 27C | Southport |
| | (C.L.C.) | | | 27D | Wigan (ex-L. |
| | | | | 27E | Walton |
| | | | | | Southport (C |

4

# EASTERN REGION

| | | | |
|---|---|---|---|
| **Stratford** | 32A | **Norwich** | |
| Brentwood | | Cromer | |
| Chelmsford | | Wells-on-Sea | |
| Epping | | Dereham | |
| Spitalfields | | Swaffham | |
| Wood St. | | Wymondham | |
| (Walthamstow) | 32B | Ipswich | |
| Palace Gates | | Felixstowe Beach | |
| Enfield Town | | Aldeburgh | |
| Ware | | Stowmarket | |
| Hertford East | 32C | Lowestoft | |
| Buntingford | 32D | Yarmouth | |
| Bishops Stortford | | (South Town) | |
| Southend (Victoria) | 32E | Yarmouth (Vauxhall) | |
| Southminster | 32F | Yarmouth Beach | |
| Wickford | 32G | Melton Constable | |
| Colchester | | Norwich City | |
| Clacton | | Cromer Beach | |
| Walton-on-Naze | 33A | **Plaistow** | |
| Kelvedon | | Upminster | |
| Maldon | 33B | Tilbury | |
| Braintree | 33C | Shoeburyness | |
| Parkeston | 34A | **Kings Cross** | |
| **Cambridge** | 34B | Hornsey | |
| Ely | 34C | Hatfield | |
| Huntingdon East | 34D | Hitchin | |
| Saffron Walden | 34E | Neasden | |
| March | | Aylesbury | |
| Wisbech | | Chesham | |
| Kings Lynn | 35A | **New England** | |
| Hunstanton | | Spalding | |
| South Lynn | | Bourne | |
| Bury St. Edmunds | | Stamford | |
| Sudbury (Suffolk) | | | |

| | |
|---|---|
| 35B | Grantham |
| 35C | Peterborough |
| | (Spital) |
| 36A | **Doncaster** |
| 36B | Mexborough |
| | Wath |
| 36C | Frodingham |
| 36D | Barnsley |
| 36E | Retford (G.N.) |
| | Retford (G.C.) |
| | Newark |
| 37A | **Ardsley** |
| 37B | Copley Hill |
| 37C | Bradford |
| 38A | **Colwick** |
| | Derby (Friargate) |
| 38B | Annesley |
| 38C | Leicester (ex-G.C.) |
| | Leicester (ex-G.N.) |
| 38D | Staveley |
| 38E | Woodford Halse |
| 39A | **Gorton** |
| | Dinting |
| | Hayfield |
| 39B | Sheffield (Darnall) |
| 40A | **Lincoln** |
| 40B | Immingham |
| 40C | Louth |
| 40D | Tuxford |
| 40E | Langwith Junction |
| 40F | Boston |

# NORTH EASTERN REGION

| | | | |
|---|---|---|---|
| **York** | | West Auckland | 51F |
| Leeds (Neville Hill) | | Wearhead | |
| Selby | 51G | Haverton Hill | |
| Starbeck | 51H | Kirkby Stephen | |
| Scarborough | 51J | Northallerton | |
| Malton | | Leyburn | |
| Pickering | 51K | Saltburn | |
| Whitby | 52A | **Gateshead** | |
| **Darlington** | | Bowes Bridge | |
| Middleton-in- | 52B | Heaton | |
| Teesdale | 52C | Blaydon | |
| Newport | | Hexham | |
| West Hartlepool | | Alston | |
| Middlesbrough | 52D | Tweedmouth | |
| Guisborough | | Alnmouth | |
| Stockton | | | |

| | |
|---|---|
| 52E | Percy Main |
| 52F | North Blyth |
| | South Blyth |
| 53A | **Hull** (Dairycoates) |
| 53B | Hull |
| | (Botanic Gardens) |
| 53C | Hull (Springhead) |
| | Alexandra Dock |
| 53D | Bridlington |
| 54A | **Sunderland** |
| | Durham |
| 54B | Tyne Dock |
| | Pelton Level |
| 54C | Borough Gardens |
| 54D | Consett |

## SCOTTISH REGION

| | | | | | |
|---|---|---|---|---|---|
| 60A | **Inverness** | 63A | **Perth South** | 65C | Parkhead |
| | Dingwall | | Aberfeldy | 65D | Dawsholm |
| | Kyle of Lochalsh | | Blair Atholl | | Dumbarton |
| 60B | Aviemore | | Crieff | 65E | Kipps |
| | Boat of Garten | 63B | Stirling | 65F | Grangemouth |
| 60C | Helmsdale | | Killin | 65G | Yoker |
| | Dornoch | | Stirling | 65H | Helensburgh |
| | Tain | | (Shore Road) | | Arrochar |
| 60D | Wick | 63C | Forfar | 65I | Balloch |
| | Thurso | | Brechin | 66A | **Polmadie** |
| 60E | Forres | 63D | Fort William | | **(Glasgow** |
| 61A | **Kittybrewster** | | Mallaig | 66B | Motherwell |
| | Ballater | 63E | Oban | | Morningside |
| | Fraserburgh | | Ballachulish | 66C | Hamilton |
| | Peterhead | 64A | **St. Margarets** | 66D | Greenock |
| 61B | Aberdeen (Ferryhill) | | **(Edinburgh)** | | (Ladyburn |
| 61C | Keith | | Dunbar | | Greenock |
| | Banff | | Galashiels | | (Princes Pier |
| | Elgin | | Longniddry | 67A | **Corkerhill** |
| 62A | **Thornton** | | North Berwick | | **(Glasgow** |
| | Anstruther | | Peebles | 67B | Hurlford |
| | Burntisland | | Seafield | | Beith |
| | Ladybank | | South Leith | | Muirkirk |
| | Methil | 64B | Haymarket | 67C | Ayr |
| 62B | Dundee (Tay Bridge) | 64C | Dalry Road | 67D | Ardrossan |
| | Arbroath | 64D | Carstairs | 68A | **Carlisle** |
| | Montrose | 64E | Polmont | | **(Kingmoor** |
| | St. Andrews | 64F | Bathgate | 68B | Dumfries |
| 62C | Dunfermline | 64G | Hawick | | Kirkcudbright |
| | (Upper) | | Kelso | 68C | Stranraer |
| | Alloa | | Riccarton | | Newton Stewart |
| | | 65A | **Eastfield** | 68D | Beattock |
| | | | **(Glasgow)** | 68E | Carlisle Canal |
| | | 65B | St. Rollox | | Silloth |


## SOUTHERN REGION

| | | | | | |
|---|---|---|---|---|---|
| 70A | **Nine Elms** | 71F | Ryde (I.O.W.) | 73B | Bricklayers Arms |
| 70B | Feltham | 71G | Bath (S. & D.) | 73C | Hither Green |
| 70C | Guildford | | Radstock | 73D | Gillingham (Kent) |
| | Bordon | 71H | Templecombe | 73E | Faversham |
| 70D | Basingstoke | 71I | Southampton | | |
| 70E | Reading | 71J | Highbridge | 74A | **Ashford (Kent)** |
| 71A | **Eastleigh** | | | | Canterbury West |
| | Winchester | 72A | **Exmouth Junction** | 74B | Ramsgate |
| | Winchester | | Seaton | 74C | Dover |
| | (ex-G.W.) | | Lyme Regis | | Folkestone |
| | Lymington | | Exmouth | 74D | Tonbridge |
| | Andover Junction | | Okehampton | 74E | St. Leonards |
| 71B | Bournemouth | | Bude | | |
| | Swanage | 72B | Salisbury | 75A | **Brighton** |
| | Hamworthy | 72C | Yeovil | | Newhaven |
| | Junction | 72D | Plymouth | | Eastbourne |
| | Branksome | | Callington | 75B | Redhill |
| 71C | Dorchester | 72E | Barnstaple Junction | 75C | Norwood Junction |
| 71D | Fratton | | Torrington | 75D | Horsham |
| | Gosport | | Ilfracombe | 75E | Three Bridges |
| | Midhurst | 72F | Wadebridge | 75F | Tunbridge Wells |
| 71E | Newport (I.O.W.) | 73A | **Stewarts Lane** | | West |

# WESTERN REGION

| | | | |
|---|---|---|---|
| **Old Oak Common** | 84A | **Wolverhampton** | 87A |
| Slough | | **(Stafford Road)** | |
| Aylesbury | 84B | Oxley | |
| Marlow | 84C | Banbury | 87B |
| Watlington | 84D | Leamington Spa | 87C |
| Southall | 84E | Tyseley | 87D |
| Staines | | Stratford-on-Avon | 87E |
| Reading | 84F | Stourbridge | 87F. |
| Henley-on-Thames | 84G | Clee Hill | |
| Didcot | | Craven Arms | |
| Newbury | | Knighton | 87G |
| Wallingford | | Builth Road | 87H |
| Oxford | | Wellington (Salop) | |
| Abingdon | 84H | Croes Newydd | |
| Fairford | 84J | Bala | |
| | | Trawsfynydd | |
| **Bristol** | | Penmaenpool | 87J |
| **(Bath Road)** | | Chester | 87K |
| Bath | 84K | | |
| Wells | | | |
| Weston-Super- | | **Worcester** | |
| Yatton [Mare | 85A | Evesham | |
| St. Philip's Marsh | | Kingham | |
| Swindon | | Gloucester | 88A |
| Andover Junction | 85B | Cheltenham | |
| Chippenham | | Brimscombe | 88B |
| Westbury | | Cirencester | 88C |
| Frome | | Lydney | 88D |
| Yeovil | | Tetbury | |
| Weymouth | | Hereford | |
| Bridport | 85C | Leominster | |
| | | Ross | 88E |
| **Newton Abbot** | | Kidderminster | 88F |
| Ashburton | 85D | | |
| Kingsbridge | | | |
| Taunton | | **Newport** | |
| Bridgwater | 86A | **(Ebbw Junction)** | |
| Minehead | | Newport (Pill) | 89A |
| Exeter | 86B | Cardiff (Canton) | |
| Tiverton Junction | 86C | Llantrisant | |
| Laira (Plymouth) | 86D | Severn Tunnel | |
| Princetown | 86E | Junction | |
| Launceston | | Tondu | 89B |
| St. Blazey | 86F | Pontypool Road | |
| Bodmin | 86G | Branches Fork | 89C |
| Moorswater | | Aberbeeg | |
| Truro | 86H | Aberdare | |
| Penzance | 86J | Abergavenny | |
| Helston | 86K | Tredegar | |
| St. Ives | | | |

| | |
|---|---|
| **Neath** | |
| Glyn Neath | |
| Neath (N. & B.) | |
| Duffryn Yard | |
| Danygraig | |
| Swansea East Dock | |
| Landore | |
| Llanelly | |
| Burry Port | |
| Pantyfynnon | |
| Carmarthen | |
| Newcastle Emlyn | |
| Neyland | |
| Cardigan | |
| Milford Haven | |
| Pembroke Dock | |
| Whitland | |
| Goodwick | |
| Swansea (Victoria) | |
| Upper Bank | |
| Gurnos | |
| Llandovery | |
| | |
| **Cardiff (Cathays)** | |
| Radyr | |
| Cardiff East Dock | |
| Barry | |
| Merthyr | |
| Cae Harris | |
| Dowlais Central | |
| Rhymney | |
| Abercynon | |
| Treherbert | |
| Ferndale | |
| | |
| **Oswestry** | |
| Llanidloes | |
| Moat Lane | |
| Welshpool | |
| (W. & L.) | |
| Brecon | |
| Builth Wells | |
| Machynlleth | |
| Aberayron | |
| Aberystwyth | |
| Portmadoc | |
| Pwllheli | |

## 2-6-2T     3MT

Introduced 1930. Fowler L.M.S. design with parallel boiler.
*Introduced 1930. Condensing locos. for working to Moorgate, London.
Weight: $\begin{cases} 70 \text{ tons } 10 \text{ cwt.} \\ 71 \text{ tons } 16 \text{ cwt.*} \end{cases}$
Pressure: 200 lb. Su.
Cyls.: (O) $17\frac{1}{2}'' \times 26''$.
Dr. Wheels: 5' 3".    T.E.: 21,485 lb.
Walschaerts Valve Gear P.V.

| | | | |
|---|---|---|---|
| 40001 | 40019 | 40037* | 40054 |
| 40002 | 40020 | 40038* | 40055 |
| 40003 | 40021 | 40039* | 40056 |
| 40004 | 40022* | 40040* | 40057 |
| 40005 | 40023* | 40041 | 40058 |
| 40006 | 40024* | 40042 | 40059 |
| 40007 | 40025* | 40043 | 40060 |
| 40008 | 40026* | 40044 | 40061 |
| 40009 | 40027* | 40045 | 40062 |
| 40010 | 40028* | 40046 | 40063 |
| 40011 | 40029* | 40047 | 40064 |
| 40012 | 40030* | 40048 | 40065 |
| 40013 | 40031* | 40049 | 40066 |
| 40014 | 40032* | 40050 | 40067 |
| 40015 | 40033* | 40051 | 40068 |
| 40016 | 40034* | 40052 | 40069 |
| 40017 | 40035* | 40053 | 40070 |
| 40018 | 40036* | | Total 70 |

## 2-6-2T     3MT

Introduced 1935. Stanier L.M.S. taper boiler development of Fowler design (*above*).
*Introduced 1941. Rebuilt with larger boiler.
Weight: $\begin{cases} 71 \text{ tons } 5 \text{ cwt.} \\ 72 \text{ tons } 10 \text{ cwt.*} \end{cases}$
Pressure: 200 lb. Su.
Cyls.: (O) $17\frac{1}{2}'' \times 26''$
Dr. Wheels: 5' 3".    T.E.: 21,485 lb.
Walschaerts Valve Gear P.V.

| | | | |
|---|---|---|---|
| 40071 | 40080 | 40089 | 40098 |
| 40072 | 40081 | 40090 | 40099 |
| 40073 | 40082 | 40091 | 40100 |
| 40074 | 40083 | 40092 | 40101 |
| 40075 | 40084 | 40093 | 40102 |
| 40076 | 40085 | 40094 | 40103 |
| 40077 | 40086 | 40095 | 40104 |
| 40078 | 40087 | 40096 | 40105 |
| 40079 | 40088 | 40097 | 40106 |

| | | | |
|---|---|---|---|
| 40107 | 40133 | 40159 | 4018 |
| 40108 | 40134 | 40160 | 4018 |
| 40109 | 40135 | 40161 | 4018 |
| 40110 | 40136 | 40162 | 4018 |
| 40111 | 40137 | 40163* | 4018 |
| 40112 | 40138 | 40164 | 4019 |
| 40113 | 40139 | 40165 | 4019 |
| 40114 | 40140 | 40166 | 4019 |
| 40115 | 40141 | 40167 | 4019 |
| 40116 | 40142 | 40168 | 4019 |
| 40117 | 40143 | 40169* | 4019 |
| 40118 | 40144 | 40170 | 4019 |
| 40119 | 40145 | 40171 | 4019 |
| 40120 | 40146 | 40172 | 4019 |
| 40121 | 40147 | 40173 | 4019 |
| 40122 | 40148* | 40174 | 4020 |
| 40123 | 40149 | 40175 | 4020 |
| 40124 | 40150 | 40176 | 4020 |
| 40125 | 40151 | 40177 | 4020 |
| 40126 | 40152 | 40178 | 4020 |
| 40127 | 40153 | 40179 | 4020 |
| 40128 | 40154 | 40180 | 4020 |
| 40129 | 40155 | 40181 | |
| 40130 | 40156 | 40182 | |
| 40131 | 40157 | 40183 | |
| 40132 | 40158 | 40184 | |
| | | | Total |

## 4-4-0

Introduced 1912. Fowler rebuild Johnson locos. with superheater piston valves.
*Introduced 1914. Locos. built new superheated design for S. & D. (taken into L.M.S. stock, 1930).
Weight: Loco. 53 tons 7 cwt.
Pressure: 160 lb. SS.
Cyls.: $20\frac{1}{2}'' \times 26''$ Su.
Dr. Wheels: 7' 0$\frac{1}{2}''$ Su.
T.E.: 17,585 lb.

| | | | |
|---|---|---|---|
| 40322* | 40351 | 40364 | 404 |
| 40323* | 40353 | 40377 | 404 |
| 40326* | 40356 | 40395 | 404 |
| 40332 | 40359 | 40396 | 404 |
| 40337 | 40362 | 40401 | 404 |

| | | | |
|---|---|---|---|
| 10 | 40444 | 40491 | 40531 |
| 11 | 40447 | 40493 | 40534 |
| 12 | 40448 | 40495 | 40535 |
| 13 | 40450 | 40501 | 40536 |
| 14 | 40452 | 40502 | 40537 |
| 16 | 40453 | 40504 | 40538 |
| 18 | 40454 | 40505 | 40539 |
| 19 | 40455 | 40509 | 40540 |
| 20 | 40458 | 40511 | 40541 |
| 21 | 40461 | 40513 | 40542 |
| 22 | 40463 | 40518 | 40543 |
| 25 | 40464 | 40519 | 40548 |
| 26 | 40472 | 40520 | 40550 |
| 32 | 40480 | 40521 | 40551 |
| 33 | 40482 | 40522 | 40552 |
| 34 | 40484 | 40524 | 40553 |
| 36 | 40485 | 40525 | 40556 |
| 38 | 40486 | 40526 | 40557 |
| 39 | 40487 | 40527 | 40559 |
| 43 | 40489 | 40529 | 40562 |

**Total 100**

## 4-0      2P

...oduced 1928. Post-Grouping devel-
...pment of Midland design, with
...odified dimensions and reduced
...oiler mountings.

...troduced 1928. Locos. built for
..., & D.J.R. (taken into L.M.S.
...tock, 1930).

...ted experimentally in 1933 with
...)abeg feed-water heater.

...ight: Loco. 54 tons 1 cwt.

...ssure: 180 lb. Su.

...s.: 19″×26″.

...Wheels: 6′9″.     T.E.: 17,730 lb.

| | | | |
|---|---|---|---|
| 563 | 40569 | 40575 | 40581 |
| 564 | 40570 | 40576 | 40582 |
| 565 | 40571 | 40577 | 40583 |
| 566 | 40572 | 40578 | 40584 |
| 567 | 40573 | 40579 | 40585 |
| 568 | 40574 | 40580 | 40586 |

| | | | |
|---|---|---|---|
| 40587 | 40616 | 40645 | 40673 |
| 40588 | 40617 | 40646 | 40674 |
| 40589 | 40618 | 40647 | 40675 |
| 40590 | 40619 | 40648 | 40676 |
| 40592 | 40620 | 40649 | 40677 |
| 40593 | 40621 | 40650 | 40678 |
| 40594 | 40622 | 40651 | 40679 |
| 40595 | 40623 | 40652 | 40680 |
| 40596 | 40624 | 40653† | 40681 |
| 40597 | 40625 | 40654 | 40682 |
| 40598 | 40626 | 40655 | 40683 |
| 40599 | 40627 | 40656 | 40684 |
| 40600 | 40628 | 40657 | 40685 |
| 40601 | 40629 | 40658 | 40686 |
| 40602 | 40630 | 40659 | 40687 |
| 40603 | 40631 | 40660 | 40688 |
| 40604 | 40632 | 40661 | 40689 |
| 40605 | 40633*† | 40662 | 40690 |
| 40606 | 40634* | 40663 | 40691 |
| 40607 | 40635* | 40664 | 40692 |
| 40608 | 40636 | 40665 | 40693 |
| 40609 | 40637 | 40666 | 40694 |
| 40610 | 40638 | 40667 | 40695 |
| 40611 | 40640 | 40668 | 40696 |
| 40612 | 40641 | 40669 | 40697 |
| 40613 | 40642 | 40670 | 40698 |
| 40614 | 40643 | 40671 | 40699 |
| 40615 | 40644 | 40672 | 40700 |

**Total 136**

*For full details of*
LONDON MIDLAND
REGION DIESEL LOCO-
MOTIVES

**See the**
ABC OF BRITISH RAIL-
WAYS LOCOMOTIVES
Pt. II. Nos. 10000-39999.

## 4-4-0 (3-Cyl. Compd.) 4P

Introduced 1924. Post-Grouping development of Johnson Midland compound with modified dimensions and (except 41045–64) reduced boiler mountings.

Weight: Loco. 61 tons 14 cwt.

Pressure: 200 lb. Su.

Cyls.: L.P. (2) 21"×26". H.P. (1) 19"×26".

Dr. Wheels: 6' 9".

T.E. (of L.P. cyls. at 80% boiler pressure) 22,650 lb

P.V.: (H.P. cyl. only).

| | | | |
|---|---|---|---|
| 40900 | 40931 | 41065 | 41093 |
| 40901 | 40932 | 41066 | 41094 |
| 40902 | 40933 | 41067 | 41095 |
| 40903 | 40934 | 41068 | 41096 |
| 40904 | 40935 | 41069 | 41097 |
| 40905 | 40936 | 41070 | 41098 |
| 40906 | 40937 | 41071 | 41099 |
| 40907 | 40938 | 41072 | 41100 |
| 40908 | 40939 | 41073 | 41101 |
| 40909 | 41045 | 41074 | 41102 |
| 40910 | 41047 | 41075 | 41103 |
| 40912 | 41048 | 41076 | 41104 |
| 40913 | 41049 | 41077 | 41105 |
| 40914 | 41050 | 41078 | 41106 |
| 40915 | 41051 | 41079 | 41107 |
| 40916 | 41052 | 41080 | 41108 |
| 40917 | 41053 | 41081 | 41110 |
| 40919 | 41054 | 41082 | 41111 |
| 40920 | 41055 | 41083 | 41112 |
| 40921 | 41056 | 41084 | 41113 |
| 40923 | 41057 | 41085 | 41114 |
| 40924 | 41058 | 41086 | 41115 |
| 40925 | 41059 | 41087 | 41116 |
| 40926 | 41060 | 41088 | 41117 |
| 40927 | 41061 | 41089 | 41118 |
| 40928 | 41062 | 41090 | 41119 |
| 40929 | 41063 | 41091 | 41120 |
| 40930 | 41064 | 41092 | 41121 |

| | | | |
|---|---|---|---|
| 41122 | 41142 | 41162 | 4118 |
| 41123 | 41143 | 41163 | 4118 |
| 41124 | 41144 | 41164 | 4118 |
| 41126 | 41145 | 41165 | 4118 |
| 41127 | 41146 | 41166 | 4118 |
| 41128 | 41147 | 41167 | 4118 |
| 41129 | 41149 | 41168 | 4118 |
| 41130 | 41150 | 41169 | 4118 |
| 41131 | 41151 | 41170 | 4119 |
| 41132 | 41152 | 41172 | 4119 |
| 41133 | 41153 | 41173 | 4119 |
| 41134 | 41154 | 41174 | 4119 |
| 41135 | 41155 | 41175 | 4119 |
| 41136 | 41156 | 41176 | 4119 |
| 41137 | 41157 | 41177 | 4119 |
| 41138 | 41158 | 41178 | 4119 |
| 41139 | 41159 | 41179 | 4119 |
| 41140 | 41160 | 41180 | 4119 |
| 41141 | 41161 | | |

Total I

## 2-6-2T 2M

Introduced 1946. Ivatt L.M.S. ta... boiler design. Nos. 41200-89 h... short L.M.S. chimney, Nos. 4129... B.R. long tapered chimney, N... 41300-29 B.R. long parallel chimne...

Weight: 63 tons 5 cwt.

Pressure: 200 lb. Su.

Cyls.: $\left\{ \begin{array}{l} \text{(O) } 16''\times24'' \\ \text{(O) } 16\frac{1}{2}''\times24''* \end{array} \right.$

Dr. Wheels: 5' 0". T.E.: $\left\{ \begin{array}{l} 17,410 \\ 18,510 \end{array} \right.$

Walschaerts Valve Gear. P.V.

| | | | |
|---|---|---|---|
| 41200 | 41210 | 41220 | 4123 |
| 41201 | 41211 | 41221 | 4123 |
| 41202 | 41212 | 41222 | 4123 |
| 41203 | 41213 | 41223 | 4123 |
| 41204 | 41214 | 41224 | 4123 |
| 41205 | 41215 | 41225 | 412. |
| 41206 | 41216 | 41226 | 412. |
| 41207 | 41217 | 41227 | 412. |
| 41208 | 41218 | 41228 | 412. |
| 41209 | 41219 | 41229 | 412. |

| 240 | 41263 | 41286 | 41308* |
|---|---|---|---|
| 241 | 41264 | 41287 | 41309* |
| 242 | 41265 | 41288 | 41310* |
| 243 | 41266 | 41289 | 41311* |
| 244 | 41267 | 41290* | 41312* |
| 245 | 41268 | 41291* | 41313* |
| 246 | 41269 | 41292* | 41314* |
| 247 | 41270 | 41293* | 41315* |
| 248 | 41271 | 41294* | 41316* |
| 249 | 41272 | 41295* | 41317* |
| 250 | 41273 | 41296* | 41318* |
| 251 | 41274 | 41297* | 41319* |
| 252 | 41275 | 41298* | 41320* |
| 253 | 41276 | 41299* | 41321* |
| 254 | 41277 | 41300* | 41322* |
| 255 | 41278 | 41301* | 41323* |
| 256 | 41279 | 41302* | 41324* |
| 257 | 41280 | 41303* | 41325* |
| 258 | 41281 | 41304* | 41326* |
| 259 | 41282 | 41305* | 41327* |
| 260 | 41283 | 41306* | 41328* |
| 261 | 41284 | 41307* | 41329* |
| 262 | 41285 | | |

Total 130

## 4-0ST 0F

roduced 1883. Johnson Midland design.
ntroduced 1897. Larger Johnson Midland design.
Wheels: 3' 10".
ssure: $\begin{cases} 140\ lb.*† \\ 150\ lb.‡ \end{cases}$

| | Weight tons cwt. | Cyls. (O) | T.E. |
|---|---|---|---|
| 516* | 23 3 | 13"×20" | 8,745 |
| 518† | 32 3 | 15"×20" | 11,640 |
| 523‡ | 32 3 | 15"×20" | 12,475 |

Total 3

## 4-0T 0F

oduced 1907. Deeley Midland design.
ight: 32 tons 16 cwt.
ssure: 160 lb.
s.: (O) 15"×22".
Wheels: 3' 9¾". T.E.: 14,635 lb.
schaerts Valve Gear.

| 41528 | 41531 | 41534 | 41536 |
|---|---|---|---|
| 41529 | 41532 | 41535 | 41537 |
| 41530 | 41533 | | |

Total 10

## 0-6-0T 1F

Introduced 1878. Johnson Midland design.
*Rebuilt with Belpaire boilers
Weight: 39 tons 11 cwt.
Pressure: $\begin{cases} 150\ lb. \\ 140\ lb.* \end{cases}$
Cyls.: 17"×24".
Dr. Wheels: 4' 7".
T.E.: $\begin{cases} 16,080\ lb. \\ 15,005\ lb.* \end{cases}$

| 41660* | 41713 | 41773* | 41839* |
|---|---|---|---|
| 41661* | 41720* | 41777 | 41844* |
| 41664* | 41724* | 41779 | 41846* |
| 41666 | 41725* | 41780* | 41847* |
| 41671* | 41726* | 41795 | 41853 |
| 41672* | 41734* | 41797* | 41855* |
| 41682* | 41739* | 41803* | 41857 |
| 41686 | 41747* | 41804* | 41859* |
| 41695* | 41748 | 41805 | 41860* |
| 41699* | 41749* | 41811* | 41865 |
| 41702* | 41752* | 41813* | 41875* |
| 41706* | 41753* | 41814* | 41878* |
| 41708* | 41754* | 41826* | 41879* |
| 41710* | 41763 | 41833* | 41885 |
| 41711* | 41769* | 41835 | 41889* |
| 41712* | 41770* | 41838* | |

Total 63

## 0-4-4T 2P

Introduced: 1932. Stanier L.M.S. design. Push-and-pull fitted
Weight: 58 tons 1 cwt.
Pressure: 160 lb.
Cyls.: 18"×26".
Dr. Wheels: 5' 7". T.E.: 17,100 lb

| 41900 | 41903 | 41906 | 41908 |
|---|---|---|---|
| 41901 | 41904 | 41907 | 41909 |
| 41902 | 41905 | | |

Total 10

## 4-4-2T　　　　　　　2P

Introduced: 1900. Whitelegg L.T. & S.
" 51 " Class.
Weight: 67 tons 15 cwt.
Pressure: 170 lb.
Cyls.: (O) 19″ × 26″.
Dr. Wheels: 6′ 6″.　　　T.E.: 17.390 lb.

| | |
|---|---|
| 41911 | 41922 |

**Total 2**

## 4-4-2T　　　　　　　3P

*Introduced 1909. L.T. & S. Whitelegg
" 79 " Class.
*Remainder.* Introduced 1923. Midland
and L.M.S. development of L.T. &
S. " 79 " Class.
Weight: { 71 tons 10 cwt.*
　　　　 { 71 tons 10 cwt.
Pressure: 170 lb.
Cyls.: (O) 19″ × 26″.
Dr. Wheels: 6′ 6″.　　　T.E.: 17,390 lb

| | | | |
|---|---|---|---|
| 41928 | 41943 | 41950 | 41972 |
| 41936 | 41944 | 41951 | 41973 |
| 41938 | 41945 | 41952 | 41974 |
| 41939 | 41946 | 41966* | 41975 |
| 41940 | 41947 | 41969 | 41976 |
| 41941 | 41948 | 41970 | 41977 |
| 41942 | 41949 | 41971 | 41978 |

**Total 28**

## 0-6-2T　　　　　　　3F

Introduced 1903. Whitelegg L.T. & S.
" 69 " Class (Nos. 41990-3 built 1912
taken directly into M.R. stock).
Weight: 64 tons 13 cwt.
Pressure: 170 lb.
Cyls.: 18″ × 26″.
Dr. Wheels: 5′ 3″.　　　T.E.: 19,320 lb.

| | | | |
|---|---|---|---|
| 41980 | 41984 | 41988 | 41991 |
| 41981 | 41985 | 41989 | 41992 |
| 41982 | 41986 | 41990 | 41993 |
| 41983 | 41987 | | |

**Total 14**

## 2-6-4T　　　　　　　4MT

*Introduced 1927. Fowler L.M.S. parallel
boiler design.

†Introduced 1933 As earlier engine
but with side-window cabs and doo

‡Introduced 1934. Stanier tape
boiler 3-cylinder design for L.T &
section.

§Introduced 1935. Stanier tap
boiler 2-cylinder design.

¶Introduced 1945. Fairburn develo
ment of Stanier design with short
wheelbase and detail alterations.

Weights: { 86 tons 5 cwt.*†
　　　　　{ 92 tons 5 cwt.‡
　　　　　{ 87 tons 17 cwt.§
　　　　　{ 85 tons 5 cwt.¶

Pressure (all types): 200 lb. Su.

Cyls.: { (O) 19″ × 26″*†
　　　 { (3) 16″ × 26″‡
　　　 { (O) 19⅝″ × 26″§¶

Dr. Wheels (all types): 5′ 9″

T.E.: { 23,125 lb.*†
　　　{ 24,600 lb.‡
　　　{ 24,670 lb.§¶

Walschaerts valve gear.　P.V

## ¶FAIRBURN LOCOS.

| | | | |
|---|---|---|---|
| 42050 | 42074 | 42098 | 4212 |
| 42051 | 42075 | 42099 | 4212 |
| 42052 | 42076 | 42100 | 4212 |
| 42053 | 42077 | 42101 | 4212 |
| 42054 | 42078 | 42102 | 4212 |
| 42055 | 42079 | 42103 | 4212 |
| 42056 | 42080 | 42104 | 4212 |
| 42057 | 42081 | 42105 | 4212 |
| 42058 | 42082 | 42106 | 4213 |
| 42059 | 42083 | 42107 | 4213 |
| 42060 | 42084 | 42108 | 4213 |
| 42061 | 42085 | 42109 | 4213 |
| 42062 | 42086 | 42110 | 4213 |
| 42063 | 42087 | 42111 | 4213 |
| 42064 | 42088 | 42112 | 4213 |
| 42065 | 42089 | 42113 | 4213 |
| 42066 | 42090 | 42114 | 4213 |
| 42067 | 42091 | 42115 | 4213 |
| 42068 | 42092 | 42116 | 4214 |
| 42069 | 42093 | 42117 | 4214 |
| 42070 | 42094 | 42118 | 4214 |
| 42071 | 42095 | 42119 | 4214 |
| 42072 | 42096 | 42120 | 4214 |
| 42073 | 42097 | 42121 | 4214 |

| | | | |
|---|---|---|---|
| 42146 | 42185 | 42224 | 42263 |
| 42147 | 42186 | 42225 | 42264 |
| 42148 | 42187 | 42226 | 42265 |
| 42149 | 42188 | 42227 | 42266 |
| 42150 | 42189 | 42228 | 42267 |
| 42151 | 42190 | 42229 | 42268 |
| 42152 | 42191 | 42230 | 42269 |
| 42153 | 42192 | 42231 | 42270 |
| 42154 | 42193 | 42232 | 42271 |
| 42155 | 42194 | 42233 | 42272 |
| 42156 | 42195 | 42234 | 42273 |
| 42157 | 42196 | 42235 | 42274 |
| 42158 | 42197 | 42236 | 42275 |
| 42159 | 42198 | 42237 | 42276 |
| 42160 | 42199 | 42238 | 42277 |
| 42161 | 42200 | 42239 | 42278 |
| 42162 | 42201 | 42240 | 42279 |
| 42163 | 42202 | 42241 | 42280 |
| 42164 | 42203 | 42242 | 42281 |
| 42165 | 42204 | 42243 | 42282 |
| 42166 | 42205 | 42244 | 42283 |
| 42167 | 42206 | 42245 | 42284 |
| 42168 | 42207 | 42246 | 42285 |
| 42169 | 42208 | 42247 | 42286 |
| 42170 | 42209 | 42248 | 42287 |
| 42171 | 42210 | 42249 | 42288 |
| 42172 | 42211 | 42250 | 42289 |
| 42173 | 42212 | 42251 | 42290 |
| 42174 | 42213 | 42252 | 42291 |
| 42175 | 42214 | 42253 | 42292 |
| 42176 | 42215 | 42254 | 42293 |
| 42177 | 42216 | 42255 | 42294 |
| 42178 | 42217 | 42256 | 42295 |
| 42179 | 42218 | 42257 | 42296 |
| 42180 | 42219 | 42258 | 42297 |
| 42181 | 42220 | 42259 | 42298 |
| 42182 | 42221 | 42260 | 42299 |
| 42183 | 42222 | 42261 | |
| 42184 | 42223 | 42262 | |

## FOWLER LOCOS.

| | | | |
|---|---|---|---|
| 42300 | 42305 | 42310 | 42315 |
| 42301 | 42306 | 42311 | 42316 |
| 42302 | 42307 | 42312 | 42317 |
| 42303 | 42308 | 42313 | 42318 |
| 42304 | 42309 | 42314 | 42319 |

| | | | |
|---|---|---|---|
| 42320 | 42339 | 42358 | 42377 |
| 42321 | 42340 | 42359 | 42378 |
| 42322 | 42341 | 42360 | 42379 |
| 42323 | 42342 | 42361 | 42380 |
| 42324 | 42343 | 42362 | 42381 |
| 42325 | 42344 | 42363 | 42382 |
| 42326 | 42345 | 42364 | 42383 |
| 42327 | 42346 | 42365 | 42384 |
| 42328 | 42347 | 42366 | 42385 |
| 42329 | 42348 | 42367 | 42386 |
| 42330 | 42349 | 42368 | 42387 |
| 42331 | 42350 | 42369 | 42388 |
| 42332 | 42351 | 42370 | 42389 |
| 42333 | 42352 | 42371 | 42390 |
| 42334 | 42353 | 42372 | 42391 |
| 42335 | 42354 | 42373 | 42392 |
| 42336 | 42355 | 42374 | 42393 |
| 42337 | 42356 | 42375 | 42394 |
| 42338 | 42357 | 42376 | |

## † FOWLER LOCOS. WITH SIDE-WINDOW CAB.

| | | | |
|---|---|---|---|
| 42395 | 42403 | 42411 | 42418 |
| 42396 | 42404 | 42412 | 42419 |
| 42397 | 42405 | 42413 | 42420 |
| 42398 | 42406 | 42414 | 42421 |
| 42399 | 42407 | 42415 | 42422 |
| 42400 | 42408 | 42416 | 42423 |
| 42401 | 42409 | 42417 | 42424 |
| 42402 | 42410 | | |

## §STANIER 2-CYL LOCOS.

| | | | |
|---|---|---|---|
| 42425 | 42440 | 42455 | 42470 |
| 42426 | 42441 | 42456 | 42471 |
| 42427 | 42442 | 42457 | 42472 |
| 42428 | 42443 | 42458 | 42473 |
| 42429 | 42444 | 42459 | 42474 |
| 42430 | 42445 | 42460 | 42475 |
| 42431 | 42446 | 42461 | 42476 |
| 42432 | 42447 | 42462 | 42477 |
| 42433 | 42448 | 42463 | 42478 |
| 42434 | 42449 | 42464 | 42479 |
| 42435 | 42450 | 42465 | 42480 |
| 42436 | 42451 | 42466 | 42481 |
| 42437 | 42452 | 42467 | 42482 |
| 42438 | 42453 | 42468 | 42483 |
| 42439 | 42454 | 42469 | 42484 |

| | | | |
|---|---|---|---|
| 42485 | 42488 | 42491 | 42493 |
| 42486 | 42489 | 42492 | 42494 |
| 42487 | 42490 | | |

## ‡STANIER 3-CYL. LOCOS.

| | | | |
|---|---|---|---|
| 42500 | 42510 | 42519 | 42528 |
| 42501 | 42511 | 42520 | 42529 |
| 42502 | 42512 | 42521 | 42530 |
| 42503 | 42513 | 42522 | 42531 |
| 42504 | 42514 | 42523 | 42532 |
| 42505 | 42515 | 42524 | 42533 |
| 42506 | 42516 | 42525 | 42534 |
| 42507 | 42517 | 42526 | 42535 |
| 42508 | 42518 | 42527 | 42536 |
| 42509 | | | |

## §STANIER 2-CYL. LOCOS.

| | | | |
|---|---|---|---|
| 42537 | 42566 | 42595 | 42624 |
| 42538 | 42567 | 42596 | 42625 |
| 42539 | 42568 | 42597 | 42626 |
| 42540 | 42569 | 42598 | 42627 |
| 42541 | 42570 | 42599 | 42628 |
| 42542 | 42571 | 42600 | 42629 |
| 42543 | 42572 | 42601 | 42630 |
| 42544 | 42573 | 42602 | 42631 |
| 42545 | 42574 | 42603 | 42632 |
| 42546 | 42575 | 42604 | 42633 |
| 42547 | 42576 | 42605 | 42634 |
| 42548 | 42577 | 42606 | 42635 |
| 42549 | 42578 | 42607 | 42636 |
| 42550 | 42579 | 42608 | 42637 |
| 42551 | 42580 | 42609 | 42638 |
| 42552 | 42581 | 42610 | 42639 |
| 42553 | 42582 | 42611 | 42640 |
| 42554 | 42583 | 42612 | 42641 |
| 42555 | 42584 | 42613 | 42642 |
| 42556 | 42585 | 42614 | 42643 |
| 42557 | 42586 | 42615 | 42644 |
| 42558 | 42587 | 42616 | 42645 |
| 42559 | 42588 | 42617 | 42646 |
| 42560 | 42589 | 42618 | 42647 |
| 42561 | 42590 | 42619 | 42648 |
| 42562 | 42591 | 42620 | 42649 |
| 42563 | 42592 | 42621 | 42650 |
| 42564 | 42593 | 42622 | 42651 |
| 42565 | 42594 | 42623 | 42652 |

| | | | |
|---|---|---|---|
| 42653 | 42658 | 42663 | 426.. |
| 42654 | 42659 | 42664 | 426.. |
| 42655 | 42660 | 42665 | 4267. |
| 42656 | 42661 | 42666 | 4267. |
| 42657 | 42662 | 42667 | 4267. |

## ¶FAIRBURN LOCOS.

| | | | |
|---|---|---|---|
| 42673 | 42680 | 42687 | 426.. |
| 42674 | 42681 | 42688 | 426.. |
| 42675 | 42682 | 42689 | 426.. |
| 42676 | 42683 | 42690 | 426.. |
| 42677 | 42684 | 42691 | 426.. |
| 42678 | 42685 | 42692 | 426.. |
| 42679 | 42686 | 42693 | |

Total

## 2-6-0     5M

Introduced 1926. Hughes L.M.S. de... built under Fowler's direction. W... schaerts Valve Gear. P.V.
*Introduced 1953. Locos. reb... experimentally with Lentz... poppet valves in 1931; rebuilt w... Reidinger rotary poppet valve g... in 1953.
Weight: Loco. 66 tons 0 cwt.
Pressure: 180 lb. Su.
Cyls.: (O) 21"×26".
Dr. Wheels: 5' 6".    T.E.: 26,58(

| | | | |
|---|---|---|---|
| 42700 | 42717 | 42734 | 427. |
| 42701 | 42718 | 42735 | 427 |
| 42702 | 42719 | 42736 | 427. |
| 42703 | 42720 | 42737 | 427. |
| 42704 | 42721 | 42738 | 427 |
| 42705 | 42722 | 42739 | 427 |
| 42706 | 42723 | 42740 | 427 |
| 42707 | 42724 | 42741 | 427 |
| 42708 | 42725 | 42742 | 427 |
| 42709 | 42726 | 42743 | 427 |
| 42710 | 42727 | 42744 | 427 |
| 42711 | 42728 | 42745 | 427 |
| 42712 | 42729 | 42746 | 427 |
| 42713 | 42730 | 42747 | 427 |
| 42714 | 42731 | 42748 | 427 |
| 42715 | 42732 | 42749 | 427 |
| 42716 | 42733 | 42750 | 427 |

| | | | |
|---|---|---|---|
| .768 | 42813 | 42857 | 42901 |
| .769 | 42814 | 42858 | 42902 |
| .770 | 42815 | 42859 | 42903 |
| .771 | 42816 | 42860 | 42904 |
| .772 | 42817 | 42861 | 42905 |
| 773 | 42818* | 42862 | 42906 |
| .774 | 42819 | 42863 | 42907 |
| 775 | 42820 | 42864 | 42908 |
| 776 | 42821 | 42865 | 42909 |
| 777 | 42822* | 42866 | 42910 |
| 778 | 42823 | 42867 | 42911 |
| .779 | 42824* | 42868 | 42912 |
| .780 | 42825* | 42869 | 42913 |
| .781 | 42826 | 42870 | 42914 |
| .782 | 42827 | 42871 | 42915 |
| 783 | 42828 | 42872 | 42916 |
| 784 | 42829* | 42873 | 42917 |
| .785 | 42830 | 42874 | 42918 |
| 786 | 42831 | 42875 | 42919 |
| 787 | 42832 | 42876 | 42920 |
| 788 | 42833 | 42877 | 42921 |
| 789 | 42834 | 42878 | 42922 |
| 790 | 42835 | 42879 | 42923 |
| 791 | 42836 | 42880 | 42924 |
| 792 | 42837 | 42881 | 42925 |
| 793 | 42838 | 42882 | 42926 |
| 794 | 42839 | 42883 | 42927 |
| 795 | 42840 | 42884 | 42928 |
| 796 | 42841 | 42885 | 42929 |
| 797 | 42842 | 42886 | 42930 |
| 798 | 42843 | 42887 | 42931 |
| 799 | 42844 | 42888 | 42932 |
| 800 | 42845 | 42889 | 42933 |
| 802 | 42846 | 42890 | 42934 |
| 803 | 42847 | 42891 | 42935 |
| 803 | 42848 | 42892 | 42936 |
| 804 | 42849 | 42893 | 42937 |
| 805 | 42850 | 42894 | 42938 |
| 806 | 42851 | 42895 | 42939 |
| 807 | 42852 | 42896 | 42940 |
| 808 | 42853 | 42897 | 42941 |
| 809 | 42854 | 42898 | 42942 |
| 810 | 42855 | 42899 | 42943 |
| 811 | 42856 | 42900 | 42944 |
| 812 | | | |

**Total 245**

## 2-6-0         5MT

Introduced 1933. Stanier L.M.S. taper boiler design, some with safety valves mounted on the top feed.
Weight: Loco. 69 tons 2 cwt.
Pressure: 225 lb. Su.
Cyls.: (O) 18″×28″.
Dr. Wheels: 5′ 6″.     T.E.: 26,290 lb.
Walschaerts Valve Gear. P.V.

| | | | |
|---|---|---|---|
| 42945 | 42955 | 42965 | 42975 |
| 42946 | 42956 | 42966 | 42976 |
| 42947 | 42957 | 42967 | 42977 |
| 42948 | 42958 | 42968 | 42978 |
| 42949 | 42959 | 42969 | 42979 |
| 42950 | 42960 | 42970 | 42980 |
| 42951 | 42961 | 42971 | 42981 |
| 42952 | 42962 | 42972 | 42982 |
| 42953 | 42963 | 42973 | 42983 |
| 42954 | 42964 | 42974 | 42984 |

**Total 40**

## 2-6-0         4MT

Introduced 1947. Ivatt L.M.S. taper boiler design with double chimney.
*Introduced 1949, with single chimney.
No. 43027 has a stovepipe chimney.
Weight: Loco. 59 tons 2 cwt.
Pressure: 225 lb. Su.
Cyls.: (O) 17½″×26″.
Dr. Wheels: 5′ 3″.     T.E.: 24,170 lb.
Walschaerts Valve Gear. P.V.

| | | | |
|---|---|---|---|
| 43000 | 43018 | 43036 | 43054* |
| 43001 | 43019 | 43037 | 43055* |
| 43002 | 43020 | 43038 | 43056* |
| 43003 | 43021 | 43039 | 43057* |
| 43004 | 43022 | 43040 | 43058* |
| 43005 | 43023 | 43041 | 43059* |
| 43006 | 43024 | 43042 | 43060* |
| 43007 | 43025 | 43043 | 43061* |
| 43008 | 43026 | 43044 | 43062* |
| 43009 | 43027* | 43045 | 43063* |
| 43010 | 43028 | 43046 | 43064* |
| 43011 | 43029 | 43047 | 43065* |
| 43012 | 43030 | 43048 | 43066* |
| 43013 | 43031 | 43049 | 43067* |
| 43014 | 43032 | 43050* | 43068* |
| 43015 | 43033 | 43051* | 43069* |
| 43016 | 43034 | 43052* | 43070* |
| 43017 | 43035 | 43053* | 43071* |

| | | | | | | | |
|---|---|---|---|---|---|---|---|
| 43072* | 43095* | 43118* | 43140* | 43219 | 43284 | 43356 | 43 |
| 43073* | 43096* | 43119* | 43141* | 43222 | 43286 | 43357 | 43 |
| 43074* | 43097* | 43120* | 43142* | 43223 | 43287 | 43359 | 43 |
| 43075* | 43098* | 43121* | 43143* | 43224 | 43290 | 43361 | 43 |
| 43076* | 43099* | 43122* | 43144* | 43225 | 43292 | 43364 | 43 |
| 43077* | 43100* | 43123* | 43145* | 43226 | 43293 | 43367 | 43 |
| 43078* | 43101* | 43124* | 43146* | 43231 | 43294 | 43368 | 43 |
| 43079* | 43102* | 43125* | 43147* | 43232 | 43295 | 43369 | 43 |
| 43080* | 43103* | 43126* | 43148* | 43233 | 43296 | 43370 | 43 |
| 43081* | 43104* | 43127* | 43149* | 43234 | 43298 | 43371 | 43 |
| 43082* | 43105* | 43128* | 43150* | 43235 | 43299 | 43373 | 43 |
| 43083* | 43106* | 43129* | 43151* | 43237 | 43300 | 43374 | 43 |
| 43084* | 43107* | 43130* | 43152* | 43239 | 43301 | 43378 | 43 |
| 43085* | 43108* | 43131* | 43153* | 43240 | 43305 | 43379 | 43 |
| 43086* | 43109* | 43132* | 43154* | 43241 | 43306 | 43381 | 43 |
| 43087* | 43110* | 43133* | 43155* | 43242 | 43307 | 43386 | 43 |
| 43088* | 43111* | 43134* | 43156* | 43243 | 43308 | 43387 | 43 |
| 43089* | 43112* | 43135* | 43157* | 43244 | 43309 | 43388 | 43 |
| 43090* | 43113* | 43136* | 43158* | 43245 | 43310 | 43389 | 43 |
| 43091* | 43114* | 43137* | 43159* | 43246 | 43312 | 43392 | 43 |
| 43092* | 43115* | 43138* | 43160* | 43247 | 43313 | 43394 | 43 |
| 43093* | 43116* | 43139* | 43161* | 43248† | 43314 | 43395 | 43 |
| 43094* | 43117* | | | 43249 | 43315 | 43396 | 43 |

**Total 162**

## 0-6-0     3F

Introduced 1885. Johnson Midland locos., rebuilt from 1916 by Fowler with Belpaire boilers.
*Introduced 1885. Johnson Midland locos., rebuilt from 1920 by Fowler with Belpaire boiler.
†Introduced 1896. Locos. built for S. & D.J. (taken into L.M.S. stock 1930).
Weight: Loco. 43 tons 17 cwt.
Pressure: 175 lb.
Cyls.: 18" × 26".
Dr. Wheels: { 5' 3", *4' 11". *T.E.: { 19,890 lb.*, 21,240 lb.

| | | | | | | | |
|---|---|---|---|---|---|---|---|
| | | | | 43250 | 43317 | 43398 | 43 |
| | | | | 43251 | 43318 | 43399 | 43 |
| | | | | 43252 | 43321 | 43400 | 43 |
| | | | | 43253 | 43323 | 43401 | 43 |
| | | | | 43254 | 43324 | 43402 | 43 |
| | | | | 43256 | 43325 | 43405 | 43 |
| | | | | 43257 | 43326 | 43406 | 43 |
| | | | | 43258 | 43327 | 43410 | 43 |
| | | | | 43259 | 43329 | 43411 | 43 |
| | | | | 43261 | 43330 | 43419 | 43 |
| | | | | 43263 | 43331 | 43427 | 43 |
| | | | | 43266 | 43332 | 43428 | 43 |
| | | | | 43267 | 43333 | 43429 | 43 |
| | | | | 43268 | 43334 | 43431 | 43 |
| 43174* | 43187* | 43200 | 43210 | 43271 | 43335 | 43433 | 43 |
| 43178*. | 43188* | 43201† | 43211† | 43273 | 43337 | 43435 | 43 |
| 43180* | 43189* | 43203 | 43212 | 43274 | 43339 | 43436 | 43 |
| 43181* | 43191 | 43204† | 43213 | 43275 | 43340 | 43440 | 43 |
| 43183* | 43192 | 43205 | 43214 | 43277 | 43341 | 43441 | 43 |
| 43185* | 43193 | 43207 | 43216† | 43278 | 43342 | 43443 | 43 |
| 43186* | 43194† | 43208 | 43218† | 43281 | 43344 | 43444 | 43 |
| | | | | 43282 | 43351 | 43446 | 43 |
| | | | | 43283 | 43355 | 43448 | 43 |

*…o bottom:* Class
…2-6-2Ts Nos.
…and 41299
…modified cab);
…3MT (Riddles),
…T No. 82014:
…3MT (Stanier),
…T No. 40209.
…*Day* (3), *P. C.*

Above: Class 3MT (Fowler) 2-6-2T No. 40001. [H. C. Casserley.

Below: Class 2P 0-4-4T No. 41908. [F. W. Day.

Above: Class 3MT (Fowler) 2-6-2T No. 40025, fitted with condensing gear. [F. W. Day.

Below: Class 4MT (Fowler) 2-6-4T No. 42341. [R. J. Buckley.

Top left: Class 1F 0-6-0T No. 41795.    Top right: Class 5MT (Fowler) 2-6-0
No. 42761.

Bottom left: Class 1F 0-6-0T No. 41726.  Bottom right: Class 5MT (Stanier)
rebuilt with Belpaire boiler.          2-6-0 No. 42973.
                [J. Davenport (2)]                    [F. W. Day (2)]

Top left: Class 4P 4-4-0 No. 41050. Top right: Class 2P 4-4-0 No. 40326. Bottom left: Class 2P 4-4-0 No. 40633 (fitted with Dabeg feed-water heater). Bottom right: Class 4P 4-4-0 No. 40936 (with high-sided tender).

[P. Ransome-Wallis, F. W. Day, R. J. Buckley (2)]

Top left: Class 2MT (Ivatt) 2-6-0 No. 46494. Bottom left: Class 2MT
(Riddles) 2-6-0 No. 78003. Top right: Class 4MT (Ivatt) 2-6-0
No. 43144. Bottom right: Class 4MT (Riddles) 2-6-0 No. 76021.
[R. J. Buckley, R. H. G. Simpson, P. Ransome-Wallis, A. M. Bowman

Beyer-Garratt 2-6-6-2 No. 47983

[H. Gordon Tidey

0-10-0 No. 58100

[R. L. Sherwood

Class 7F 2-8-0 No. 53800

[R. J. Buckley

Class 7F 2-8-0 No. 53806 (with larger boiler)

[R. E. Toop

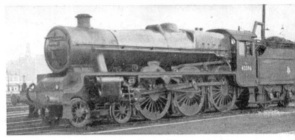

Class 6P 4-6-0 No. 45596 *Bahamas*.

Class 6P 4-6-0 No. 45520 *Llandudno*.

Class 7P 4-6-0 No. 45535 *Sir Herbert Walker, K.C.B.*

| | | | | | | | |
|---|---|---|---|---|---|---|---|
| 3572 | 43621 | 43667 | 43723 | 43797 | 43808 | 43817 | 43826 |
| 3574 | 43622 | 43668 | 43727 | 43798 | 43809 | 43819 | 43828 |
| 3575 | 43623 | 43669 | 43728 | 43799 | 43810 | 43821 | 43829 |
| 3578 | 43624 | 43673 | 43729 | 43800 | 43812 | 43822 | 43832 |
| 3579 | 43627 | 43674 | 43731 | 43803 | 43814 | 43823 | 43833 |
| 3580 | 43629 | 43675 | 43734 | 43806 | 43815 | 43825 | |
| 3581 | 43630 | 43676 | 43735 | | | | |
| 3583 | 43631 | 43678 | 43737 | | | | |

**Total 39**

| | | | |
|---|---|---|---|
| 3584 | 43633 | 43679 | 43742 |
| 3585 | 43634 | 43680 | 43745 |
| 3586 | 43636 | 43681 | 43748 |
| 3587 | 43637 | 43682 | 43749 |
| 3593 | 43638 | 43683 | 43750* |
| 3594 | 43639 | 43684 | 43751 |

## 0-6-0      4F

Introduced 1911. Fowler superheated Midland design.
Weight: 48 tons 15 cwt.
Pressure: 175 lb. Su.
Cyls.: 20″×26″.
Dr. Wheels: 5′ 3″.    T.E.: 24,555 lb
P.V.

| | | | |
|---|---|---|---|
| 3595 | 43644 | 43686 | 43753 |
| 3596 | 43645 | 43687 | 43754 |
| 3598 | 43650 | 43690 | 43755 |
| 3599 | 43651 | 43693 | 43756 |
| 3600 | 43652 | 43698 | 43757 |
| 3604 | 43653 | 43705 | 43759 |
| 3605 | 43656 | 43709 | 43760 |
| 3607 | 43657 | 43710 | 43762 |
| 3608 | 43658 | 43711 | 43763 |
| 3612 | 43660 | 43712 | 43766 |
| 3615 | 43661 | 43714 | 43767 |
| 3618 | 43662 | 43715 | 43770 |
| 3619 | 43664 | 43717 | 43771 |
| 3620 | 43665 | 43721 | 43773 |

**Total 324**

## 6-0      3F

Introduced 1906. Deeley Midland design, rebuilt by Fowler with Belpaire boiler.
Weight: Loco. 46 tons 3 cwt.
Pressure: 175 lb.
Cyls.: 18½″×26″.
Dr. Wheels: 5′ 3″.    T.E.: 21,010 lb.

| | | | |
|---|---|---|---|
| 775 | 43781 | 43786 | 43791 |
| 776 | 43782 | 43787 | 43792 |
| 778 | 43784 | 43789 | 43793 |
| 779 | 43785 | 43790 | 43795 |

| | | | |
|---|---|---|---|
| 43835 | 43862 | 43889 | 43916 |
| 43836 | 43863 | 43890 | 43917 |
| 43837 | 43864 | 43891 | 43918 |
| 43838 | 43865 | 43892 | 43919 |
| 43839 | 43866 | 43893 | 43920 |
| 43840 | 43867 | 43894 | 43921 |
| 43841 | 43868 | 43895 | 43922 |
| 43842 | 43869 | 43896 | 43923 |
| 43843 | 43870 | 43897 | 43924 |
| 43844 | 43871 | 43898 | 43925 |
| 43845 | 43872 | 43899 | 43926 |
| 43846 | 43873 | 43900 | 43927 |
| 43847 | 43874 | 43901 | 43928 |
| 43848 | 43875 | 43902 | 43929 |
| 43849 | 43876 | 43903 | 43930 |
| 43850 | 43877 | 43904 | 43931 |
| 43851 | 43878 | 43905 | 43932 |
| 43852 | 43879 | 43906 | 43933 |
| 43853 | 43880 | 43907 | 43934 |
| 43854 | 43881 | 43908 | 43935 |
| 43855 | 43882 | 43909 | 43936 |
| 43856 | 43883 | 43910 | 43937 |
| 43857 | 43884 | 43911 | 43938 |
| 43858 | 43885 | 43912 | 43939 |
| 43859 | 43886 | 43913 | 43940 |
| 43860 | 43887 | 43914 | 43941 |
| 43861 | 43888 | 43915 | 43942 |

| | | | |
|---|---|---|---|
| 43943 | 43964 | 43985 | 44006 |
| 43944 | 43965 | 43986 | 44007 |
| 43945 | 43966 | 43987 | 44008 |
| 43946 | 43967 | 43988 | 44009 |
| 43947 | 43968 | 43989 | 44010 |
| 43948 | 43969 | 43990 | 44011 |
| 43949 | 43970 | 43991 | 44012 |
| 43950 | 43971 | 43992 | 44013 |
| 43951 | 43972 | 43993 | 44014 |
| 43952 | 43973 | 43994 | 44015 |
| 43953 | 43974 | 43995 | 44016 |
| 43954 | 43975 | 43996 | 44017 |
| 43955 | 43976 | 43997 | 44018 |
| 43956 | 43977 | 43998 | 44019 |
| 43957 | 43978 | 43999 | 44020 |
| 43958 | 43979 | 44000 | 44021 |
| 43959 | 43980 | 44001 | 44022 |
| 43960 | 43981 | 44002 | 44023 |
| 43961 | 43982 | 44003 | 44024 |
| 43962 | 43983 | 44004 | 44025 |
| 43963 | 43984 | 44005 | 44026 |

Total 192

## 0-6-0 4F

Introduced 1924. Post-grouping development of Midland design with reduced boiler mountings.
*Introduced 1922. Locos. built for S. & D.J.R. to M.R. design (taken into L.M.S. stock, 1930).
Weight: Loco. 48 tons 15 cwt.
Pressure: 175 lb. Su.
Cyls.: 20″×26″.
Dr. Wheels: 5′ 3″.     T.E.: 24,555 lb.
P.V.

| | | | | | | | |
|---|---|---|---|---|---|---|---|
| 44027 | 44039 | 44051 | 44063 | 44075 | 44121 | 44167 | 44213 |
| 44028 | 44040 | 44052 | 44064 | 44076 | 44122 | 44168 | 44214 |
| 44029 | 44041 | 44053 | 44065 | 44077 | 44123 | 44169 | 44215 |
| 44030 | 44042 | 44054 | 44066 | 44078 | 44124 | 44170 | 44216 |
| 44031 | 44043 | 44055 | 44067 | 44079 | 44125 | 44171 | 44217 |
| 44032 | 44044 | 44056 | 44068 | 44080 | 44126 | 44172 | 44218 |
| 44033 | 44045 | 44057 | 44069 | 44081 | 44127 | 44173 | 44219 |
| 44034 | 44046 | 44058 | 44070 | 44082 | 44128 | 44174 | 44220 |
| 44035 | 44047 | 44059 | 44071 | 44083 | 44129 | 44175 | 44221 |
| 44036 | 44048 | 44060 | 44072 | 44084 | 44130 | 44176 | 44222 |
| 44037 | 44049 | 44061 | 44073 | 44085 | 44131 | 44177 | 44223 |
| 44038 | 44050 | 44062 | 44074 | 44086 | 44132 | 44178 | 44224 |
| | | | | 44087 | 44133 | 44179 | 44225 |
| | | | | 44088 | 44134 | 44180 | 44226 |
| | | | | 44089 | 44135 | 44181 | 44227 |
| | | | | 44090 | 44136 | 44182 | 44228 |
| | | | | 44091 | 44137 | 44183 | 44229 |
| | | | | 44092 | 44138 | 44184 | 44230 |
| | | | | 44093 | 44139 | 44185 | 44231 |
| | | | | 44094 | 44140 | 44186 | 44232 |
| | | | | 44095 | 44141 | 44187 | 44233 |
| | | | | 44096 | 44142 | 44188 | 44234 |
| | | | | 44097 | 44143 | 44189 | 44235 |
| | | | | 44098 | 44144 | 44190 | 44236 |
| | | | | 44099 | 44145 | 44191 | 44237 |
| | | | | 44100 | 44146 | 44192 | 44238 |
| | | | | 44101 | 44147 | 44193 | 44239 |
| | | | | 44102 | 44148 | 44194 | 44240 |
| | | | | 44103 | 44149 | 44195 | 44241 |
| | | | | 44104 | 44150 | 44196 | 44242 |
| | | | | 44105 | 44151 | 44197 | 44243 |
| | | | | 44106 | 44152 | 44198 | 44244 |
| | | | | 44107 | 44153 | 44199 | 44245 |
| | | | | 44108 | 44154 | 44200 | 44246 |
| | | | | 44109 | 44155 | 44201 | 44247 |
| | | | | 44110 | 44156 | 44202 | 44248 |
| | | | | 44111 | 44157 | 44203 | 44249 |
| | | | | 44112 | 44158 | 44204 | 44250 |
| | | | | 44113 | 44159 | 44205 | 44251 |
| | | | | 44114 | 44160 | 44206 | 44252 |
| | | | | 44115 | 44161 | 44207 | 44253 |
| | | | | 44116 | 44162 | 44208 | 44254 |
| | | | | 44117 | 44163 | 44209 | 44255 |
| | | | | 44118 | 44164 | 44210 | 44256 |
| | | | | 44119 | 44165 | 44211 | 44257 |
| | | | | 44120 | 44166 | 44212 | 44258 |

| | | | | | | | |
|---|---|---|---|---|---|---|---|
| 44259 | 44305 | 44351 | 44397 | 44443 | 44484 | 44525 | 44566 |
| 44260 | 44306 | 44352 | 44398 | 44444 | 44485 | 44526 | 44567 |
| 44261 | 44307 | 44353 | 44399 | 44445 | 44486 | 44527 | 44568 |
| 44262 | 44308 | 44354 | 44400 | 44446 | 44487 | 44528 | 44569 |
| 44263 | 44309 | 44355 | 44401 | 44447 | 44488 | 44529 | 44570 |
| 44264 | 44310 | 44356 | 44402 | 44448 | 44489 | 44530 | 44571 |
| 44265 | 44311 | 44357 | 44403 | 44449 | 44490 | 44531 | 44572 |
| 44266 | 44312 | 44358 | 44404 | 44450 | 44491 | 44532 | 44573 |
| 44267 | 44313 | 44359 | 44405 | 44451 | 44492 | 44533 | 44574 |
| 44268 | 44314 | 44360 | 44406 | 44452 | 44493 | 44534 | 44575 |
| 44269 | 44315 | 44361 | 44407 | 44453 | 44494 | 44535 | 44576 |
| 44270 | 44316 | 44362 | 44408 | 44454 | 44495 | 44536 | 44577 |
| 44271 | 44317 | 44363 | 44409 | 44455 | 44496 | 44537 | 44578 |
| 44272 | 44318 | 44364 | 44410 | 44456 | 44497 | 44538 | 44579 |
| 44273 | 44319 | 44365 | 44411 | 44457 | 44498 | 44539 | 44580 |
| 44274 | 44320 | 44366 | 44412 | 44458 | 44499 | 44540 | 44581 |
| 44275 | 44321 | 44367 | 44413 | 44459 | 44500 | 44541 | 44582 |
| 44276 | 44322 | 44368 | 44414 | 44460 | 44501 | 44542 | 44583 |
| 44277 | 44323 | 44369 | 44415 | 44461 | 44502 | 44543 | 44584 |
| 44278 | 44324 | 44370 | 44416 | 44462 | 44503 | 44544 | 44585 |
| 44279 | 44325 | 44371 | 44417 | 44463 | 44504 | 44545 | 44586 |
| 44280 | 44326 | 44372 | 44418 | 44464 | 44505 | 44546 | 44587 |
| 44281 | 44327 | 44373 | 44419 | 44465 | 44506 | 44547 | 44588 |
| 44282 | 44328 | 44374 | 44420 | 44466 | 44507 | 44548 | 44589 |
| 44283 | 44329 | 44375 | 44421 | 44467 | 44508 | 44549 | 44590 |
| 44284 | 44330 | 44376 | 44422 | 44468 | 44509 | 44550 | 44591 |
| 44285 | 44331 | 44377 | 44423 | 44469 | 44510 | 44551 | 44592 |
| 44286 | 44332 | 44378 | 44424 | 44470 | 44511 | 44552 | 44593 |
| 44287 | 44333 | 44379 | 44425 | 44471 | 44512 | 44553 | 44594 |
| 44288 | 44334 | 44380 | 44426 | 44472 | 44513 | 44554 | 44595 |
| 44289 | 44335 | 44381 | 44427 | 44473 | 44514 | 44555 | 44596 |
| 44290 | 44336 | 44382 | 44428 | 44474 | 44515 | 44556 | 44597 |
| 44291 | 44337 | 44383 | 44429 | 44475 | 44516 | 44557* | 44598 |
| 44292 | 44338 | 44384 | 44430 | 44476 | 44517 | 44558* | 44599 |
| 44293 | 44339 | 44385 | 44431 | 44477 | 44518 | 44559* | 44600 |
| 44294 | 44340 | 44386 | 44432 | 44478 | 44519 | 44560* | 44601 |
| 44295 | 44341 | 44387 | 44433 | 44479 | 44520 | 44561* | 44602 |
| 44296 | 44342 | 44388 | 44434 | 44480 | 44521 | 44562 | 44603 |
| 44297 | 44343 | 44389 | 44435 | 44481 | 44522 | 44563 | 44604 |
| 44298 | 44344 | 44390 | 44436 | 44482 | 44523 | 44564 | 44605 |
| 44299 | 44345 | 44391 | 44437 | 44483 | 44524 | 44565 | 44606 |
| 44300 | 44346 | 44392 | 44438 | | | | Total 580 |
| 44301 | 44347 | 44393 | 44439 | | | | |
| 44302 | 44348 | 44394 | 44440 | | | | |
| 44303 | 44349 | 44395 | 44441 | | | | |
| 44304 | 44350 | 44396 | 44442 | | | | |

## 4-6-0             5MT

Introduced 1934. Stanier L.M.S. taper boiler design.

**Experimental locomotives:—**
1. Introduced 1947. Stephenson link motion (outside), Timken roller bearings, double chimney.
2. Introduced 1948. Caprotti Valve Gear.
3. Introduced 1948. Caprotti Valve Gear, Timken roller bearings.
4. Introduced 1948. Caprotti Valve Gear, Timken roller bearings, double chimney.
5. Introduced 1948. Timken roller bearings.
6. Introduced 1948. Timken roller bearings, double chimney.
7. Introduced 1949. Fitted with steel firebox.
8. Introduced 1950. Skefco roller bearings.
9. Introduced 1950. Timken roller bearings on driving coupled axle only.
10. Introduced 1950. Skefco roller bearings on driving coupled axle only.
11. Introduced 1951. Caprotti valve gear, Skefco roller bearings.

Weights: Loco.
- 72 tons 2 cwt.
- 75 tons 6 cwt. (1, 5, 6, 8, 9, 10).
- 74 tons 0 cwt. (2, 3, 4, 11).
- 72 tons 2 cwt. (7).

Pressure: 225 lb. Su.
Cyls.: (O) 18½″ × 28″.
Dr. Wheels: 6′ 0″.     T.E.: 25,455 lb.
Walschaerts Valve Gear, and P.V. except where otherwise shown.

| | | | |
|---|---|---|---|
| 44658 | 44671[10] | 44684[8] | 44697[9] |
| 44659 | 44672[10] | 44685[8] | 44698 |
| 44660 | 44673[10] | 44686[11] | 44699 |
| 44661 | 44674[10] | 44687[11] | 44700 |
| 44662 | 44675[10] | 44688[9] | 44701 |
| 44663 | 44676[10] | 44689[9] | 44702 |
| 44664 | 44677[10] | 44690[9] | 44703 |
| 44665 | 44678[8] | 44691[9] | 44704 |
| 44666 | 44679[8] | 44692[9] | 44705 |
| 44667 | 44680[8] | 44693[9] | 44706 |
| 44668[10] | 44681[8] | 44694[9] | 44707 |
| 44669[10] | 44682[8] | 44695[9] | 44708 |
| 44670[10] | 44683[8] | 44696[9] | 44709 |

| | | | |
|---|---|---|---|
| 44710 | 44756[4] | 44802 | 44848 |
| 44711 | 44757[4] | 44803 | 44849 |
| 44712 | 44758[5] | 44804 | 44850 |
| 44713 | 44759[5] | 44805 | 44851 |
| 44714 | 44760[5] | 44806 | 44852 |
| 44715 | 44761[5] | 44807 | 44853 |
| 44716 | 44762[5] | 44808 | 44854 |
| 44717 | 44763[5] | 44809 | 44855 |
| 44718[7] | 44764[5] | 44810 | 44856 |
| 44719[7] | 44765[6] | 44811 | 44857 |
| 44720[7] | 44766[6] | 44812 | 44858 |
| 44721[7] | 44767[1] | 44813 | 44859 |
| 44722[7] | 44768 | 44814 | 44860 |
| 44723[7] | 44769 | 44815 | 44861 |
| 44724[7] | 44770 | 44816 | 44862 |
| 44725[7] | 44771 | 44817 | 44863 |
| 44726[7] | 44772 | 44818 | 44864 |
| 44727[7] | 44773 | 44819 | 44865 |
| 44728 | 44774 | 44820 | 44866 |
| 44729 | 44775 | 44821 | 44867 |
| 44730 | 44776 | 44822 | 44868 |
| 44731 | 44777 | 44823 | 44869 |
| 44732 | 44778 | 44824 | 44870 |
| 44733 | 44779 | 44825 | 44871 |
| 44734 | 44780 | 44826 | 44872 |
| 44735 | 44781 | 44827 | 44873 |
| 44736 | 44782 | 44828 | 44874 |
| 44737 | 44783 | 44829 | 44875 |
| 44738[2] | 44784 | 44830 | 44876 |
| 44739[2] | 44785 | 44831 | 44877 |
| 44740[2] | 44786 | 44832 | 44878 |
| 44741[2] | 44787 | 44833 | 44879 |
| 44742[2] | 44788 | 44834 | 44880 |
| 44743[2] | 44789 | 44835 | 44881 |
| 44744[2] | 44790 | 44836 | 44882 |
| 44745[2] | 44791 | 44837 | 44883 |
| 44746[2] | 44792 | 44838 | 44884 |
| 44747[2] | 44793 | 44839 | 44885 |
| 44748[3] | 44794 | 44840 | 44886 |
| 44749[3] | 44795 | 44841 | 44887 |
| 44750[3] | 44796 | 44842 | 44888 |
| 44751[3] | 44797 | 44843 | 44889 |
| 44752[3] | 44798 | 44844 | 44890 |
| 44753[3] | 44799 | 44845 | 44891 |
| 44754[3] | 44800 | 44846 | 44892 |
| 44755[4] | 44801 | 44847 | 44893 |

| | | | |
|---|---|---|---|
| 44894 | 44934 | 44974 | 45014 |
| 44895 | 44935 | 44975 | 45015 |
| 44896 | 44936 | 44976 | 45016 |
| 44897 | 44937 | 44977 | 45017 |
| 44898 | 44938 | 44978 | 45018 |
| 44899 | 44939 | 44979 | 45019 |
| 44900 | 44940 | 44980 | 45020 |
| 44901 | 44941 | 44981 | 45021 |
| 44902 | 44942 | 44982 | 45022 |
| 44903 | 44943 | 44983 | 45023 |
| 44904 | 44944 | 44984 | 45024 |
| 44905 | 44945 | 44985 | 45025 |
| 44906 | 44946 | 44986 | 45026 |
| 44907 | 44947 | 44987 | 45027 |
| 44908 | 44948 | 44988 | 45028 |
| 44909 | 44949 | 44989 | 45029 |
| 44910 | 44950 | 44990 | 45030 |
| 44911 | 44951 | 44991 | 45031 |
| 44912 | 44952 | 44992 | 45032 |
| 44913 | 44953 | 44993 | 45033 |
| 44914 | 44954 | 44994 | 45034 |
| 44915 | 44955 | 44995 | 45035 |
| 44916 | 44956 | 44996 | 45036 |
| 44917 | 44957 | 44997 | 45037 |
| 44918 | 44958 | 44998 | 45038 |
| 44919 | 44959 | 44999 | 45039 |
| 44920 | 44960 | 45000 | 45040 |
| 44921 | 44961 | 45001 | 45041 |
| 44922 | 44962 | 45002 | 45042 |
| 44923 | 44963 | 45003 | 45043 |
| 44924 | 44964 | 45004 | 45044 |
| 44925 | 44965 | 45005 | 45045 |
| 44926 | 44966 | 45006 | 45046 |
| 44927 | 44967 | 45007 | 45047 |
| 44928 | 44968 | 45008 | 45048 |
| 44929 | 44969 | 45009 | 45049 |
| 44930 | 44970 | 45010 | 45050 |
| 44931 | 44971 | 45011 | 45051 |
| 44932 | 44972 | 45012 | 45052 |
| 44933 | 44973 | 45013 | 45053 |

| | | | |
|---|---|---|---|
| 45054 | 45095 | 45136 | 45177 |
| 45055 | 45096 | 45137 | 45178 |
| 45056 | 45097 | 45138 | 45179 |
| 45057 | 45098 | 45139 | 45180 |
| 45058 | 45099 | 45140 | 45181 |
| 45059 | 45100 | 45141 | 45182 |
| 45060 | 45101 | 45142 | 45183 |
| 45061 | 45102 | 45143 | 45184 |
| 45062 | 45103 | 45144 | 45185 |
| 45063 | 45104 | 45145 | 45186 |
| 45064 | 45105 | 45146 | 45187 |
| 45065 | 45106 | 45147 | 45188 |
| 45066 | 45107 | 45148 | 45189 |
| 45067 | 45108 | 45149 | 45190 |
| 45068 | 45109 | 45150 | 45191 |
| 45069 | 45110 | 45151 | 45192 |
| 45070 | 45111 | 45152 | 45193 |
| 45071 | 45112 | 45153 | 45194 |
| 45072 | 45113 | 45154* | 45195 |
| 45073 | 45114 | 45155 | 45196 |
| 45074 | 45115 | 45156* | 45197 |
| 45075 | 45116 | 45157* | 45198 |
| 45076 | 45117 | 45158* | 45199 |
| 45077 | 45118 | 45159 | 45200 |
| 45078 | 45119 | 45160 | 45201 |
| 45079 | 45120 | 45161 | 45202 |
| 45080 | 45121 | 45162 | 45203 |
| 45081 | 45122 | 45163 | 45204 |
| 45082 | 45123 | 45164 | 45205 |
| 45083 | 45124 | 45165 | 45206 |
| 45084 | 45125 | 45166 | 45207 |
| 45085 | 45126 | 45167 | 45208 |
| 45086 | 45127 | 45168 | 45209 |
| 45087 | 45128 | 45169 | 45210 |
| 45088 | 45129 | 45170 | 45211 |
| 45089 | 45130 | 45171 | 45212 |
| 45090 | 45131 | 45172 | 45213 |
| 45091 | 45132 | 45173 | 45214 |
| 45092 | 45133 | 45174 | 45215 |
| 45093 | 45134 | 45175 | 45216 |
| 45094 | 45135 | 45176 | 45217 |

---

## NOTE

To understand the system of reference marks used in this book it is essential to read the notes on page 2.

**\* NAMES:**

45154 Lanarkshire Yeomanry.
45156 Ayrshire Yeomanry.
45157 The Glasgow Highlander
45158 Glasgow Yeomanry.

| | | | | | | | |
|---|---|---|---|---|---|---|---|
| 45218 | 45264 | 45310 | 45356 | 45402 | 45427 | 45452 | 45476 |
| 45219 | 45265 | 45311 | 45357 | 45403 | 45428 | 45453 | 45477 |
| 45220 | 45266 | 45312 | 45358 | 45404 | 45429 | 45454 | 45478 |
| 45221 | 45267 | 45313 | 45359 | 45405 | 45430 | 45455 | 45479 |
| 45222 | 45268 | 45314 | 45360 | 45406 | 45431 | 45456 | 45480 |
| 45223 | 45269 | 45315 | 45361 | 45407 | 45432 | 45457 | 45481 |
| 45224 | 45270 | 45316 | 45362 | 45408 | 45433 | 45458 | 45482 |
| 45225 | 45271 | 45317 | 45363 | 45409 | 45434 | 45459 | 45483 |
| 45226 | 45272 | 45318 | 45364 | 45410 | 45435 | 45460 | 45484 |
| 45227 | 45273 | 45319 | 45365 | 45411 | 45436 | 45461 | 45485 |
| 45228 | 45274 | 45320 | 45366 | 45412 | 45437 | 45462 | 45486 |
| 45229 | 45275 | 45321 | 45367 | 45413 | 45438 | 45463 | 45487 |
| 45230 | 45276 | 45322 | 45368 | 45414 | 45439 | 45464 | 45488 |
| 45231 | 45277 | 45323 | 45369 | 45415 | 45440 | 45465 | 45489 |
| 45232 | 45278 | 45324 | 45370 | 45416 | 45441 | 45466 | 45490 |
| 45233 | 45279 | 45325 | 45371 | 45417 | 45442 | 45467 | 45491 |
| 45234 | 45280 | 45326 | 45372 | 45418 | 45443 | 45468 | 45492 |
| 45235 | 45281 | 45327 | 45373 | 45419 | 45444 | 45469 | 45493 |
| 45236 | 45282 | 45328 | 45374 | 45420 | 45445 | 45470 | 45494 |
| 45237 | 45283 | 45329 | 45375 | 45421 | 45446 | 45471 | 45495 |
| 45238 | 45284 | 45330 | 45376 | 45422 | 45447 | 45472 | 45496 |
| 45239 | 45285 | 45331 | 45377 | 45423 | 45448 | 45473 | 45497 |
| 45240 | 45286 | 45332 | 45378 | 45424 | 45449 | 45474 | 45498 |
| 45241 | 45287 | 45333 | 45379 | 45425 | 45450 | 45475 | 45499 |
| 45242 | 45288 | 45334 | 45380 | 45426 | 45451 | | |
| 45243 | 45289 | 45335 | 45381 | | | | |
| 45244 | 45290 | 45336 | 45382 | | | | |
| 45245 | 45291 | 45337 | 45383 | | | | |
| 45246 | 45292 | 45338 | 45384 | | | | |
| 45247 | 45293 | 45339 | 45385 | | | | |
| 45248 | 45294 | 45340 | 45386 | | | | |
| 45249 | 45295 | 45341 | 45387 | | | | |
| 45250 | 45296 | 45342 | 45388 | | | | |
| 45251 | 45297 | 45343 | 45399 | | | | |
| 45252 | 45298 | 45344 | 45390 | | | | |
| 45253 | 45299 | 45345 | 45391 | | | | |
| 45254 | 45300 | 45346 | 45392 | | | | |
| 45255 | 45301 | 45347 | 45393 | | | | |
| 45256 | 45302 | 45348 | 45394 | | | | |
| 45257 | 45303 | 45349 | 45395 | | | | |
| 45258 | 45304 | 45350 | 45396 | | | | |
| 45259 | 45305 | 45351 | 45397 | | | | |
| 45260 | 45306 | 45352 | 45398 | | | | |
| 45261 | 45307 | 45353 | 45399 | | | | |
| 45262 | 45308 | 45354 | 45400 | | | | |
| 45263 | 45309 | 45355 | 45401 | | | | |

Total 84

## 4-6-0 " Patriot " 6P & 7P

*6P Introduced 1930. Fowler 3-cyl.
rebuild of L.N.W. ' Claughton '
Class (introduced 1912), retaining
original wheels and other details.

Remainder. Introduced 1933. New
locos. to Fowler design (45502–4
were officially considered as rebuilds

†7P Introduced 1946. Ivatt rebuild of
Fowler locos. with large taper boiler,
new cylinders and double chimney.

Weights: Loco. $\begin{cases} 80 \text{ tons } 15 \text{ cwt.} \\ 82 \text{ tons } 0 \text{ cwt.} † \end{cases}$

Pressure: $\begin{cases} 200 \text{ lb. Su.} \\ 250 \text{ lb. Su.} † \end{cases}$

Cyls.: $\begin{cases} (3) \ 18" \times 26" \\ (3) \ 17" \times 26" † \end{cases}$

Dr. Wheels: 6′ 9″

T.E.: $\begin{cases} 26,520 \text{ lb.} \\ 29,570 \text{ lb.} † \end{cases}$

Walschaerts Valve Gear. P.V.

| | |
|---|---|
| 45500*Patriot | 45541 Duke of Sutherland |
| 45501*St. Dunstan's | 45542 |
| 45502 Royal Naval Division | 45543 Home Guard |
| 45503 The Royal Leicestershire Regiment | 45544 |
| 45504 Royal Signals | 45545†Planet |
| 45505 The Royal Army Ordnance Corps | 45546 Fleetwood |
| 45506 The Royal Pioneer Corps | 45547 |
| 45507 Royal Tank Corps | 45548 Lytham St. Annes |
| 45508 | 45549 |
| 45509 The Derbyshire Yeomanry | 45550 |
| 45510 | 45551 |

**Total 52**

## "Jubilee" Class

### 4-6-0        6P & 7P

**6P** Introduced 1934. Stanier L.M.S. taper boiler development of the "Patriot" class.

*Introduced 1936. Boiler fitted with double chimney; this boiler was acquired by 45742 in 1940.

†**7P** Introduced 1942. Rebuilt with larger boiler and double chimney

Weights: Loco. $\begin{cases} 79 \text{ tons } 11 \text{ cwt.} \\ 82 \text{ tons } 0 \text{ cwt.}† \end{cases}$

Pressure: $\begin{cases} 225 \text{ lb. Su.} \\ 250 \text{ lb. Su.}† \end{cases}$

Cyls.: (3) $17'' \times 26''$.
Dr. Wheels: 6' 9".

T.E.: $\begin{cases} 26,610 \text{ lb.} \\ 29,570 \text{ lb.}† \end{cases}$

Walschaerts Valve Gear. P.V.

| | |
|---|---|
| 45511 Isle of Man | |
| 45512†Bunsen | |
| 45513 | |
| 45514†Holyhead | |
| 45515 Caernarvon | |
| 45516 The Bedfordshire and Hertfordshire Regiment | |
| 45517 | |
| 45518 Bradshaw | |
| 45519 Lady Godiva | |
| 45520 Llandudno | |
| 45521†Rhyl | |
| 45522†Prestatyn | |
| 45523†Bangor | |
| 45524 Blackpool | |
| 45525†Colwyn Bay | |
| 45526†Morecambe and Heysham | |
| 45527†Southport | |
| 45528† | |
| 45529†Stephenson | |
| 45530†Sir Frank Ree | 45552 Silver Jubilee |
| 45531†Sir Frederick Harrison | 45553 Canada |
| 45532†Illustrious | 45554 Ontario |
| 45533 Lord Rathmore | 45555 Quebec |
| 45534†E. Tootal Broadhurst | 45556 Nova Scotia |
| 45535†Sir Herbert Walker, K.C.B. | 45557 New Brunswick |
| 45536†Private W. Wood, V.C. | 45558 Manitoba |
| 45537 Private E. Sykes, V.C. | 45559 British Columbia |
| 45538 Giggleswick | 45560 Prince Edward Island |
| 45539 E. C. Trench | 45561 Saskatchewan |
| 45540†Sir Robert Turnbull | 45562 Alberta |
| | 45563 Australia |
| | 45564 New South Wales |
| | 45565 Victoria |

| | | | |
|---|---|---|---|
| 45566 | Queensland | 45612 | Jamaica |
| 45567 | South Australia | 45613 | Kenya |
| 45568 | Western Australia | 45614 | Leeward Islands |
| 45569 | Tasmania | 45615 | Malay States |
| 45570 | New Zealand | 45616 | Malta G.C. |
| 45571 | South Africa | 45617 | Mauritius |
| 45572 | Eire | 45618 | New Hebrides |
| 45573 | Newfoundland | 45619 | Nigeria |
| 45574 | India | 45620 | North Borneo |
| 45575 | Madras | 45621 | Northern Rhodesia |
| 45576 | Bombay | 45622 | Nyasaland |
| 45577 | Bengal | 45623 | Palestine |
| 45578 | United Provinces | 45624 | St. Helena |
| 45579 | Punjab | 45625 | Sarawak |
| 45580 | Burma | 45626 | Seychelles |
| 45581 | Bihar and Orissa | 45627 | Sierra Leone |
| 45582 | Central Provinces | 45628 | Somaliland |
| 45583 | Assam | 45629 | Straits Settlements |
| 45584 | North West Frontier | 45630 | Swaziland |
| 45585 | Hyderabad | 45631 | Tanganyika |
| 45586 | Mysore | 45632 | Tonga |
| 45587 | Baroda | 45633 | Aden |
| 45588 | Kashmir | 45634 | Trinidad |
| 45589 | Gwalior | 45635 | Tobago |
| 45590 | Travancore | 45636 | Uganda |
| 45591 | Udaipur | 45638 | Zanzibar |
| 45592 | Indore | 45639 | Raleigh |
| 45593 | Kolhapur | 45640 | Frobisher |
| 45594 | Bhopal | 45641 | Sandwich |
| 45595 | Southern Rhodesia | 45642 | Boscawen |
| 45596 | Bahamas | 45643 | Rodney |
| 45597 | Barbados | 45644 | Howe |
| 45598 | Basutoland | 45645 | Collingwood |
| 45599 | Bechuanaland | 45646 | Napier |
| 45600 | Bermuda | 45647 | Sturdee |
| 45601 | British Guiana | 45648 | Wemyss |
| 45602 | British Honduras | 45649 | Hawkins |
| 45603 | Solomon Islands | 45650 | Blake |
| 45604 | Ceylon | 45651 | Shovell |
| 45605 | Cyprus | 45652 | Hawke |
| 45606 | Falkland Islands | 45653 | Barham |
| 45607 | Fiji | 45654 | Hood |
| 45608 | Gibraltar | 45655 | Keith |
| 45609 | Gilbert and Ellice Islands | 45656 | Cochrane |
| 45610 | Gold Coast | 45657 | Tyrwhitt |
| 45611 | Hong Kong | 45658 | Keyes |

| | | | |
|---|---|---|---|
| 45659 | Drake | 45705 | Seahorse |
| 45660 | Rooke | 45706 | Express |
| 45661 | Vernon | 45707 | Valiant |
| 45662 | Kempenfelt | 45708 | Resolution |
| 45663 | Jervis | 45709 | Implacable |
| 45664 | Nelson | 45710 | Irresistible |
| 45665 | Lord Rutherford of | 45711 | Courageous |
| 45666 | Cornwallis    [Nelson | 45712 | Victory |
| 45667 | Jellicoe | 45713 | Renown |
| 45668 | Madden | 45714 | Revenge |
| 45669 | Fisher | 45715 | Invincible |
| 45670 | Howard of Effingham | 45716 | Swiftsure |
| 45671 | Prince Rupert | 45717 | Dauntless |
| 45672 | Anson | 45718 | Dreadnought |
| 45673 | Keppel | 45719 | Glorious |
| 45674 | Duncan | 45720 | Indomitable |
| 45675 | Hardy | 45721 | Impregnable |
| 45676 | Codrington | 45722 | Defence |
| 45677 | Beatty | 45723 | Fearless |
| 45678 | De Robeck | 45724 | Warspite |
| 45679 | Armada | 45725 | Repulse |
| 45680 | Camperdown | 45726 | Vindictive |
| 45681 | Aboukir | 45727 | Inflexible |
| 45682 | Trafalgar | 45728 | Defiance |
| 45683 | Hogue | 45729 | Furious |
| 45684 | Jutland | 45730 | Ocean |
| 45685 | Barfleur | 45731 | Perseverance |
| 45686 | St. Vincent | 45732 | Sanspareil |
| 45687 | Neptune | 45733 | Novelty |
| 45688 | Polyphemus | 45734 | Meteor |
| 45689 | Ajax | 45735†Comet | |
| 45690 | Leander | 45736†Phoenix | |
| 45691 | Orion | 45737 | Atlas |
| 45692 | Cyclops | 45738 | Samson |
| 45693 | Agamemnon | 45739 | Ulster |
| 45694 | Bellerophon | 45740 | Munster |
| 45695 | Minotaur | 45741 | Leinster |
| 45696 | Arethusa | 45742*Connaught | |
| 45697 | Achilles | | |
| 45698 | Mars | | **Total 190** |
| 45699 | Galatea | | |
| 45700 | Amethyst | | |
| 45701 | Conqueror | | |
| 45702 | Colossus | | |
| 45703 | Thunderer | | |
| 45704 | Leviathan | | |

*For full details of*
BRITISH RAILWAYS CLASS
" WD " 2–8–0s and 2-10-0s
**see the**
A.B.C. OF BRITISH RAILWAYS
LOCOMOTIVES PT. IV.

33

# "Royal Scot" Class

## 4-6-0        7P

Introduced 1927. Fowler L.M.S. parallel boiler design.

*Introduced 1935. Stanier taper boiler rebuild with simple cyls. of experimental high pressure loco. No. 6399 *Fury*.

†Introduced 1943. Stanier rebuild of Fowler locos. with taper boiler, new cylinders and double chimney.

Weights: Loco. $\begin{cases} 84 \text{ tons } 18 \text{ cwt.} \\ 84 \text{ tons } 1 \text{ cwt.*} \\ 83 \text{ tons.†} \end{cases}$

Pressure: 250 lb. Su.

Cyls.: (3) $18'' \times 26''$.

Dr. Wheels: 6′ 9″.    T.E.: 33,150 lb.

Walschaerts Valve Gear. P.V.

46100†Royal Scot
46101†Royal Scots Grey
46102†Black Watch
46103†Royal Scots Fusilier
46104†Scottish Borderer
46105†Cameron Highlander
46106†Gordon Highlander
46107†Argyll and Sutherland Highlander
46108†Seaforth Highlander
46109†Royal Engineer
46110†Grenadier Guardsman
46111†Royal Fusilier
46112†Sherwood Forester
46113†Cameronian
46114†Coldstream Guardsman
46115†Scots Guardsman
46116†Irish Guardsman
46117†Welsh Guardsman
46118†Royal Welch Fusilier
46119†Lancashire Fusilier
46120†Royal Inniskilling Fusilier
46121†Highland Light Infantry, City of Glasgow Regiment
46122†Royal Ulster Rifleman
46123†Royal Irish Fusilier
46124†London Scottish
46125†3rd Carabinier
46126†Royal Army Service Corps
46127†Old Contemptibles
46128†The Lovat Scouts
46129†The Scottish Horse
46130†The West Yorkshire Regiment
46131†The Royal Warwickshire Regiment
46132†The King's Regiment Liverpool
46133†The Green Howards
46134 The Cheshire Regiment
46135†The East Lancashire Regiment
46136†The Border Regiment
46137 The Prince of Wales' Volunteers (South Lancashire)
46138†The London Irish Rifleman
46139†The Welch Regiment
46140†The King's Royal Rifle Corps
46141†The North Staffordshire Regiment
46142†The York & Lancaster Regiment
46143†The South Staffordshire Regiment
46144†Honourable Artillery Company
46145†The Duke of Wellington Regt. (West Riding)
46146†The Rifle Brigade
46147†The Northamptonshire Regiment
46148 The Manchester Regiment
46149†The Middlesex Regiment
46150†The Life Guardsman,
46151†The Royal Horse Guardsman
46152†The King's Dragoon Guardsman

153†The Royal Dragoon
154†The Hussar
155†The Lancer
156 The South Wales Borderer
157†The Royal Artilleryman
158†The Loyal Regiment
159†The Royal Air Force
160†Queen Victoria's Rifleman
161†King's Own
162†Queen's Westminster Rifleman
163 Civil Service Rifleman
164†The Artists' Rifleman
165†The Ranger (12th London Regt.)
166†London Rifle Brigade
167†The Hertfordshire Regiment
168†The Girl Guide
169†The Boy Scout
170*British Legion

**Total 71**

## "Princess Royal " Class

### 6-2                               8P

troduced 1933. Stanier L.M.S. taper boiler design.

troduced 1935. Experimental turbine-driven locomotive (" Turbomotive "). Rebuilt 1952 as reciprocating steam engine.

mainder. Introduced 1935. Development of original design with alterations to valve gear, boiler and other details.

eight.: Loco. $\begin{cases} 104 \text{ tons } 10 \text{ cwt.} \\ 105 \text{ tons } 4 \text{ cwt.}† \end{cases}$

essure: 250 lb. Su.

ls.: (4) $\begin{cases} 16\frac{1}{4}"\times28". \\ 16\frac{1}{4}"\times23"†. \end{cases}$

. Wheels: 6' 6".   T.E.: $\begin{cases} 40,285 \text{ lb.} \\ 41,540 \text{ lb.}† \end{cases}$

alschaerts Valve Gear and rocking shafts, P.V.

200*The Princess Royal
201*Princess Elizabeth

46202†Princess Anne
46203 Princess Margaret Rose
46204 Princess Louise
46205 Princess Victoria
46206 Princess Marie Louise
46207 Princess Arthur of Connaught
46208 Princess Helena Victoria
46209 Princess Beatrice
46210 Lady Patricia
46211 Queen Maud
46212 Duchess of Kent

**Total 13**

## " Princess Coronation " Class

### 4-6-2                               8P

Introduced 1938. Stanier L.M.S. enlargement of " Princess Royal " class. All except Nos. 46230–4/49–55 originally streamlined (introduced 1937. Streamlining removed from 1946).

*Introduced 1947. Ivatt development with roller bearings and detail alterations.

Weights: $\begin{cases} 105 \text{ tons } 5 \text{ cwt.} \\ 106 \text{ tons } 8 \text{ cwt.}* \end{cases}$

Pressure: 250 lb. Su.

Cyls.: (4) $16\frac{1}{4}"\times28"$.

Dr. Wheels: 6' 9".   T.E.: 40,000 lb.

Walschaerts Valve Gear and rocking shafts, P.V.

46220 Coronation
46221 Queen Elizabeth
46222 Queen Mary
46223 Princess Alice
46224 Princess Alexandra
46225 Duchess of Gloucester
46226 Duchess of Norfolk
46227 Duchess of Devonshire
46228 Duchess of Rutland
46229 Duchess of Hamilton
46230 Duchess of Buccleuch

46231 Duchess of Atholl
46232 Duchess of Montrose
46233 Duchess of Sutherland
46234 Duchess of Abercorn
46235 City of Birmingham
46236 City of Bradford
46237 City of Bristol
46238 City of Carlisle
46239 City of Chester
46240 City of Coventry
46241 City of Edinburgh
46242 City of Glasgow
46243 City of Lancaster
46244 King George VI
46245 City of London
46246 City of Manchester
46247 City of Liverpool
46248 City of Leeds
46249 City of Sheffield
46250 City of Lichfield
46251 City of Nottingham
46252 City of Leicester
46253 City of St. Albans
46254 City of Stoke-on-Trent
46255 City of Hereford
46256*Sir William A. Stanier, F.R.S.
46257*City of Salford

**Total 38**

| 46420 | 46447 | 46474* | 4650 |
| 46421 | 46448 | 46475* | 4650 |
| 46422 | 46449 | 46476* | 4650 |
| 46423 | 46450 | 46477* | 4650 |
| 46424 | 46451 | 46478* | 4650 |
| 46425 | 46452 | 46479* | 4650 |
| 46426 | 46453 | 46480* | 4650 |
| 46427 | 46454 | 46481* | 4650 |
| 46428 | 46455 | 46482* | 4650 |
| 46429 | 46456 | 46483* | 4651 |
| 46430 | 46457 | 46484* | 4651 |
| 46431 | 46458 | 46485* | 4651 |
| 46432 | 46459 | 46486* | 4651 |
| 46433 | 46460 | 46487* | 4651 |
| 46434 | 46461 | 46488* | 4651 |
| 46435 | 46462 | 46489* | 4651 |
| 46436 | 46463 | 46490* | 4651 |
| 46437 | 46464 | 46491* | 4651 |
| 46438 | 46465* | 46492* | 4651 |
| 46439 | 46466* | 46493* | 4652 |
| 46440 | 46467* | 46494* | 4652 |
| 46441 | 46468* | 46495* | 4652 |
| 46442 | 46469* | 46496* | 4652 |
| 46443 | 46470* | 46497* | 4652 |
| 46444 | 46471* | 46498* | 4652 |
| 46445 | 46472* | 46499* | 4652 |
| 46446 | 46473* | 46500* | 4652 |

## 2-6-0 2MT

Introduced 1946. Ivatt L.M.S. taper boiler design. Nos. 46400-64 have short L.M.S. chimney, Nos. 46465-89 have long B.R. tapered chimney, remainder B.R. long parallel chimney.
Weight: Loco. 47 tons 2 cwt.
Pressure: 200 lb. Su.
Cyls.: $\begin{cases} \text{(O) } 16'' \times 24''. \\ \text{(O) } 16\frac{1}{2}'' \times 24''* \end{cases}$
Dr. Wheels: 5' 0". T.E.: $\begin{cases} 17,410 \text{ lb.} \\ 18,510 \text{ lb.*} \end{cases}$
Walschaerts Valve Gear, P.V.

| 46400 | 46405 | 46410 | 46415 |
| 46401 | 46406 | 46411 | 46416 |
| 46402 | 46407 | 46412 | 46417 |
| 46403 | 46408 | 46413 | 46418 |
| 46404 | 46409 | 46414 | 46419 |

## 2-4-2T 1

Introduced 1890. Webb L.N.W design.
Weight: 50 tons 10 cwt.
Pressure: 150 lb.
Cyls.: 17" × 24".
Dr. Wheels: 5' 8½". T.E.: 12,910
Allan straight link gear.

| 46601 | 46620 | 46683 | 4675 |
| 46604 | 46654 | 46701 | |
| 46616 | 46666 | 46712 | |

**Total 1**

## 0-6-2T 2M

Introduced 1898. Webb L.N.W. " Passenger tank."
Weight: 52 tons 6 cwt.
Pressure: 150 lb.

36

yls.: 18″ × 24 .
r. Wheels: 5′ 2½″.　　T.E.: 15,865 lb.
y Valve Gear.

6900　　　　　　　　　　Total 1

## -4-0ST　　　　　　　　　0F

ntroduced 1932. Kitson design pre-
pared to Stanier's requirements for
L.M.S.
Weight: 33 tons 0 cwt.
ressure: 160 lb.
yls.: (O) 15½″ × 30″.
r. Wheels: 3′ 10″.　　T.E.: 14,205 lb.

| | | | |
|---|---|---|---|
| 7000 | 47003 | 47006 | 47008 |
| 7001 | 47004 | 47007 | 47009 |
| 7002 | 47005 | | |

**N.B.—Locos. of this class are still being delivered.**

## -6-0T　　　　　　　　　2F

ntroduced 1928. Fowler L.M.S. short-
wheel-base dock tanks.
Weight: 43 tons 12 cwt.
ressure: 160 lb.
yls.: (O) 17″ × 22″.
r. Wheels: 3′ 11″.　　T.E.: 18,400 lb.
Walschaerts Valve Gear.

| | | | |
|---|---|---|---|
| 47160 | 47163 | 47166 | 47168 |
| 47161 | 47164 | 47167 | 47169 |
| 47162 | 47165 | | |

Total 10

## 0-4-0T　　　　　　　Sentinel

**Geared Sentinel locos.**
*Introduced 1929. Single-speed locos.
for S. & D.J. (taken into L.M.S. stock
1930).
†Introduced 1930. Two-speed locos.
for L.M.S.
‡Introduced 1932 Single-speed loco.
for L.M.S.

Weight:
$\left\{\begin{array}{l} 27 \text{ tons } 15 \text{ cwt.*} \\ 20 \text{ tons } 17 \text{ cwt.†} \\ 18 \text{ tons } 18 \text{ cwt.‡} \end{array}\right.$

Pressure: 275 lb Su.

Cyls.:
$\left\{\begin{array}{l} (4) 6\frac{3}{4}″ × 9″.* \\ 6\frac{3}{4}″ × 9″.†‡ \end{array}\right.$

Dr. Wheels:
$\left\{\begin{array}{l} 3′ 1\frac{1}{2}″.* \\ 2′ 6″.†‡ \end{array}\right.$

T.E.:
$\left\{\begin{array}{l} 15,500 \text{ lb.*} \\ 11,800 \text{ lb.†‡} \end{array}\right.$

Poppet Valves.

| | | | |
|---|---|---|---|
| 47180† | 47182† | 47184‡ | 47191* |
| 47181† | 47183† | 47190* | |

Total 7

## 0-6-0T 3F

Introduced 1899. Johnson large Midland design, rebuilt with Belpaire boiler from 1919; fitted with condensers for London area.
*Introduced 1899 Non-condensing locos.
Weight: 48 tons 15 cwt.
Pressure: 160 lb.
Cyls.: 18″ × 26″.
Dr. Wheels: 4′ 7″.    T.E.: 20,835 lb.

| | | | |
|---|---|---|---|
| 47200 | 47215 | 47230* | 47245 |
| 47201 | 47216 | 47231* | 47246* |
| 47202 | 47217 | 47232* | 47247 |
| 47203 | 47218 | 47233* | 47248* |
| 47204 | 47219 | 47234* | 47249 |
| 47205 | 47220 | 47235* | 47250* |
| 47206 | 47221 | 47236* | 47251 |
| 47207 | 47222 | 47237* | 47252* |
| 47208 | 47223 | 47238* | 47253* |
| 47209 | 47224 | 47239* | 47254* |
| 47210 | 47225 | 47240 | 47255* |
| 47211 | 47226 | 47241 | 47256* |
| 47212 | 47227 | 47242 | 47257* |
| 47213 | 47228 | 47243 | 47258* |
| 47214 | 47229 | 47244 | 47259* |

**Total 60**

## 0-6-0T 3F

Introduced 1924. Post-grouping development of Midland design with detail alterations.
*Introduced 1929. Locos. built for S. & D.J. (taken into L.M.S. stock 1930).
Weight: 49 tons 10 cwt.
Pressure: 160 lb.
Cyls.: 18″ × 26″.
Dr. Wheels: 4′ 7″.    T.E.: 20,835 lb.

| | | | |
|---|---|---|---|
| 47260 | 47270 | 47280 | 47290 |
| 47261 | 47271 | 47281 | 47291 |
| 47262 | 47272 | 47282 | 47292 |
| 47263 | 47273 | 47283 | 47293 |
| 47264 | 47274 | 47284 | 47294 |
| 47265 | 47275 | 47285 | 47295 |
| 47266 | 47276 | 47286 | 47296 |
| 47267 | 47277 | 47287 | 47297 |
| 47268 | 47278 | 47288 | 47298 |
| 47269 | 47279 | 47289 | 47299 |

| | | | |
|---|---|---|---|
| 47300 | 47346 | 47392 | 47438 |
| 47301 | 47347 | 47393 | 47439 |
| 47302 | 47348 | 47394 | 47440 |
| 47303 | 47349 | 47395 | 47441 |
| 47304 | 47350 | 47396 | 47442 |
| 47305 | 47351 | 47397 | 47443 |
| 47306 | 47352 | 47398 | 47444 |
| 47307 | 47353 | 47399 | 47445 |
| 47308 | 47354 | 47400 | 47446 |
| 47309 | 47355 | 47401 | 47447 |
| 47310* | 47356 | 47402 | 47448 |
| 47311* | 47357 | 47403 | 47449 |
| 47312* | 47358 | 47404 | 47450 |
| 47313* | 47359 | 47405 | 47451 |
| 47314* | 47360 | 47406 | 47452 |
| 47315* | 47361 | 47407 | 47453 |
| 47316* | 47362 | 47408 | 47454 |
| 47317 | 47363 | 47409 | 47455 |
| 47318 | 47364 | 47410 | 47457 |
| 47319 | 47365 | 47411 | 47458 |
| 47320 | 47366 | 47412 | 47459 |
| 47321 | 47367 | 47413 | 47460 |
| 47322 | 47368 | 47414 | 47461 |
| 47323 | 47369 | 47415 | 47462 |
| 47324 | 47370 | 47416 | 47463 |
| 47325 | 47371 | 47417 | 47464 |
| 47326 | 47372 | 47418 | 47465 |
| 47327 | 47373 | 47419 | 47466 |
| 47328 | 47374 | 47420 | 47467 |
| 47329 | 47375 | 47421 | 47468 |
| 47330 | 47376 | 47422 | 47469 |
| 47331 | 47377 | 47423 | 47470 |
| 47332 | 47378 | 47424 | 47471 |
| 47333 | 47379 | 47425 | 47472 |
| 47334 | 47380 | 47426 | 47473 |
| 47335 | 47381 | 47427 | 47474 |
| 47336 | 47382 | 47428 | 47475 |
| 47337 | 47383 | 47429 | 47476 |
| 47338 | 47384 | 47430 | 47477 |
| 47339 | 47385 | 47431 | 47478 |
| 47340 | 47386 | 47432 | 47479 |
| 47341 | 47387 | 47433 | 47480 |
| 47342 | 47388 | 47434 | 47481 |
| 47343 | 47389 | 47435 | 47482 |
| 47344 | 47390 | 47436 | 47483 |
| 47345 | 47391 | 47437 | 47484 |

| | | | | | | | |
|---|---|---|---|---|---|---|---|
| 485 | 47531 | 47578 | 47626 | 47673 | 47676 | 47678 | 47680 |
| 486 | 47532 | 47579 | 47627 | 47674 | 47677 | 47679 | 47681 |
| 487 | 47533 | 47580 | 47628 | 47675 | | | **Total 417** |
| 488 | 47534 | 47581 | 47629 | | | | |
| 489 | 47535 | 47582 | 47630 | | | | |
| 490 | 47536 | 47583 | 47631 | | | | |
| 491 | 47537 | 47584 | 47632 | | | | |
| 492 | 47538 | 47585 | 47633 | | | | |
| 493 | 47539 | 47586 | 47634 | | | | |
| 494 | 47540 | 47587 | 47635 | | | | |
| 495 | 47541 | 47588 | 47636 | | | | |
| 496 | 47542 | 47589 | 47637 | | | | |
| 497 | 47543 | 47590 | 47638 | | | | |
| 498 | 47544 | 47591 | 47639 | | | | |
| 499 | 47545 | 47592 | 47640 | | | | |
| 500 | 47546 | 47593 | 47641 | | | | |
| 501 | 47547 | 47594 | 47642 | | | | |
| 502 | 47548 | 47595 | 47643 | | | | |
| 503 | 47549 | 47596 | 47644 | | | | |
| 504 | 47550 | 47597 | 47645 | | | | |
| 505 | 47551 | 47598 | 47646 | | | | |
| 506 | 47552 | 47599 | 47647 | | | | |
| 507 | 47554 | 47600 | 47648 | | | | |
| 508 | 47555 | 47601 | 47649 | | | | |
| 509 | 47556 | 47602 | 47650 | | | | |
| 510 | 47557 | 47603 | 47651 | | | | |
| 511 | 47558 | 47604 | 47652 | | | | |
| 512 | 47559 | 47605 | 47653 | | | | |
| 513 | 47560 | 47606 | 47654 | | | | |
| 514 | 47561 | 47607 | 47655 | | | | |
| 515 | 47562 | 47608 | 47656 | | | | |
| 516 | 47563 | 47609 | 47657 | | | | |
| 517 | 47564 | 47610 | 47658 | | | | |
| 518 | 47565 | 47611 | 47659 | | | | |
| 519 | 47566 | 47612 | 47660 | | | | |
| 520 | 47567 | 47614 | 47661 | | | | |

## 0-4-2ST        1F

Introduced 1896. · Webb L.N.W.
  Bissel truck design.
Weight: 34 tons 17 cwt.
Pressure: 150 lb.
Cyls.: 17″ × 24″.
Dr. Wheels: 4′ 5½″.    T.E.: 16,530 lb.

| | | |
|---|---|---|
| 47862 | 47865 | **Total 2** |

## 2-6-6-2T    Beyer-Garratt

*Introduced 1927. Fowler & Beyer-
  Peacock, L.M.S. design with fixed
  coal bunker.
*Remainder.* Introduced 1930. Develop-
  ment with detail alterations, later
  fitted with revolving coal bunkers.
  No. 47997 built 1927 to original
  design.
Weights: $\begin{cases} 148 \text{ tons } 15 \text{ cwt.*} \\ 155 \text{ tons } 10 \text{ cwt.} \end{cases}$
Pressure: 190 lb. Su.
Cyls. (4) 18½″ × 26″.
Dr. Wheels: 5′ 3″.    T.E.: 45,620 lb.
Walschaerts Valve Gear. P.V.

| | | | |
|---|---|---|---|
| 47967 | 47976 | 47984 | 47992 |
| 47968 | 47977 | 47985 | 47993 |
| 47969 | 47978 | 47986 | 47994 |
| 47970 | 47979 | 47987 | 47995 |
| 47971 | 47980 | 47988 | 47996 |
| 47972 | 47981 | 47989 | 47997 |
| 47973 | 47982 | 47990 | 47998* |
| 47974 | 47983 | 47991 | 47999* |
| 47975 | | | |

**Total 33**

Continuation of left columns:

| | | | |
|---|---|---|---|
| 521 | 47568 | 47615 | 47662 |
| 522 | 47569 | 47616 | 47664 |
| 523 | 47570 | 47618 | 47665 |
| 524 | 47571 | 47619 | 47666 |
| 525 | 47572 | 47620 | 47667 |
| 526 | 47573 | 47621 | 47668 |
| 527 | 47574 | 47622 | 47669 |
| 528 | 47563 | 47623 | 47670 |
| 529 | 47576 | 47624 | 47671 |
| 530 | 47577 | 47625 | 47672 |

## 2-8-0          8F

Introduced 1935. Stanier L.M.S. taper
  boiler design.
Weight: Loco. 72 tons 2 cwt.
Pressure: 225 lb. Su.
Cyls.: (O) 18½″ × 28″.
Dr. Wheels: 4′ 8½″.   T.E.: 32,440 lb.
Walschaerts Valve Gear.   P.V.

| | | | |
|---|---|---|---|
| 48000 | 48064 | 48109 | 48147 |
| 48001 | 48065 | 48110 | 48148 |
| 48002 | 48067 | 48111 | 48149 |
| 48003 | 48069 | 48112 | 48150 |
| 48004 | 48070 | 48113 | 48151 |
| 48005 | 48073 | 48114 | 48152 |
| 48006 | 48074 | 48115 | 48153 |
| 48007 | 48075 | 48116 | 48154 |
| 48008 | 48076 | 48117 | 48155 |
| 48009 | 48077 | 48118 | 48156 |
| 48010 | 48078 | 48119 | 48157 |
| 48011 | 48079 | 48120 | 48158 |
| 48012 | 48080 | 48121 | 48159 |
| 48016 | 48081 | 48122 | 48160 |
| 48017 | 48082 | 48123 | 48161 |
| 48018 | 48083 | 48124 | 48162 |
| 48020 | 48084 | 48125 | 48163 |
| 48024 | 48085 | 48126 | 48164 |
| 48026 | 48088 | 48127 | 48165 |
| 48027 | 48089 | 48128 | 48166 |
| 48029 | 48090 | 48129 | 48167 |
| 48033 | 48092 | 48130 | 48168 |
| 48035 | 48093 | 48131 | 48169 |
| 48036 | 48094 | 48132 | 48170 |
| 48037 | 48095 | 48133 | 48171 |
| 48039 | 48096 | 48134 | 48172 |
| 48045 | 48097 | 48135 | 48173 |
| 48046 | 48098 | 48136 | 48174 |
| 48050 | 48099 | 48137 | 48175 |
| 48053 | 48100 | 48138 | 48176 |
| 48054 | 48101 | 48139 | 48177 |
| 48055 | 48102 | 48140 | 48178 |
| 48056 | 48103 | 48141 | 48179 |
| 48057 | 48104 | 48142 | 48180 |
| 48060 | 48106 | 48143 | 48181 |
| 48061 | 48107 | 48144 | 48182 |
| 48062 | 48108 | 48145 | 48183 |
| 48063 | 48108 | 48146 | 48184 |

| | | | |
|---|---|---|---|
| 48185 | 48251 | 48297 | 4834 |
| 48186 | 48252 | 48301 | 4834 |
| 48187 | 48253 | 48302 | 4834 |
| 48188 | 48254 | 48303 | 4834 |
| 48189 | 48255 | 48304 | 4835 |
| 48190 | 48256 | 48305 | 4835 |
| 48191 | 48257 | 48306 | 4835 |
| 48192 | 48258 | 48307 | 4835 |
| 48193 | 48259 | 48308 | 4835 |
| 48194 | 48260 | 48309 | 4835 |
| 48195 | 48261 | 48310 | 4835 |
| 48196 | 48262 | 48311 | 4835 |
| 48197 | 48263 | 48312 | 4835 |
| 48198 | 48264 | 48313 | 4835 |
| 48199 | 48265 | 48314 | 4836 |
| 48200 | 48266 | 48315 | 4836 |
| 48201 | 48267 | 48316 | 4836 |
| 48202 | 48268 | 48317 | 4836 |
| 48203 | 48269 | 48318 | 4836 |
| 48204 | 48270 | 48319 | 4836 |
| 48205 | 48271 | 48320 | 4836 |
| 48206 | 48272 | 48321 | 4837 |
| 48207 | 48273 | 48322 | 4837 |
| 48208 | 48274 | 48323 | 4837 |
| 48209 | 48275 | 48324 | 4837 |
| 48210 | 48276 | 48325 | 4837 |
| 48211 | 48277 | 48326 | 4837 |
| 48212 | 48278 | 48327 | 4837 |
| 48213 | 48279 | 48328 | 4837 |
| 48214 | 48280 | 48329 | 4837 |
| 48215 | 48281 | 48330 | 4838 |
| 48216 | 48282 | 48331 | 4838 |
| 48217 | 48283 | 48332 | 4838 |
| 48218 | 48284 | 48333 | 4838 |
| 48219 | 48285 | 48334 | 4838 |
| 48220 | 48286 | 48335 | 4838 |
| 48221 | 48287 | 48336 | 4838 |
| 48222 | 48288 | 48337 | 4838 |
| 48223 | 48289 | 48338 | 4838 |
| 48224 | 48290 | 48339 | 4838 |
| 48225 | 48291 | 48340 | 4838 |
| 48246 | 48292 | 48341 | 4838 |
| 48247 | 48293 | 48342 | 4838 |
| 48248 | 48294 | 48343 | 4838 |
| 48249 | 48295 | 48344 | 4839 |
| 48250 | 48296 | 48345 | 4839 |

Class 8P 4-6-2
46203 Princess
~~aret~~ Rose.
[E. D. Bruton

: Class 8P 4-6-2
46238 City of
~~sle.~~
[J. E. Wilkinson

: Class 7P 4-6-0
46156 The South
~~es~~ Borderer.
[E. Treacy

Above: Class 2F 0-6-0 No. 52053. [C. B. Golding

Below: Class 2P 2-4-2T No. 50660. [C. B. Golding

[F. W. Day

Above: Class 7F 0-8-0 No. 49547.

Below: Class 2P 2-4-2T No. 50855 (with larger tanks and bunker)
[C. B. Golding

[E. Treacy (2), R. J. Buckley, W. H. Foster

Top left: Class 3F 0-6-0 No. 52119. Top right: Class 3F 0-6-0 No. 52582 (superheated). Bottom left: Class 3F 0-6-0 No. 52201 (Belpaire boiler). Bottom right: Class 3F 0-6-0 No. 52494.

[C. L. Kerr (2), Dr. G. D. Parkes, J. Robertson]

*Top left:* Class 2F 0-6-0 No. 57270 (with cut-down chimney).
*Top right:* Class 2F 0-6-0 No. 57254 (with built-up tender for snow-plough work). *Bottom left:* Class 3F 0-6-0 No. 57659. *Bottom right:* Class 4MT 4-6-0 No. 54650.

Top left: Class 2P 0-4-4T No. 55175. Top right: Class 2P 0-4-4T No. 55261. Bottom left: Class 3P 4-4-0 No. 54450. Bottom right: Class 3P 4-4-0 No. 54508.

[H. C. Casserley (2). J. N. Westwood. W. A. C. Smith

Top left: Class 2F 0-6-0 No. 58240. Top right: Class 2F 0-6-0 No. 58209 (rebuilt with Belpaire boiler). Bottom left: Class 1P 0-4-4T No. 58077. Bottom right: Class 3F 0-6-0 No. 43568.

[R. J. Buckley, E. D. Bruton, J. F. Henton, J. B. Snell

Top left: Class 2F 0-6-0 No. 58409 (fitted for snow-plough work).
Top right: Class 2F 0-6-0 No. 58323. Bottom left: Class 1P 2-4-2T
No. 46666. Bottom right: Class 2F 0-6-2T No. 58900.
[W. H. Whitworth, F. W. Day, R. J. Buckley (2).

Top left.: Class 2F 0-6-0T No. 58860. Top right.: Class 1F 0-4-2ST No. 47865 and Class 0F 0-4-0ST No. 56032. Bottom left.: Horwich works 18-in. gauge 0-4-0 Wren. Bottom right.: Class 2F 0-6-0ST No. 51321.

[P. H. Wells, B. K. B. Green, T. K. Widd, F. W. Doy

| | | | | | | | |
|---|---|---|---|---|---|---|---|
| 92 | 48438 | 48494 | 48544 | 48630 | 48666 | 48702 | 48738 |
| 93 | 48439 | 48495 | 48545 | 48631 | 48667 | 48703 | 48739 |
| 94 | 48440 | 48500 | 48546 | 48632 | 48668 | 48704 | 48740 |
| 95 | 48441 | 48501 | 48547 | 48633 | 48669 | 48705 | 48741 |
| 96 | 48442 | 48502 | 48548 | 48634 | 48670 | 48706 | 48742 |
| 97 | 48443 | 48503 | 48549 | 48635 | 48671 | 48707 | 48743 |
| 98 | 48444 | 48504 | 48550 | 48636 | 48672 | 48708 | 48744 |
| 99 | 48445 | 48505 | 48551 | 48637 | 48673 | 48709 | 48745 |
| 00 | 48446 | 48506 | 48552 | 48638 | 48674 | 48710 | 48746 |
| 01 | 48447 | 48507 | 48553 | 48639 | 48675 | 48711 | 48747 |
| 02 | 48448 | 48508 | 48554 | 48640 | 48676 | 48712 | 48748 |
| 03 | 48449 | 48509 | 48555 | 48641 | 48677 | 48713 | 48749 |
| 04 | 48450 | 48510 | 48556 | 48642 | 48678 | 48714 | 48750 |
| 05 | 48451 | 48511 | 48557 | 48643 | 48679 | 48715 | 48751 |
| 06 | 48452 | 48512 | 48558 | 48644 | 48680 | 48716 | 48752 |
| 07 | 48453 | 48513 | 48559 | 48645 | 48681 | 48717 | 48753 |
| 08 | 48454 | 48514 | 48600 | 48646 | 48682 | 48718 | 48754 |
| 09 | 48455 | 48515 | 48601 | 48647 | 48683 | 48719 | 48755 |
| 10 | 48456 | 48516 | 48602 | 48648 | 48684 | 48720 | 48756 |
| 11 | 48457 | 48517 | 48603 | 48649 | 48685 | 48721 | 48757 |
| 12 | 48458 | 48518 | 48604 | 48650 | 48686 | 48722 | 48758 |
| 13 | 48459 | 48519 | 48605 | 48651 | 48687 | 48723 | 48759 |
| 14 | 48460 | 48520 | 48606 | 48652 | 48688 | 48724 | 48760 |
| 15 | 48461 | 48521 | 48607 | 48653 | 48689 | 48725 | 48761 |
| 16 | 48462 | 48522 | 48608 | 48654 | 48690 | 48726 | 48762 |
| 17 | 48463 | 48523 | 48609 | 48655 | 48691 | 48727 | 48763 |
| 18 | 48464 | 48524 | 48610 | 48656 | 48692 | 48728 | 48764 |
| 19 | 48465 | 48525 | 48611 | 48657 | 48693 | 48729 | 48765 |
| 20 | 48466 | 48526 | 48612 | 48658 | 48694 | 48730 | 48766 |
| 21 | 48467 | 48527 | 48613 | 48659 | 48695 | 48731 | 48767 |
| 22 | 48468 | 48528 | 48614 | 48660 | 48696 | 48732 | 48768 |
| 23 | 48469 | 48529 | 48615 | 48661 | 48697 | 48733 | 48769 |
| 24 | 48470 | 48530 | 48616 | 48662 | 48698 | 48734 | 48770 |
| 25 | 48471 | 48531 | 48617 | 48663 | 48699 | 48735 | 48771 |
| 26 | 48472 | 48532 | 48618 | 48665 | 48700 | 48736 | 48772 |
| 27 | 48473 | 48533 | 48619 | | 48701 | 48737 | |
| 28 | 48474 | 48534 | 48620 | | | | |
| 29 | 48475 | 48535 | 48621 | | | | |
| 30 | 48476 | 48536 | 48622 | | | | |
| 31 | 48477 | 48537 | 48623 | | | | |
| 32 | 48478 | 48538 | 48624 | | | | |
| 33 | 48479 | 48539 | 48625 | | | | |
| 34 | 48490 | 48540 | 48626 | | | | |
| 35 | 48491 | 48541 | 48627 | | | | |
| 36 | 48492 | 48542 | 48628 | | | | |
| 37 | 48493 | 48543 | 48629 | | | | |

**Total 663**

---

*For full details of*
LONDON MIDLAND REGION DIESEL LOCOMOTIVES
**See the**
ABC OF BRITISH RAILWAYS LOCOMOTIVES Pt. II. Nos. 10000–39999.

# 0-8-0 6F & 7F

### G1 Class 6F
*Introduced 1912. Bowen Cooke L.N.W. superheated design, developed from earlier saturated design (many rebuilt from earlier Webb, Whale and Bowen Cooke compound and simple designs introduced 1892 onwards). Many later rebuilt with Belpaire boilers.

### G2 Class 7F
†Introduced 1921. Development of G1 with higher pressure boiler. Many later rebuilt with Belpaire boilers.

### G2a Class 7F
*Remainder.* Introduced 1936. G1 locos. rebuilt with G2 Belpaire boilers.

Weights: Loco. $\begin{cases} 60 \text{ tons } 15 \text{ cwt. (G1).} \\ 62 \text{ tons } 0 \text{ cwt. (G2, G2a).} \end{cases}$

Pressure: $\begin{cases} 160 \text{ lb. Su. (G1).} \\ 175 \text{ lb. Su. (G2, G2a).} \end{cases}$

Cyls.: $20\frac{1}{2}'' \times 24''$.

Dr. Wheels: $4' 5\frac{1}{4}''$.

T.E.: $\begin{cases} 25,640 \text{ lb. (G1).} \\ 28,045 \text{ lb. (G2, G2a).} \end{cases}$

Joy Valve Gear. P.V.

---

Nos. 48893–49394 CLASSES G1* AND G2a.

---

| | | | |
|---|---|---|---|
| 48893 | 48921 | 48944 | 49007 |
| 48895 | 48922 | 48945 | 49008 |
| 48898 | 48926 | 48950 | 49009 |
| 48899 | 48927 | 48951 | 49010 |
| 48905 | 48930 | 48952 | 49018 |
| 48907 | 48932 | 48953 | 49020 |
| 48914 | 48940 | 48964 | 49021 |
| 48915 | 48942 | 49002 | 49023 |
| 48917 | 48943 | 49005 | 49024 |

| | | | |
|---|---|---|---|
| 49025 | 49121 | 49203 | 493 |
| 49027 | 49122 | 49209 | 493 |
| 49028 | 49125 | 49210 | 493 |
| 49033 | 49126 | 49212 | 493 |
| 49034 | 49129 | 49214 | 493 |
| 49035 | 49130 | 49216 | 493 |
| 49037 | 49132 | 49223 | 493 |
| 49044 | 49134 | 49224 | 493 |
| 49045 | 49137 | 49226 | 493 |
| 49046 | 49139 | 49228 | 493 |
| 49047 | 49140* | 49229 | 493 |
| .49048 | 49141 | 49230 | 493 |
| 49049 | 49142 | 49234 | 493 |
| 49051 | 49143 | 49239 | 493 |
| 49057 | 49144 | 49240 | 493 |
| 49061 | 49145 | 49243 | 493 |
| 49063 | 49146 | 49245 | 493 |
| 49064 | 49147 | 49246 | 493 |
| 49066 | 49148 | 49247 | 493 |
| 49068 | 49149 | 49249 | 493 |
| 49070 | 49150 | 49252 | 493 |
| 49073 | 49153 | 49254 | 493 |
| 49077 | 49154 | 49260 | 493 |
| 49078 | 49155 | 49262 | 493 |
| 49079 | 49157 | 49266 | 493 |
| 49081 | 49158 | 49267 | 493 |
| 49082 | 49160 | 49268 | 493 |
| 49087 | 49161 | 49270 | 493 |
| 49088 | 49162* | 49271 | 493 |
| 49089* | 49164 | 49275 | 493 |
| 49093 | 49167 | 49276 | 493 |
| 49094 | 49168 | 49277 | 493 |
| 49099 | 49172 | 49278 | 493 |
| 49104 | 49173 | 49281 | 493 |
| 49105 | 49174 | 49287 | 493 |
| 49106 | 49177 | 49288 | 493 |
| 49108 | 49180 | 49289 | 493 |
| 49109 | 49181 | 49293 | 493 |
| 49112 | 49186 | 49301 | 493 |
| 49113 | 49189 | 49304 | 493 |
| 49114 | 49191 | 49306 | 493 |
| 49115 | 49196 | 49308 | 493 |
| 49116 | 49198 | 49310 | 493 |
| 49117 | 49199 | 49311 | 493 |
| 49119 | 49200 | 49313 | 493 |
| 49120 | 49202 | 49314 | |

**. 49395–49454† CLASS G2.**

| | | | |
|---|---|---|---|
| 95 | 49410 | 49425 | 49440 |
| 96 | 49411 | 49426 | 49441 |
| 97 | 49412 | 49427 | 49442 |
| 98 | 49413 | 49428 | 49443 |
| 99 | 49414 | 49429 | 49444 |
| 00 | 49415 | 49430 | 49445 |
| 01 | 49416 | 49431 | 49446 |
| 02 | 49417 | 49432 | 49447 |
| 03 | 49418 | 49433 | 49448 |
| 04 | 49419 | 49434 | 49449 |
| 05 | 49420 | 49435 | 49450 |
| 06 | 49421 | 49436 | 49451 |
| 07 | 49422 | 49437 | 49452 |
| 08 | 49423 | 49438 | 49453 |
| 09 | 49424 | 49439 | 49454 |

**otals G2 60 GI 4 G2a 215**

**8-0**     **7F**

oduced 1929. Fowler L.M.S. design,
eveloped from L.N.W. G2.
ght: Loco. 60 tons 15 cwt.
ssure: 200 lb. Su.
s.: 19½″ × 26″.
Wheels: 4′ 8½″.    T.E.: 29,745 b.
Ischaerts Valve Gear. P.V.

| | | | |
|---|---|---|---|
| 03 | 49547 | 49598 | 49640 |
| 05 | 49552 | 49600 | 49648 |
| 08 | 49554 | 49602 | 49657 |
| 09 | 49557 | 49603 | 49659 |
| 11 | 49557 | 49608 | 49662 |
| 15 | 49560 | 49612 | 49664 |
| 24 | 49566 | 49618 | 49666 |
| 32 | 49570 | 49620 | 49667 |
| 36 | 49578 | 49624 | 49668 |
| 38 | 49582 | 49627 | 49672 |
| 44 | 49586 | 49637 | 49674 |
| 45 | 49592 | 49638 | |

**Total 47**

**4-2T**     **2P**

oduced 1889. Aspinall L. & Y. Class
with 2 tons coal capacity.

*Introduced 1892. Locos. built or
rebuilt with smaller cylinders.
†Introduced 1898. Locos. with longer
tanks and 4 tons coal capacity.
‡Introduced 1905. Hughes loco. built
with Belpaire boiler and extended
smokebox.
¶Introduced 1910. Loco. rebuilt with
Belpaire boiler.

Weights: $\begin{cases} 55 \text{ tons } 19 \text{ cwt.} \\ 55 \text{ tons } 19 \text{ cwt.}^* \\ 59 \text{ tons } 3 \text{ cwt.}†‡¶ \end{cases}$

Pressure: 180 lb.
Cyls.: $\begin{cases} 17½″ \times 26″.^* \\ 18″ \times 26″ \text{ (remainder).} \end{cases}$
Dr. Wheels: 5′ 8″.
T.E.: $\begin{cases} 18,360 \text{ lb.}^* \\ 18,955 \text{ lb. (remainder)} \end{cases}$
Joy Valve Gear.

| | | | |
|---|---|---|---|
| 50621 | 50656* | 50731¶ | 50807* |
| 50636 | 50660 | 50746 | 50818 |
| 50643* | 50678* | 50752* | 50829†¶ |
| 50644 | 50686 | 50757 | 50831† |
| 50646 | 50687 | 50762 | 50850†¶ |
| 50647 | 50703 | 50764 | 50855*† |
| 50648 | 50705 | 50765¶ | 50859† |
| 50650¶ | 50714* | 50777 | 50865*† |
| 50651¶ | 50715* | 50778 | 50869† |
| 50652*¶ | 50721 | 50781 | 50887‡ |
| 50653* | | 50788 | |
| 50655¶ | 50725 | 50795* | |

**Total 46**

**0-4-0ST**     **0F**

Introduced 1891. Aspinall L. & Y.
Class 21.
Weight! 21 tons 5 cwt.
Pressure: 160 lb.
Cyls.: (O) 13″ × 18″
Dr. Wheels: 3′ 0⅜″.    T.E.: 11,335 lb.

| | | | |
|---|---|---|---|
| 51202 | 51217 | 51230 | 51240 |
| 51204 | 51218 | 51231 | 51241 |
| 51206 | 51221 | 51232 | 51244 |
| 51207 | 51222 | 51234 | 51246 |
| 51212 | 51227 | 51235 | 51253 |
| 51216 | 51229 | 51237 | |

**Total 23**

## 0-6-0ST (See also p. 60) 2F

Introduced 1891. Aspinall rebuild of
L. & Y. Barton Wright Class 23 0–6–0.
Originally introduced 1876.
Weight: 43 tons 17 cwt.
Pressure: 140 lb.   Cyls.: $17\frac{1}{2}'' \times 26''$.
Dr. Wheels: 4' 6".   T.E.: 17,545 lb.

| | | | |
|---|---|---|---|
| 51307 | 51396 | 51447 | 51496 |
| 51313 | 51397 | 51453 | 51497 |
| 51316 | 51404 | 51457 | 51498 |
| 51319 | 51408 | 51458 | 51499 |
| 51321 | 51410 | 51460 | 51500 |
| 51323 | 51412 | 51462 | 51503 |
| 51336 | 51413 | 51464 | 51504 |
| 51338 | 51415 | 51470 | 51506 |
| 51343 | 51419 | 51471 | 51510 |
| 51345 | 51423 | 51472 | 51511 |
| 51348 | 51424 | 51474 | 51512 |
| 51353 | 51425 | 51477 | 51513 |
| 51358 | 51429 | 51479 | 51514 |
| 51361 | 51432 | 51481 | 51516 |
| 51371 | 51436 | 51484 | 51519 |
| 51375 | 51439 | 51486 | 51521 |
| 51376 | 51441 | 51488 | 51524 |
| 51379 | 51444 | 51489 | 51526 |
| 51381 | 51445 | 51490 | 51530 |
| 51390 | 51446 | 51491 | |

Total 79

## 0-6-0T 1F

Introduced 1897. Aspinall L. & Y.
Class 24 dock tanks.
Weight: 50 tons 0 cwt.
Pressure: 140 lb.
Cyls.: (O) $17'' \times 24''$.
Dr. Wheels: 4' 0".   T.E.: 45,285 lb.
Allan straight link gear.

| | | | |
|---|---|---|---|
| 51535 | 51537 | 51544 | 51546 |
| 51536 | | | |

Total 5

## 0-6-0 2F

Introduced 1887. Barton Wright
L. & Y. Class 25.
Weight: Loco. 39 tons 1 cwt.
Pressure: 140 lb.
Cyls.: $17\frac{1}{2}'' \times 26''$.
Dr. Wheels: 4' 6".   T.E.: 17,545 lb.

| | | |
|---|---|---|
| 52016 | 52031 | 52045 |
| 52021 | 52043 | 52051 |
| 52024 | 52044 | 52053 |

Tot

## 0-6-0

Introduced 1889. Aspinall L. & Y
27.
*Introduced 1911. Rebuilt with
paire boiler and extended smoke
†Introduced 1913. Pettigrew Fu
Rly. design.
‡Furness 0-6-0s rebuilt with ex-L
boiler.
Weights: Loco. $\begin{cases} 42 \text{ tons 3 cwt.} \\ 43 \text{ tons 11 cwt.*} \\ 42 \text{ tons 13 cwt.†} \end{cases}$
Pressure: $\begin{cases} 180 \text{ lb.} \\ 170 \text{ lb.†} \end{cases}$
Cyls.: $18'' \times 26''$.
Dr. Wheels: $\begin{cases} 5' 1''. \\ 4' 7\frac{1}{2}'' \text{ †} \end{cases}$
T.E.: $\begin{cases} 21,130 \text{ lb.} \\ 21,935 \text{ lb.†} \\ 23,225 \text{ lb.‡} \end{cases}$
Joy Valve Gear.

| | | | |
|---|---|---|---|
| 52089 | 52137 | 52177 | 52 |
| 52091* | 52138 | 52179 | 52 |
| 52093 | 52139 | 52182 | 52 |
| 52094* | 52140* | 52183 | 52 |
| 52095 | 52141 | 52186 | 52 |
| 52098 | 52143 | 52189 | 52 |
| 52099 | 52150 | 52194 | 52 |
| 52104 | 52154* | 52196 | 52 |
| 52105 | 52156 | 52197* | 52 |
| 52107 | 52157 | 52201* | 52 |
| 52108 | 52159 | 52203 | 52 |
| 52118 | 52160 | 52207 | 52 |
| 52119 | 52161* | 52212 | 52 |
| 52120 | 52162 | 52215 | 52 |
| 52121 | 52163 | 52216 | 52 |
| 52123 | 52164 | 52217 | 52 |
| 52124 | 52165 | 52218 | 52 |
| 52125 | 52166 | 52220 | 52 |
| 52129 | 52167 | 52225 | 52 |
| 52132* | 52171 | 52230 | 52 |
| 52133 | 52172 | 52232 | 52 |
| 52135 | 52174 | 52235 | 52 |
| 52136 | 52175 | 52236 | 52 |

| 3 | 52355 | 52410 | 52458 |
| 9 | 52356 | 52411 | 52459 |
| 0 | 52358 | 52412 | 52461 |
| 5 | 52360 | 52413 | 52464 |
| 9 | 52365 | 52415 | 52465 |
|   | 52366 | 52416 | 52466 |
| 2* | 52368 | 52418 | 52494† |
| 7 | 52369 | 52427 | 52499‡ |
| 9* | 52376 | 52429 | 52501‡ |
|   | 52378 | 52431* | 52509‡ |
| 2 | 52379* | 52432 | 52510‡ |
| 8 | 52381 | 52435 | 52515 |
| 1 | 52382 | 52437 | 52517 |
| 3 | 52387 | 52438* | 52521 |
| 4 | 52388 | 52441 | 52522 |
| 6 | 52389 | 52443 | 52523 |
| 8 | 52390 | 52445* | 52524 |
| 1 | 52393 | 52447 | 52525 |
| 3 | 52397 | 52449 | 52526 |
| 5 | 52399 | 52450 | 52527 |
| 8 | 52400* | 52452 | 52529 |
| 9 | 52404 | 52453 | |
| 0 | 52405 | 52455 | |
| 1 | 52408 | 52456 | |

**Totals: L. & Y. 180, F.R. 5**

## -0     3F

oduced 1912. Hughes L. & Y. ass 28, superheated development Class 27.

...inder. Introduced 1913. Rebuilds Class 27.

ght: Loco. 46 tons 10 cwt

sure: 180 lb. Su.

: 20½″×26″.

Wheels: 5′ 1″.    T.E.: 27,405 lb.

Valve Gear. P.V.

| 49* | 52569 | 52580 | 52608 |
| 51* | 52572 | 52581 | 52615 |
| 58 | 52575 | 52582 | 52616 |
| 61 | 52576 | 52592 | 52619 |
| | | | Total 16 |

## 2-8-0     7F

Introduced 1914. Fowler design for S. & D.J. with 4′ 9″ boiler (some rebuilt from 1925 series).

*Introduced 1925. Fowler design with 5′ 3″ boiler.

(All taken into L.M.S. stock, 1930.)

Weights: Loco. $\begin{cases} 64 \text{ tons } 15 \text{ cwt.} \\ 68 \text{ tons } 11 \text{ cwt.*} \end{cases}$

Pressure: 190 lb. Su.

Cyls.: (O) 21″×28″.

Dr. Wheels: 4′ 8½″.    T.E.: 35,295 lb.

Walschaerts Valve Gear. P.V.

| 53800 | 53803 | 53806* | 53809 |
| 53801 | 53804 | 53807* | 53810 |
| 53802 | 53805 | 53808* | |

**Total 11**

## 4-4-0     3P

Introduced 1910. McIntosh Caledonian "Dunalastair IV Superheater" or "139" class.

*Introduced 1915. Superheated rebuild of McIntosh Caledonian "Dunalastair IV" or "140" class (originally introduced 1904).

Weight: Loco. 61 tons 5 cwt.

Pressure: 180 lb. Su.

Cyls.: 20¼″×26″.

Dr. Wheels: 6′ 6″.    T.E.: 20,915 lb. P.V.

| 54438* | 54446 | 54451 | 54456 |
| 54439* | 54447 | 54452 | 54457 |
| 54440 | 54448 | 54453 | 54458 |
| 54441 | 54449 | 54454 | 54459 |
| 54443 | 54450 | 54455 | 54460 |
| 54444 | | | Total 21 |

## 4-4-0      3P

Introduced 1916. Pickersgill Caledonian " 113 " and " 928 " classes.
Weight: Loco. 61 tons 5 cwt.
Pressure: 180 lb. Su.
Cyls.: 20″ × 26″.
Dr. Wheels: 6′ 6″.     T.E.: 20,400 lb.
P.V.

| | | | |
|---|---|---|---|
| 54461 | 54465 | 54469 | 54473 |
| 54462 | 54466 | 54470 | 54474 |
| 54463 | 54467 | 54471 | 54475 |
| 54464 | 54468 | 54472 | 54476 |

**Total 16**

## 4-4-0      3P

Introduced 1920. Pickersgill Caledonian " 72 " class.
Weight: Loco. 61 tons 5 cwt.
Pressure: 180 lb. Su.
Cyls.: 20½″ × 26″.
Dr. Wheels: 6′ 6″.     T.E.: 21,435 lb.
P.V.

| | | | |
|---|---|---|---|
| 54477 | 54485 | 54493 | 54501 |
| 54478 | 54486 | 54494 | 54502 |
| 54479 | 54487 | 54495 | 54503 |
| 54480 | 54488 | 54496 | 54504 |
| 54481 | 54489 | 54497 | 54505 |
| 54482 | 54490 | 54498 | 54506 |
| 54483 | 54491 | 54499 | 54507 |
| 54484 | 54492 | 54500 | 54508 |

**Total 32**

## 4-6-0      4

Introduced 1925. Post-Grouping opment of Caledonian " 60 " C
Weight: Loco. 74 tons 15 cwt.
Pressure: 180 lb. Su.
Cyls.: (O) 20½″ × 26″.
Dr. Wheels: 6′ 1″.     T.E.: 22,9
P.V.

| | |
|---|---|
| 54639 | **Tot** |

## 4-6-0      4

Introduced 1916. Pickersgill donian " 60 " Class.
Weight: Loco. 75 tons 0 cwt.
Pressure: 180 lb. Su.
Cyls.: (O) 20″ × 26″.
Dr. Wheels: 6′ 1″.     T.E.: 21,7
P.V.

| | |
|---|---|
| 54650 | **Tot** |

## 0-4-4T

Introduced 1905. Drummond Hig design.
Weight: 35 tons 15 cwt.
Pressure: 150 lb.
Cyls.: 14″ × 20″.
Dr. Wheels: 4′ 6″.     T.E.: 9,2

| | | |
|---|---|---|
| 55051 | 55053 | **Tot** |

## 0-4-4T

*Introduced 1895. McIntosh donian " 19 " class, with raile bunkers.
*Remainder.* Introduced 1897. Mc " 92 " class, developed from " class with larger tanks and hig coal bunkers (both classes ori fitted for condensing on G Central Low Level lines).
Weights: $\begin{cases} 53 \text{ tons } 16 \text{ cwt.*} \\ 53 \text{ tons } 19 \text{ cwt.} \end{cases}$
Pressure: 180 lb.
Cyls.: 18″ × 26″.
Dr. Wheels: 5′ 9″.     T.E.: 18,6

| | | | |
|---|---|---|---|
| 55119* | 55126 | 55141 | 55 |
| 55124* | 55135 | 55143 | 55 |
| 55125 | | | **Tot** |

## 4T      2P

duced 1900. McIntosh Cale-
nian " 439 " or " Standard Passen-
- " class.
oduced 1915. Pickersgill locos.
th detail alterations.
hts: $\begin{cases} 53 \text{ tons } 19 \text{ cwt.} \\ 57 \text{ tons } 12 \text{ cwt.*} \end{cases}$
ure: 180 lb.
: 18"×26".
Wheels: 5' 9".     T.E.: 18,680 lb.

| | | | |
|---|---|---|---|
| 50 | 55185 | 55207 | 55222 |
| 1 | 55187 | 55208 | 55223 |
| 2 | 55189 | 55209 | 55224 |
| 4 | 55193 | 55210 | 55225 |
| 4 | 55194 | 55211 | 55226 |
| 6 | 55195 | 55212 | 55227* |
| 7 | 55196 | 55213 | 55228* |
| 8 | 55197 | 55214 | 55229* |
| 9 | 55198 | 55215 | 55230* |
| 3 | 55199 | 55216 | 55231* |
| 4 | 55200 | 55217 | 55232* |
| 6 | 55201 | 55218 | 55233* |
| 7 | 55202 | 55219 | 55234* |
| 8 | 55203 | 55220 | 55235* |
| 9 | 55204 | 55221 | 55236* |
| 2 | 55206 | | Total 62 |

## 4T      2P

oduced 1922. Pickersgill Cale-
nian " 431 " class (developed from
439 " class) with cast-iron front
ffer beam for banking.
ght: 57 tons 17 cwt.
sure: 180 lb.
.: 18½"×26".
Wheels: 5' 9".     T.E.: 19,200 lb.

| | | |
|---|---|---|
| 37 | 55238 | 55239 | 55240 |

Total 4

---

**IMPORTANT NOTE**

A careful reading of the notes
n page 2 is essential to
understand the use of refer-
nce marks in this book.

---

## 0-4-4T      2P

Introduced 1925. Post-Grouping devel-
opment of Caledonian " 439 " class.
Weight: 59 tons 12 cwt.
Pressure: 180 lb.
Cyls.: 18½"×26".
Dr. Wheels: 5' 9".     T.E.: 19,200 lb

| | | | |
|---|---|---|---|
| 55260 | 55263 | 55266 | 55268 |
| 55261 | 55264 | 55267 | 55269 |
| 55262 | 55265 | | |

Total 10

## 4-6-2T      4P

Introduced 1917. Pickersgill Cale-
donian " 944 " class.
Weight: 91 tons 13 cwt.
Pressure: 180 lb. Su.Cyls.: (O) 19½"×26".
Dr. Wheels: 5' 9".     T.E.: 21,920 lb.
P.V.

55359

Total 1

## 0-4-0ST      0F

Introduced 1885. Drummond and
McIntosh Caledonian " Pugs."
Weight: 27 tons 7 cwt.
Pressure: 160 lb. Cyls: (O) 14"×20".
Dr. Wheels: 3' 8".     T.E.: 12,115 lb.

| | | | |
|---|---|---|---|
| 56011 | 56027 | 56030 | 56035 |
| 56020 | 56028 | 56031 | 56038 |
| 56025 | 56029 | 56032 | 56039 |

Total 12

## 0-6-0T      2F

Introduced 1911. McIntosh Cale-
donian dock shunters, " 498 " class.
Weight: 47 tons 15 cwt.
Pressure: 160 lb. Cyls.: (O) 17"×22".
Dr. Wheels: 4' 0".     T.E.: 18,015 lb.

| | | | |
|---|---|---|---|
| 56151 | 56157 | 56163 | 56169 |
| 56152 | 56158 | 56164 | 56170 |
| 56153 | 56159 | 56165 | 56171 |
| 56154 | 56160 | 56166 | 56172 |
| 56155 | 56161 | 56167 | 56173 |
| 56156 | 56162 | 56168 | |

Total 23

## 0-6-0T 3F | 0-6-0

Introduced 1895. McIntosh Caledonian " 29 " and " 782 " classes (56231-9 originally condensing).

Weight: 47 tons 15cwt.

Pressure: 160 lb.  Cyls.: 18″×26″.

Dr. Wheels: 4′ 6″.  T.E.: 21,215 lb.

Introduced 1883. Drummond Caledonian " Standard Goods "; additions by Lambie and McInt

*Rebuilt with L.M.S. boilers.

Weight: Loco. { 41 tons 6 cwt. / 42 tons 4 cwt.*

Pressure: 180 lb.

Cyls.: 18″×26″.

Dr. Wheels: 5′ 0″  T.E.: 21,4

| | | | | | | | | |
|---|---|---|---|---|---|---|---|---|
| 56230 | 56267 | 56306 | 56342 | | 57230 | 57270 | 57336 | 57 |
| 56231 | 56269 | 56307 | 56343 | | 57232 | 57271 | 57338 | 57 |
| 56232 | 56271 | 56308 | 56344 | | 57233 | 57273 | 57339 | 57 |
| 56233 | 56272 | 56309 | 56345 | | 57234 | 57274 | 57340 | 57 |
| 56234 | 56273 | 56310 | 56346 | | 57235 | 57275 | 57341 | 57 |
| 56235 | 56274 | 56311 | 56347 | | 57236 | 57276 | 57345 | 57 |
| 56236 | 56275 | 56312 | 56348 | | 57237 | 57278 | 57346 | 57 |
| 56238 | 56277 | 56313 | 56349 | | 57238 | 57279 | 57347 | 57 |
| 56239 | 56278 | 56314 | 56350 | | 57239 | 57282 | 57348 | 57 |
| 56240 | 56279 | 56315 | 56352 | | 57240 | 57284 | 57349 | 57 |
| 56241 | 56280 | 56316 | 56353 | | 57241 | 57285 | 57350 | 57 |
| 56242 | 56281 | 56317 | 56354 | | 57242 | 57287 | 57353 | 57 |
| 56243 | 56282 | 56318 | 56355 | | 57243 | 57288 | 57354 | 57 |
| 56244 | 56283 | 56319 | 56356 | | 57244 | 57291 | 57355 | 57 |
| 56245 | 56284 | 56320 | 56357 | | 57245 | 57292 | 57356 | 57 |
| 56246 | 56285 | 56321 | 56358 | | 57246 | 57295 | 57357 | 57 |
| 56247 | 56286 | 56322 | 56359 | | 57247 | 57296 | 57359 | 57 |
| 56248 | 56287 | 56323 | 56360 | | 57249 | 57299 | 57360 | 57 |
| 56249 | 56288 | 56324 | 56361 | | 57250 | 57300 | 57361 | 57 |
| 56250 | 56289 | 56325 | 56362 | | 57251 | 57302 | 57362 | 57 |
| 56251 | 56290 | 56326 | 56363 | | 57252 | 57303 | 57363 | 57 |
| 56252 | 56291 | 56327 | 56364 | | 57253 | 57307 | 57364 | 57 |
| 56253 | 56292 | 56328 | 56365 | | 57254 | 57309 | 57365 | 57 |
| 56254 | 56293 | 56329 | 56366 | | 57256 | 57311 | 57366 | 57 |
| 56255 | 56294 | 56330 | 56367 | | 57257 | 57314 | 57367 | 57 |
| 56256 | 56295 | 56331 | 56368 | | 57258 | 57315 | 57368 | 57 |
| 56257 | 56296 | 56332 | 56369 | | 57259 | 57317 | 57369 | 57 |
| 56258 | 56297 | 56333 | 56370 | | 57260 | 57319 | 57370 | 57 |
| 56259 | 56298 | 56334 | 56371 | | 57261 | 57320 | 57373 | 57 |
| 56260 | 56299 | 56335 | 56372 | | 57262 | 57321 | 57375 | 57 |
| 56261 | 56300 | 56336 | 56373 | | 57263 | 57324 | 57377 | 57 |
| 56262 | 56301 | 56337 | 56374 | | 57264 | 57325 | 57378 | 57 |
| 56263 | 56302 | 56338 | 56375 | | 57265 | 57326 | 57383 | 57 |
| 56264 | 56303 | 56339 | 56376 | | 57266 | 57328 | 57384 | 57 |
| 56265 | 56304 | 56340 | | | 57267 | 57329 | 57385 | 57 |
| 56266 | 56305 | 56341 | | | 57268 | 57331 | 57386 | 57 |
| | | | | | 57269 | 57335 | 57389 | 57 |

Total 142

| 50 | 57462 | 57465 | 57472 |
| 51 | 57463 | 57470 | 57473 |

**Total 156**

| 57650 | 57661 | 57670 | 57682 |
| 57651 | 57663 | 57671 | 57684 |
| 57652 | 57665 | 57672 | 57686 |
| 57653 | 57666 | 57673 | 57688 |
| 57654 | 57667 | 57674 | 57689 |
| 57655 | 57668 | 57679 | 57690 |
| 57658 | 57669 | 57681 | 57691 |
| 57659 | | | |

**Total 29**

**–0**     **3F**

oduced 1899. McIntosh Caledonian
12 '' (Nos. 57550-57628) and " 652''
emainder) classes.
ght: Loco. 45 tons 14 cwt.
sure: 180 lb.
.: 18½"×26".
Wheels: 5' 0".    T.E.: 22,690 lb.

| 50 | 57575 | 57597 | 57621 |
| 52 | 57576 | 57599 | 57622 |
| 53 | 57577 | 57600 | 57623 |
| 54 | 57579 | 57601 | 57625 |
| 55 | 57580 | 57602 | 57626 |
| 56 | 57581 | 57603 | 57627 |
| 57 | 57582 | 57604 | 57628 |
| 58 | 57583 | 57605 | 57630 |
| 59 | 57585 | 57607 | 57631 |
| 60 | 57586 | 57608 | 57632 |
| 62 | 57587 | 57609 | 57633 |
| 63 | 57588 | 57611 | 57634 |
| 64 | 57589 | 57612 | 57635 |
| 65 | 57590 | 57613 | 57637 |
| 66 | 57591 | 57614 | 57638 |
| 68 | 57592 | 57615 | 57640 |
| 69 | 57593 | 57617 | 57642 |
| 70 | 57594 | 57618 | 57643 |
| 71 | 57595 | 57619 | 57644 |
| 72 | 57596 | 57620 | 57645 |
| 73 | | | |

**Total 81**

**0-4-4T**     **IP**

Introduced 1875. Johnson Midland
design, later rebuilt with Belpaire
boiler.
Weight: 53 tons 4 cwt.
Pressure: 140 lb.
Cyls.: 18"×24".
Dr. Wheels: 5' 7".    T.E.: 13,810 lb.
*(Former L.M.S. number in brackets)*

58038 (1261)     **Total 1**

**0-4-4T**     **IP**

Introduced 1881. Johnson Midland
design, rebuilt with Belpaire boiler
(except 58071)
\*Locos. with increased boiler pressure.
†Fitted with condensing gear.
Weight: 53 tons 4 cwt.
Pressure: { 140 lb. / 150 lb.†
Cyls.: 18"×24".   T.E.: { 14,460 lb. / 15,490 lb.†
Dr. Wheels: 5' 4".
*(Former L.M.S. numbers in brackets)*

| Nos. | 58040-56 LOCOS. WITH 140 lb. PRESSURE. | | |
|---|---|---|---|
| 58040 (1273) | | 58054 (1341) | |
| 58050 (1324) | | 58056 (1344) | |
| 58051 (1330) | | | |

**–0**     **3F**

oduced 1918. Pickersgill Cale-
onian " 294 '' class (superheated)
nd " 670 '' classes.
ight: Loco. 50 tons 13 cwt.
sure: 180 lb. Su.
s.: 18½"×26".
Wheels: 5' 0".    T.E.: 22,690 lb.

## *Nos. 58062-91 LOCOS. WITH 150 lb. PRESSURE.

| | | | |
|---|---|---|---|
| 58062 | (1360) | 58080 | (1411) |
| 58065 | (1367) | 58083 | (1420) |
| 58066 | (1368) | 58084 | (1421) |
| 58068† | (1371) | 58085 | (1422) |
| 58071† | (1377) | 58086 | (1423) |
| 58072† | (1379) | 58087 | (1424) |
| 58073† | (1382) | 58089 | (1426) |
| 58075 | (1390) | 58090 | (1429) |
| 58077 | (1397) | 58091 | (1430) |

**Total 23**

## 0-10-0

Introduced 1919. Fowler Midland banker for Lickey incline.
Weight: Loco. 73 tons 13 cwt.
Pressure: 180 lb. Su.
Cyls. (4): 16¾″ × 28″.
Dr .Wheels: 4′ 7½″.    T.E.: 43,315 lb.
Walschaerts Valve Gear.
(Former L.M.S. number in brackets)

58100    (22290)    **Total 1**

## 0-6-0    2P

*Introduced 1875. Johnson Midland 4′ 11″ design with round top boiler.
†Introduced 1917. Rebuilt with Belpaire boiler.
‡Introduced 1878. Johnson Midland 5′ 3″ design, with round top boiler.
§Introduced 1917. Rebuilt with Belpaire boiler.
Weight: Loco. Various.
37 tons 12 cwt. to 40 tons 3 cwt.
Pressure: 160 lb.
Cyls.: 18″ × 26″.

Dr. Wheels: $\begin{cases} 4'\ 11''^* \\ 4'\ 11''\dagger \\ 5'\ 3''\ddagger \\ 5'\ 3''\S \end{cases}$ T.E.: $\begin{cases} 19{,}420\ \text{lb.} \\ 19{,}420\ \text{lb.} \\ 18{,}185\ \text{lb.} \\ 18{,}185\ \text{lb.} \end{cases}$

(Former L.M.S. numbers in brackets)

| | | | |
|---|---|---|---|
| 58114† | (22900) | 58128† | (22929) |
| 58115† | (22901) | 58129† | (22931) |
| 58116† | (22902) | 58130† | (22932) |
| 58117† | (22904) | 58131† | (22933) |
| 58118† | (22907) | 58132† | (22934) |
| 58119† | (22911) | 58133† | (22935) |
| 58120† | (22912) | 58135† | (22944) |
| 58121† | (22913) | 58136† | (22945) |
| 58122† | (22915) | 58137† | (22946) |
| 58123† | (22918) | 58138† | (22947) |
| 58124† | (22920) | 58139† | (22950) |
| 58125† | (22921) | 58140† | (22951) |
| 58126† | (22924) | 58142† | (22954) |
| 58127† | (22926) | 58143† | (22955) |

## HISTORIC LOCOMOTIVES PRESERVED IN STORE

| Type | Originating Company | Pre-Grouping No. | L.M.S. No. | Name | Place of Preservation |
|---|---|---|---|---|---|
| 4-2-2 | M.R. | 118 | (673) | — | Derby |
| 2-4-0 | M.R. | 158A | — | — | Derby |
| 2-2-2 | L.N.W. | (49) | — | Columbine | York Museum |
| 2-2-2 | L.N.W. | 3020 | — | Cornwall | Crewe |
| 2-4-0 | L.N.W. | 790 | (5031) | Hardwicke | Crewe |
| *0-4-0T | L.N.W. | — | — | Pet | Crewe |
| 0-4-0 | F.R. | 3 | — | Coppernob | Horwich |
| 0-4-2 | Liverpool & Manchester | — | — | Lion | Crewe |
| 4-2-2 | C.R. | 123 | (14010) | — | St. Rollox |
| 4-6-0 | H.R. | 103 | (17916) | — | St. Rollox |

The un-bracketed numbers are the ones at present carried by the locos.
*18in. gauge works shunter.

| | | | |
|---|---|---|---|
| 44† | (22958) | 58196§ | (3044) |
| 45† | (22959) | 58197§ | (3045) |
| 46† | (22963) | 58198§ | (3047) |
| 48† | (22967) | 58199§ | (3048) |
| 52† | (22971) | 58200§ | (3049) |
| 53† | (22974) | 58203§ | (3054) |
| 54† | (22975) | 58204§ | (3058) |
| 56† | (22977) | 58206§ | (3062) |
| 57† | (22978) | 58207§ | (3064) |
| 58† | (22982) | 58209§ | (3071) |
| 59* | (22983) | 58211§ | (3074) |
| 60† | (22984) | 58212§ | (3078) |
| 162† | (2988) | 58213§ | (3084) |
| 163† | (2989) | 58214§ | (3090) |
| 164† | (2990) | 58215§ | (3094) |
| 165† | (2992) | 58216§ | (3095) |
| 166† | (2993) | 58217§ | (3096) |
| 167† | (2994) | 58218§ | (3098) |
| 168† | (2995) | 58219§ | (3099) |
| 169† | (2996) | 58220§ | (3101) |
| 170† | (2997) | 58221§ | (3103) |
| 171† | (2998) | 58224§ | (3113) |
| 172† | (2999) | 58225§ | (3118) |
| 173† | (23000) | 58228§ | (3127) |
| 174† | (23001) | 58229* | (3130) |
| 175† | (23002) | 58230† | (3134) |
| 176† | (23003) | 58232† | (3140) |
| 177† | (23005) | 58233† | (3144) |
| 178† | (23006) | 58234† | (3149) |
| 179† | (23007) | 58235† | (3150) |
| 180† | (23008) | 58236* | (3151) |
| 181† | (23009) | 58238† | (3156) |
| 182† | (23010) | 58240* | (3161) |
| 183† | (23011) | 58241† | (3164) |
| 184† | (23012) | 58242† | (3166) |
| 185† | (23013) | 58244† | (3171) |
| 186† | (23014) | 58246* | (3175) |
| 187† | (23018) | 58247† | (3176) |
| 188§ | (3023) | 58249§ | (3190) |
| 189§ | (3027) | 58257§ | (3372) |
| 190§ | (3031) | 58258§ | (3377) |
| 191§ | (3035) | 58260§ | (3420) |
| 192§ | (3037) | 58261§ | (3423) |
| 193§ | (3038) | 58264§ | (3445) |
| 194§ | (3039) | 58265§ | (3451) |
| 195§ | (3042) | 58269§ | (3485) |

| | | | |
|---|---|---|---|
| 58271§ | (3492) | 58291§ | (3564) |
| 58272§ | (3493) | 58293§ | (3571) |
| 58273§ | (3503) | 58295§ | (3603) |
| 58276§ | (3512) | 58298§ | (3648) |
| 58277§ | (3516) | 58299§ | (3655) |
| 58278§ | (3517) | 58300§ | (3688) |
| 58279§ | (3525) | 58303§ | (3696) |
| 58281§ | (3527) | 58305§ | (3707) |
| 58283§ | (3536) | 58306§ | (3725) |
| 58286§ | (3543) | 58308§ | (3738) |
| 58287§ | (3545) | 58309§ | (3739) |
| 58288§ | (3551) | 58310§ | (3764) |
| 58290§ | (3561) | | |

**Total 145**

## 0-6-0 **2F**

Introduced 1873. Webb L.N.W. " Coal Engines."

Weight: Loco. 32 tons 0 cwt.

Pressure: 150 lb..

Cyls.: 17″×24″.

Dr. Wheels: 4′ 5½″. T.E.: 16,530 lb.

*(Former L.M.S. numbers in brackets)*

| | | | |
|---|---|---|---|
| 58321 | (28091) | 58332 | (28141) |
| 58323 | (28100) | 58336 | (28172) |
| 58326 | (28106) | 58343 | (28227) |
| 58328 | (28115) | 58347 | (28245) |
| 58330 | (28128) | 58354 | (28263) |

**Total 10**

## 0-6-0 **2F**

Introduced 1887. Webb L.N.W. " 18 in. Goods " (" Cauliflowers ") many later rebuilt with Belpaire boilers.

Weight: Loco. 36 tons 10 cwt.

Pressure: 150 lb.

Cyls.: 18″×24″.

Dr. Wheels: 5′ 2½″. T.E.: 15,865 lb

Joy Valve Gear.

*(Former L.M.S. numbers in brackets)*

| | | | |
|---|---|---|---|
| 58362 | (28318) | 58376 | (28417) |
| 58375 | (28408) | 58378 | (28430) |

| | | | |
|---|---|---|---|
| 58382 | (28451) | 58413 | (28555) |
| 58394 | (28509) | 58415 | (28559) |
| 58396 | (28512) | 58427 | (28616) |
| 58409 | (28548) | 58430 | (28622) |
| 58412 | (28553) | | |

Total 13

## 0-6-0T 2F

Introduced 1879. Park North London design.
Weight: 45 tons 10 cwt.
Pressure: 160 lb.
Cyls.: (O) 17″ × 24″.
Dr. Wheels: 4′ 4″.   T.E.: 18,140 lb.

(Former L.M.S. numbers in brackets)

| | | | |
|---|---|---|---|
| 58850 | (27505) | 58857 | (27517) |
| 58851 | (27509) | 58858 | (27520) |
| 58852 | (27510) | 58859 | (27522) |
| 58853 | (27512) | 58860 | (27527) |
| 58854 | (27513) | 58861 | (27528) |
| 58855 | (27514) | 58862 | (27530) |
| 58856 | (27515) | | |

Total 13

## 0-6-2T 2F

Introduced 1882. Webb L.N.W. " Coal Tanks."
Weight: 43 tons 15 cwt.
Pressure: 150 lb.
Cyls.: 17″ × 24″.
Dr. Wheels: 4′ 5½″.   T.E.: 16,530 lb.

(Former L.M.S. numbers in brackets)

| | | | |
|---|---|---|---|
| 58880 | (27553) | 58903 | (7711) |
| 58887 | (27596) | 58904 | (7720) |
| 58888 | (27602) | 58911 | (7746) |
| 58889 | (27603) | 58915 | (7757) |
| 58891 | (27621) | 58921 | (7782) |
| 58899 | (7692) | 58924 | (7791) |
| 58900 | (7699) | 58925 | (7794) |
| 58902 | (7710) | 58926 | (7799) |

Total 16

# FORMER L.M.S. SERVICE LOCOS.

## 0-6-0ST 2

Introduced 1870. Webb version Ramsbottom " Special Tank."
Weight: 34 tons 10 cwt.
Pressure: 140 lb.
Cyls.: 17″ × 24″.
Dr. Wheels: 4′ 5½″.   T.E.: 17,005

3323 (L.N.W. No.) Crewe Loco Works
C.D.3 Wolverton Carriage Works
C.D.6 ,, ,, ,,
C.D.7 ,, ,, ,,
C.D.8 "Earlestown" Wolvert Carriage Works

## 0-6-0ST 2

Introduced 1891. Aspinall rebuild L. & Y. Barton Wright class 0-6-0 tender loco. (introduced 187
Weight: 43 tons 17 cwt.
Pressure: 140 lb.
Cyls.: 17½″ × 26″.
Dr. Wheels: 4′ 6″.   T.E.: 17,545

| |
|---|
| 51304 |
| 51305 |
| 51324 } Horwich Loco. Work |
| 51368 |
| 51394 |

(see p. 52 for remainder of class)

## 0-4-0 Dies

Introduced 1936. Fowler diesel.
Weight: 21 tons 5 cwt.

| | | |
|---|---|---|
| E.D.1 | E.D.3 | E.D.5 |
| E.D.2 | E.D.4 | E.D.6 |

Tota

(E.D.1. renumbered from E.D.2.)

# ELECTRIC MOTOR COACH NUMBERS

## LONDON DISTRICT

### OERLIKON STOCK

| | | | | | | | |
|---|---|---|---|---|---|---|---|
| )00 | 28231 | 28242 | 28251 | 28260 | 28270 | 28280 | 28290 |
| 223 | 28233 | 28243 | 28252 | 28261 | 28271 | 28281 | 28291 |
| 224 | 28234 | 28244 | 28253 | 28262 | 28272 | 28282 | 28292 |
| 225 | 28235 | 28245 | 28254 | 28263 | 28273 | 28283 | 28293 |
| 226 | 28237 | 28246 | 28255 | 28264 | 28274 | 28284 | 28294 |
| 227 | 28238 | 28247 | 28256 | 28265 | 28275 | 28285 | 28295 |
| 228 | 28239 | 28248 | 28257 | 28266 | 28276 | 28286 | 28296 |
| 229 | 28240 | 28249 | 28258 | 28267 | 28277 | 28287 | 28297 |
| 230 | 28241 | 28250 | 28259 | 28268 | 28278 | 28288 | 28298 |
| | | | | 28269 | 28279 | 28289 | 28299 |

### COMPARTMENT STOCK

| | | | | | | | |
|---|---|---|---|---|---|---|---|
| )01 | 28004 | 28007 | 28010 | 28013 | 28017 | 28021 | 28025 |
| )02 | 28005 | 28008 | 28011 | 28014 | 28018 | 28022 | |
| )03 | 28006 | 28009 | 28012 | 28015 | 28019 | 28023 | |
| | | | | 28016 | 28020 | 28024 | |

## LIVERPOOL—SOUTHPORT LINE

### COMPARTMENT STOCK

| | | | | | | | |
|---|---|---|---|---|---|---|---|
| 301 | 28304 | 28307 | 28310 | 28332 | 28342 | 28353 | 28363 |
| 302 | 28305 | 28308 | | 28333 | 28343 | 28354 | 28364 |
| 303 | 28306 | 28309 | | 28334 | 28344 | 28355 | 28365 |
| | | | | 28335 | 28345 | 28356 | 28366 |
| | | | | 28336 | 28347 | 28357 | 28367 |
| | | | | 28337 | 28348 | 28358 | 28368 |
| | | | | 28338 | 28349 | 28359 | 28369 |

### FLUSH-PANELLED STOCK

| | | | | | | | |
|---|---|---|---|---|---|---|---|
| 311 | 28316 | 28322 | 28327 | 28339 | 28350 | 28360 | |
| 312 | 28317 | 28323 | 28328 | 28340 | 28351 | 28361 | |
| 313 | 28318 | 28324 | 28329 | 28341 | 28352 | 28362 | |
| 314 | 28319 | 28325 | 28330 | | | | |
| 315 | 28321 | 28326 | 28331 | | | | |

**BAGGAGE CARS**
M28496*    28497*

## MERSEY RAILWAY

| 1st CLASS | | | | 3rd CLASS | | | |
|---|---|---|---|---|---|---|---|
| 405 | 28409 | 28413 | 28417 | M28419 | 28423 | 28427 | 28431 |
| 406 | 28410 | 28414 | 28418 | 28420 | 28424 | 28428 | 28432 |
| 407 | 28411 | 28415 | | 28421 | 28425 | 28429 | |
| 408 | 28412 | 28416 | | 28422 | 28426 | 28430 | |

## MANCHESTER—BURY

| | | | | | | | |
|---|---|---|---|---|---|---|---|
| 500 | 28505 | 28510 | 28515 | 28520 | 28525 | 28529 | 28533 |
| 501 | 28506 | 28511 | 28516 | 28521 | 28526 | 28530 | 28534 |
| 502 | 28507 | 28512 | 28517 | 28522 | 28527 | 28531 | 28535 |
| 503 | 28508 | 28513 | 28518 | 28523 | 28528 | 28532 | 28537 |
| 504 | 28509 | 28514 | 28519 | 28524 | | | |

## LANCASTER—MORECAMBE—HEYSHAM

M28219*    |    28220    |    28221*    |    28222*

*Not yet in service.

## WIRRAL RAILWAY

| | | | |
|---|---|---|---|
| **M** 28672 | 28677 | 28682 | 28687 |
| 28673 | 28678 | 28683 | 28688 |
| 28674 | 28679 | 28684 | 28689 |
| 28675 | 28680 | 28685 | 28690 |
| 28676 | 28681 | 28686 | |

## MANCHESTER, S. JUNCTION & ALTRINCHAM RAILWAY

| | | | | | |
|---|---|---|---|---|---|
| 28571 | 28575 | 28579 | 28583 | 28587 | 28591 |
| 28572 | 28576 | 28580 | 28584 | 28588 | 28592 |
| 28573 | 28577 | 28581 | 28585 | 28589 | 28593 |
| 28574 | 28578 | 28582 | 28586 | 28590 | 28594 |

# THE **ABC** OF
# BRITISH RAILWAYS
# LOCOMOTIVES

## PART 4 - Nos. 60000-99999
EASTERN, NORTH EASTERN,
SCOTTISH REGION, EX-W.D. &
B.R. STANDARD STEAM
LOCOMOTIVES
also E. & N.E.R. Electric Units

*SUMMER*
*1953*
*EDITION*

# FOREWORD

THIS booklet lists all British Railways locomotives numbered between 60000 and 99999 and E. & N.E. electric *train* units. This series of numbers includes all Eastern, North Eastern and Scottish (ex-L.N.E.R.) Region steam locomotives, i.e. steam locomotives of the former L.N.E.R., new British Railways standard locomotives and ex-Ministry of Supply locos. Under the general British Railways renumbering scheme, the numbers of L.N.E.R. steam locomotives were increased by 60000, with the exception of Classes W1 and L1. A later scheme involved the renumbering of all ex-M.o.S. locomotives in the 90000 series, and there have also been minor amendments to Classes B16 and D31 to make way for new locomotives.

Former L.N.E.R. electric, diesel electric and petrol *locomotives* have been renumbered in the 20000 and 15000 series, and details of them will be found in ABC of British Railways Locomotives, Part (Nos. 10000-39999).

## NOTES ON THE USE OF THIS BOOK

In the lists of locomotives which follow:

1. Many of the classes listed are sub-divided, the sub-division being denoted in some cases by " Parts " shown thus: D16, At the head of each class will be found a list of such sub-divisions, if any, usually arranged in order of introduction. Each part is given there a reference mark by which its relevant dimensions, differing from other parts, and the locos in the list it comprises may be identified. Any other differences between locomotives are also indicated, with reference marks, below the details of the class's introduction.

2. The lists of dimensions at the head of each class show locomotives fitted with two inside cylinders, Stephenson gear and slide valves, unless otherwise stated, e.g. (O) = two outside cylinders. P.V. = piston valves.

3. The following method is used to denote superheated locomotives, the letters being inserted, where applicable, after the boiler pressure details: Su = All engines superheated.
SS = Some engines superheated.

4. The date on which the first locomotive of a class was built is denoted by " Introduced."

5. The numbers of locomotives in service have been checked to April 11th, 1953.

6. S denotes Service (Departmental) locomotive still carrying B.R. number (see page 43). This reference letter is introduced only for the reader's guidance and is not borne by the locomotive concerned.

# BRITISH RAILWAYS
## EASTERN & NORTH EASTERN REGION
### Chief Mechanical Engineer
A. H. Peppercorn  -  -  1948-1949
*(post abolished)*

---

# LOCOMOTIVE SUPERINTENDENTS AND CHIEF MECHANICAL ENGINEERS OF THE L.N.E.R.

Sir Nigel Gresley 1923—1941 | E. Thompson 1941—1946
A. H. Peppercorn 1946—1947

## Great Northern Railway

| | | |
|---|---|---|
| A. Sturrock | .. | 1850—1866 |
| P. Stirling | .. | 1866—1895 |
| H. A. Ivatt | .. | 1896—1911 |
| H. N. Gresley | .. | 1911—1922 |

## North Eastern Railway

| | | |
|---|---|---|
| E. Fletcher | .. | 1854—1883 |
| A. McDonnell* | .. | 1883—1884 |
| T. W. Worsdell | .. | 1885—1890 |
| W. Worsdell | .. | 1890—1910 |
| Sir Vincent Raven | | 1910—1922 |

## Great Eastern Railway

| | | |
|---|---|---|
| R. Sinclair | .. | 1862—1866 |
| S. W. Johnson | .. | 1866—1873 |
| W. Adams | .. | 1873—1878 |
| M. Bromley | .. | 1878—1881 |
| T. W. Worsdell | .. | 1881—1885 |
| J. Holden | .. | 1885—1907 |
| S. D. Holden | .. | 1908—1912 |
| A. J. Hill | .. | 1912—1922 |

## Lancashire, Derbyshire and East Coast Railway

| | | |
|---|---|---|
| R. A. Thom | .. | 1902—1907 |

## Manchester, Sheffield and Lincolnshire Railway

| | | |
|---|---|---|
| Richard Peacock | | —1854 |
| W. G. Craig | .. | 1854—1859 |

| | | |
|---|---|---|
| Charles Sacré | .. | 1859—1886 |
| T. Parker | .. | 1886—1893 |
| H. Pollitt | .. | 1893—1897 |

## Great Central Railway

| | | |
|---|---|---|
| H. Pollitt | .. | 1897—1900 |
| J. G. Robinson | .. | 1900—1922 |

## Hull and Barnsley Railway

| | | |
|---|---|---|
| M. Stirling | .. | 1885—1922 |

## Midland and Great Northern Joint Railway

| | | |
|---|---|---|
| W. Marriott | .. | 1884—1924 |

## North British Railway

| | | |
|---|---|---|
| T. Wheatley† | .. | 1867—1874 |
| D. Drummond | .. | 1875—1882 |
| M. Holmes | .. | 1882—1903 |
| W. P. Reid | .. | 1903—1919 |
| W. Chalmers | .. | 1919—1922 |

## Great North of Scotland Railway

| | | |
|---|---|---|
| D. K. Clark | .. | 1853—1855 |
| J. F. Ruthven | .. | 1855—1857 |
| W. Cowan | .. | 1857—1883 |
| J. Manson | .. | 1883—1890 |
| J. Johnson | .. | 1890—1894 |
| W. Pickersgill | .. | 1894—1914 |
| T. E. Heywood | .. | 1914—1922 |

* Between McDonnell and T. W. Worsdell there was an interval during which the office was covered by a Locomotive Committee.

† Previous to whom, the records are indeterminate.

3

# BRITISH RAILWAYS LOCOMOTIVE SHEDS AND SHED CODES

## LONDON MIDLAND REGION

1A **Willesden**
1B Camden
1C Watford
1D Devons Road (Bow)
1E Bletchley
    Leighton Buzzard
    Newport Pagnell

2A **Rugby**
    Market Harborough
    Seaton
2B Nuneaton
2C Warwick
2D Coventry
2E Northampton

3A **Bescot**
3B Bushbury
3C Walsall
3D Aston
3E Monument Lane

5A **Crewe North**
    Whitchurch
    Whitchurch (ex-G.W.)
5B Crewe South
    Crewe (Gresty Lane)
5C Stafford
    Coalport
5D Stoke
5E Alsager
5F Uttoxeter

6A **Chester**
6B Mold Junction
6C Birkenhead
6D Chester (Northgate)
6E Wrexham
6F Bidston
6G Llandudno Junction
6H Bangor
6J Holyhead
6K Rhyl
    Denbigh

8A **Edge Hill**
8B Warrington
8C Speke Junction
8D Widnes
    Widnes (C.L.C.)
8E Brunswick (Liverpool)
    Warrington (C.L.C.)

9A **Longsight**
9B Stockport (Edgeley)
9C Macclesfield
9D Buxton
9E Trafford Park
9F Heaton Mersey
9G Northwich

10A **Springs Branch (Wigan)**
10B Preston
10C Patricroft
10D Plodder Lane (Bolton)
10E Sutton Oak

11A **Carnforth**
11B Barrow
    Coniston
11C Oxenholme
11D Tebay
11E Lancaster

12A **Carlisle (Upperby)**
12C Penrith
12D Workington
12E Moor Row

14A **Cricklewood**
14B Kentish Town
14C St. Albans

15A **Wellingborough**
15B Kettering
15C Leicester
15D Bedford

16A **Nottingham**
    Southwell
    Lincoln (Midland)
16C Kirkby
16D Mansfield

17A **Derby**
17B Burton
    Overseal
17C Coalville
17D Rowsley
    Cromford
    Middleton
    Sheep Pasture

18A **Toton**
18B Westhouses
18C Hasland
    Clay Cross
18D Staveley
    Sheepbridge

19A **Sheffield**
19B Millhouses
19C Canklow

20A **Leeds (Holbeck)**
20B Stourton
20C Royston
20D Normanton
20E Manningham
    Ilkley
    Ilkley (ex-L.N.E.)
20F Skipton
    Keighley
20G Hellifield
    Ingleton

21A **Saltley**
21B Bournville
    Redditch
21C Bromsgrove
21D Stratford-on-Avon

22A **Bristol**
22B Gloucester
    Tewkesbury
    Dursley

24A **Accrington**
24B Rose Grove
24C Lostock Hall
24D Lower Darwen
24E Blackpool
    Blackpool North
24F Fleetwood

25A **Wakefield**
25B Huddersfield
25C Goole
25D Mirfield
25E Sowerby Bridge
25F Low Moor
25G Farnley Junction

26A **Newton Heath**
26B Agecroft
26C Bolton
26D Bury
26E Bacup
26F Lees
26G Belle Vue

27A **Bank Hall**
27B Aintree
27C Southport
27D Wigan (ex-L. & Y.)
27E Walton
    Southport (C.L.

# EASTERN REGION

**Stratford**
Brentwood
Chelmsford
Epping
Spitalfields
Wood St.
  (Walthamstow)
Palace Gates
Enfield Town
Ware
**Hertford East**
Buntingford
**Bishops Stortford**
**Southend (Victoria)**
Southminster
Wickford
**Colchester**
Clacton
Walton-on-Naze
Kelvedon
Maldon
Braintree
**Parkeston**

**Cambridge**
Ely
Huntingdon East
Saffron Walden
**March**
Wisbech
**Kings Lynn**
Hunstanton
South Lynn
Bury St. Edmunds
Sudbury (Suffolk)

**32A Norwich**
Cromer
Wells-on-Sea
Dereham
Swaffham
Wymondham
**32B Ipswich**
Felixstowe Beach
Aldeburgh
Stowmarket
**32C** Lowestoft
**32D** Yarmouth (South
Town)
**32E** Yarmouth (Vauxhall)
**32F** Yarmouth Beach
**32G** Melton Constable
Norwich City
Cromer Beach

**33A Plaistow**
Upminster
**33B** Tilbury
**33C** Shoeburyness

**34A Kings Cross**
**34B** Hornsey
**34C** Hatfield
**34D** Hitchin
**34E** Neasden
Aylesbury
Chesham

**35A New England**
Spalding
Bourne
Stamford

**35B** Grantham
**35C** Peterborough (Spital)

**36A Doncaster**
**36B** Mexborough
Wath
**36C** Frodingham
**36D** Barnsley
**36E** Retford (G.N.)
Retford (G.C.)
Newark

**37A Ardsley**
**37B** Copley Hill
**37C** Bradford

**38A Colwick**
Derby (Friargate)
**38B** Annesley
**38C** Leicester (ex-G.C.)
Leicester (ex-G.N.)
**38D** Staveley
**38E** Woodford Halse

**39A Gorton**
Dinting
Hayfield
**39B** Sheffield (Darnall)

**40A Lincoln**
**40B** Immingham
**40C** Louth
**40D** Tuxford
**40E** Langwith Junction
**40F** Boston

# NORTH EASTERN REGION

**York**
Leeds (Neville Hill)
Selby
Starbeck
Scarborough
Malton
Pickering
Whitby

**Darlington**
Middleton-in-
  Teesdale
Newport
West Hartlepool
Middlesbrough
Guisborough
Stockton

**51F** West Auckland
Wearhead
**51G** Haverton Hill
**51H** Kirkby Stephen
**51J** Northallerton
Leyburn
**51K** Saltburn

**52A Gateshead**
Bowes Bridge
**52B** Heaton
**52C** Blaydon
Hexham
Alston
**52D** Tweedmouth
Alnmouth
**52E** Percy Main

**52F** North Blyth
South Blyth

**53A Hull (Dairycoates)**
**53B** Hull (Botanic
Gardens)
**53C** Hull (Springhead)
Alexandra Dock
**53D** Bridlington

**54A Sunderland**
Durham
**54B** Tyne Dock
Pelton Level
**54C** Borough Gardens
**54D** Consett

5

# SCOTTISH REGION

| | | |
|---|---|---|
| **60A Inverness** | **63A Perth South** | 65C Parkhead |
| Dingwall | Aberfeldy | 65D Dawsholm |
| Kyle of Lochalsh | Blair Atholl | Dumbarton |
| **60B Aviemore** | Crieff | 65E Kipps |
| Boat of Garten | **63B Stirling** | 65F Grangemouth |
| **60C Helmsdale** | Killin | 65G Yoker |
| Dornoch | Stirling (Shore | 65H Helensburgh |
| Tain | Road) | Arrochar |
| **60D Wick** | **63C Forfar** | 65I Balloch |
| Thurso | Brechin | |
| **60E Forres** | **63D Fort William** | |
| | Mallaig | **66A Polmadie (Gl** |
| **61A Kittybrewster** | **63E Oban** | **66B Motherwell** |
| Ballater | Ballachulish | Morningside |
| Fraserburgh | | **66C Hamilton** |
| Peterhead | | **66D Greenock (Lad** |
| **61B Aberdeen (Ferryhill)** | **64A St. Margarets** | Greenock ( |
| **61C Keith** | **(Edinburgh)** | |
| Banff | Dunbar | |
| Elgin | Galashiels | **67A Corkerhill** |
| | Longniddry | **(Gl** |
| | North Berwick | **67B Hurlford** |
| **62A Thornton** | Peebles | Beith |
| Anstruther | Seafield | Muirkirk |
| Burntisland | South Leith | **67C Ayr** |
| Ladybank | **64B Haymarket** | **67D Ardrossan** |
| Methil | **64C Dalry Road** | |
| **62B Dundee (Tay Bridge)** | **64D Carstairs** | |
| Arbroath | **64E Polmont** | **68A Carlisle (King** |
| Montrose | **64F Bathgate** | **68B Dumfries** |
| St. Andrews | **64G Hawick** | Kirkcudbrig |
| **62C Dunfermline (Upper)** | Kelso | **68C Stranraer** |
| Alloa | Riccarton | Newton Ste |
| Inverkeithing | | **68D Beattock** |
| Kelty | **65A Eastfield (Glasgow)** | **68E Carlisle Canal** |
| | **65B St. Rollox** | Silloth |

# SOUTHERN REGION

| | | |
|---|---|---|
| **70A Nine Elms** | **71E Newport (I.O.W.)** | **73A Stewarts Lan** |
| 70B Feltham | **71F Ryde (I.O.W.)** | 73B Bricklayers Ar |
| 70C Guildford | **71G Bath (S. & D.)** | 73C Hither Green |
| Bordon | Radstock | 73D Gillingham (K |
| 70D Basingstoke | **71H Templecombe** | 73E Faversham |
| 70E Reading | **71I Southampton Docks** | |
| | **71J Highbridge** | **74A Ashford (Ker** |
| **71A Eastleigh** | | Canterbury |
| Winchester | | 74B Ramsgate |
| Winchester (ex- | **72A Exmouth Junction** | 74C Dover |
| G.W.) | Seaton | Folkestone |
| Lymington | Lyme Regis | 74D Tonbridge |
| Andover Junction | Exmouth | 74E St. Leonards |
| **71B Bournemouth** | Okehampton | |
| Swanage | Bude | **75A Brighton** |
| Hamworthy | **72B Salisbury** | Newhaven |
| Junction | **72C Yeovil** | Eastbourne |
| Branksome | **72D Plymouth** | 75B Redhill |
| **71C Dorchester** | Callington | 75C Norwood Junc |
| **71D Fratton** | **72E Barnstaple Junction** | 75D Horsham |
| Gosport | Torrington | 75E Three Bridges |
| Midhurst | Ilfracombe | 75F Tunbridge We |
| | **72F Wadebridge** | |

# WESTERN REGION

| | | |
|---|---|---|
| **ld Oak Common** | 84A **Wolverhampton** | 87A **Neath** |
| ough | **(Stafford Road)** | Glyn Neath |
| Aylesbury | 84B Oxley | Neath (N. & B.) |
| Marlow | 84C Banbury | 87B Duffryn Yard |
| Watlington | 84D Leamington Spa | 87C Danygraig |
| outhall | 84E Tyseley | 87D Swansea East Dock |
| eading | Stratford-on-Avon | 87E Landore |
| Henley-on-Thames | 84F Stourbridge | 87F Llanelly |
| idcot | 84G Shrewsbury | Burry Port |
| Newbury | Clee Hill | Pantyfynnon |
| Wallingford | Craven Arms | 87G Carmarthen |
| xford | Knighton | Newcastle Emlyn |
| Abingdon | Builth Road | 87H Neyland |
| Fairford | 84H Wellington (Salop) | Cardigan |
| | 84J Croes Newydd | Milford Haven |
| **ristol (Bath Road)** | Bala | Pembroke Dock |
| Bath | Trawsfynydd | Whitland |
| Wells | Penmaenpool | 87J Goodwick |
| Weston-super-Mare | 84K Chester | 87K Swansea (Victoria) |
| Yatton | | Upper Bank |
| t. Philip's Marsh | 85A **Worcester** | Gurnos |
| windon | Evesham | Llandovery |
| Chippenham | Kingham | |
| Westbury | 85B Gloucester | 88A **Cardiff (Cathays)** |
| Frome | Cheltenham | Radyr |
| eovil | Brimscombe | 88B Cardiff East Dock |
| Weymouth | Cirencester | 88C Barry |
| Bridport | Lydney | 88D Merthyr |
| | Tetbury | Cae Harris |
| **Newton Abbot** | 85C Hereford | Dowlais Central |
| Ashburton | Leominster | Rhymney |
| Kingsbridge | Ross | 88E Abercynon |
| aunton | 85D Kidderminster | 88F Treherbert |
| Bridgwater | | Ferndal |
| Minehead | 86A **Newport (Ebbw** | |
| xeter | **Junction)** | 89A **Oswestry** |
| Tiverton Junction | 86B Newport Pill | Llanidloes |
| aira (Plymouth) | 86C Cardiff (Canton) | Moat Lane |
| Princetown | 86D Llantrisant | Welshpool |
| Launceston | 86E Severn Tunnel | (W. & L. |
| t. Blazey | Junction | 89B Brecon |
| Bodmin | 86F Tondu | Builth Wells |
| Moorswater | 86G Pontypool Road | 89C Machynlleth |
| ruro | Branches Fork | Aberayron |
| enzance | 86H Aberbeeg | Aberystwyth |
| Helston | 86J Aberdare | Portmadoc |
| St. Ives | 86K Abergavenny | Pwllheli |
| | Tredegar | |

# NUMERICAL LIST OF ENGINES

## 4-6-2  8P  Class A4

Introduced 1935. Gresley streamlined design with corridor tender (except those marked †).
*Inside cylinder reduced to 17".
†Non-corridor tender (remainder corridor).
‡Kylchap blast pipe and double chimney.
Weights: Loco. 102 tons 19 cwt.

Tender $\begin{cases} 64 \text{ tons } 19 \text{ cwt.} \\ 60 \text{ tons } 7 \text{ cwt.}† \end{cases}$

Pressure. 250 lb. Su.
Cyls.: $\begin{cases} (3) \ 18\frac{1}{2}" \times 26". \\ (2) \ 18\frac{1}{2}" \times 26". \ (1) \ 17" \times 26"* \end{cases}$
Driving Wheels: 6' 8".
T.E.: $\begin{cases} 35,455 \text{ lb.} \\ 33,616 \text{ lb.}* \end{cases}$
Walschaerts gear and derived motion P.V.

| | |
|---|---|
| 60001†  | Sir Ronald Matthews |
| 60002†  | Sir Murrough Wilson |
| 60003*† | Andrew K. McCosh |
| 60004   | William Whitelaw |
| 60005††‡ | Sir Charles Newton |
| 60006   | Sir Ralph Wedgwood |
| 60007   | Sir Nigel Gresley |
| 60008   | Dwight D. Eisenhower |
| 60009   | Union of South Africa |
| 60010   | Dominion of Canada |
| 60011   | Empire of India |
| 60012*  | Commonwealth of Australia |
| 60013   | Dominion of New [Zealand |
| 60014   | Silver Link |
| 60015   | Quicksilver |
| 60016   | Silver King |
| 60017   | Silver Fox |
| 60018†  | Sparrow Hawk |
| 60019†  | Bittern |
| 60020*† | Guillemot |
| 60021†  | Wild Swan |
| 60022‡  | Mallard |
| 60023†  | Golden Eagle |
| 60024   | Kingfisher |
| 60025   | Falcon |
| 60026†  | Miles Beevor |
| 60027   | Merlin |
| 60028   | Walter K. Whigham |
| 60029   | Woodcock |

| | |
|---|---|
| 60030†  | Golden Fleece |
| 60031*  | Golden Plover |
| 60032   | Gannet |
| 60033‡  | Seagull |
| 60034‡  | Lord Faringdon |
|         | **Total** |

## 4-6-2  7P  Class

**A3** Introduced 1927. Develop of Gresley G.N. 180 lb. Pacific (i duced 1922, L.N.E.R. A1, later with 220 lb. pressure (prototyp other rebuilt from A10). Some G.N.-type tender† with coal remainder L.N.E.R. pattern.
*Kylchap blast pipe and double chim
Weights: Loco. 96 tons 5 cwt

Tender $\begin{cases} 56 \text{ tons } 6 \text{ cwt} \\ 57 \text{ tons } 18 \text{ cwt.} \end{cases}$

Pressure: 220 lb. Su. Cyls.: 19" ×
Driving Wheels: 6' 8". T.E.: 32,9
Walschaerts gear and derived mo P.V.

| | |
|---|---|
| 60035 | Windsor Lad |
| 60036 | Colombo |
| 60037 | Hyperion |
| 60038 | Firdaussi |
| 60039 | Sandwich |
| 60040 | Cameronian |
| 60041 | Salmon Trout |
| 60042 | Singapore |
| 60043 | Brown Jack |
| 60044 | Melton |
| 60045 | Lemberg |
| 60046 | Diamond Jubilee |
| 60047 | Donovan |
| 60048 | Doncaster |
| 60049 | Galtee More |
| 60050 | Persimmon |
| 60051 | Blink Bonny |
| 60052 | Prince Palatine |
| 60053 | Sansovino |
| 60054 | Prince of Wales |
| 60055 | Woolwinder |
| 60056 | Centenary |
| 60057 | Ormonde |
| 60058 | Blair Athol |

| | | | |
|---|---|---|---|
| 059 | Tracery | 60107 | Royal Lancer |
| 060 | The Tetrarch | 60108 | Gay Crusader |
| 061 | Pretty Polly | 60109 | Hermit |
| 062 | Minoru | 60110 | Robert the Devil |
| 063 | Isinglass | 60111 | Enterprise |
| 064 | Tagalie | 60112 | St. Simon |
| 065 | Knight of Thistle | | |
| 066 | Merry Hampton | | **Total 78** |
| 067 | Ladas | | |
| 068 | Sir Visto | | |
| 069 | Sceptre | | |
| 070 | Gladiateur | **4-6-2** | **8P Class A1** |
| 071 | Tranquil | | |
| 072 | Sunstar | | |
| 073 | St. Gatien | | |
| 074 | Harvester | | |
| 075 | St. Frusquin | | |
| 076 | Galopin | | |

A1/1* Introduced 1945. Thompson rebuild of A10.

A1 Peppercorn development of A1/1 for new construction.

A1† Fitted with roller bearings.

Weights: Loco. $\begin{cases} 101 \text{ tons.*} \\ 104 \text{ tons 2 cwt.} \end{cases}$

Tender 60 tons 7 cwt.

Pressure: 250 lb. Su.

Cyls.: (3) $19'' \times 26''$.

Driving Wheels: 6' 8". T.E.: 37,400 lb.

Walschaerts gear. P.V.

| | | | |
|---|---|---|---|
| 077 | The White Knight | 60113* | Great Northern |
| 078 | Night Hawk | 60114 | W. P. Allen |
| 079 | Bayardo | 60115 | Meg Merrilies |
| 080 | Dick Turpin | 60116 | Hal o' the Wynd |
| 081 | Shotover | 60117 | Bois Roussel |
| 082 | Neil Gow | 60118 | Archibald Sturrock |
| 083 | Sir Hugo | 60119 | Patrick Stirling |
| 084 | Trigo | 60120 | Kittiwake |
| 085 | Manna | 60121 | Silurian |
| 086 | Gainsborough | 60122 | Curlew |
| 087 | Blenheim | 60123 | H. A. Ivatt |
| 088 | Book Law | 60124 | Kenilworth |
| 089 | Felstead | 60125 | Scottish Union |
| 090 | Grand Parade | 60126 | Sir Vincent Raven |
| 091 | Captain Cuttle | 60127 | Wilson Worsdell |
| 092 | Fairway | 60128 | Bongrace |
| 093 | Coronach | 60129 | Guy Mannering |
| 094 | Colorado | 60130 | Kestrel |
| 095 | Flamingo | 60131 | Osprey |
| 096 | Papyrus | 60132 | Marmion |
| 097* | Humorist | 60133 | Pommern |
| 098 | Spion Kop | 60134 | Foxhunter |
| 099 | Call Boy | 60135 | Madge Wildfire |
| 100 | Spearmint | 60136 | Alcazar |
| 101 | Cicero | 60137 | Redgauntlet |
| 102 | Sir Frederick Banbury | 60138 | Boswell |
| 103 | Flying Scotsman | | |
| 104 | Solario | | |
| 105 | Victor Wild | | |
| 106 | Flying Fox | | |

| | |
|---|---|
| 60139 | Sea Eagle |
| 60140 | Balmoral |
| 60141 | Abbotsford |
| 60142 | Edward Fletcher |
| 60143 | Sir Walter Scott |
| 60144 | King's Courier |
| 60145 | Saint Mungo |
| 60146 | Peregrine |
| 60147 | North Eastern |
| 60148 | Aboyeur |
| 60149 | Amadis |
| 60150 | Willbrook |
| 60151 | Midlothian |
| 60152 | Holyrood |
| 60153† | Flamboyant |
| 60154† | Bon Accord |
| 60155† | Borderer |
| 60156† | Great Central |
| 60157† | Great Eastern |
| 60158 | Aberdonian |
| 60159 | Bonnie Dundee |
| 60160 | Auld Reekie |
| 60161 | North British |
| 60162 | Saint Johnstoun |

**Total 50**

---

# 4-6-2 (A2/1 : 6MT) $\frac{7MT}{}$ Class A2

**A2/2\*** Introduced 1943. Original Thompson Pacific, rebuilt from Gresley Class P2 2-8-2 (introduced 1934).
Weight: Loco. 101 tons 10 cwt.
Pressure: 225 lb. Su.
Cyls.: (3) 20″ × 26″.
Driving Wheels: 6′ 2″. T.E.: 40,320 lb.

**A2/1†** Introduced 1944. Development of Class A2/2, incorporating Class V2 2-6-2 boiler.
Weight: Loco. 98 tons.
Pressure: 225 lb. Su.
Cyls.: (3) 19″ × 26″.
Driving Wheels: 6′ 2″. T.E.: 36,385 lb.

**A2/3‡** Introduced 1946. Development of Class A2/2 for new construction.
Weight: Loco. 101 tons 10 cwt.
Pressure: 250 lb. Su.
Cyls.: (3) 19″ × 26″.
Driving Wheels: 6′ 2″. T.E.: 40,430 lb.

**A2§** Introduced 1947. Peppercorn development of Class A2/2 with shorter wheelbase. (No. 60539 b with double blast pipe.)

**A2\*\*** Rebuilt with double blast pipe and multiple valve regulator.
Weight: Loco. 101 tons.
Pressure: 250 lb. Su.
Cyls.: (3) 19″ × 26″.
Driving Wheels: 6′ 2″. T.E.: 40,430 lb.
Tender weight (all parts): 60 tons 7 c (except Nos. 60509-10, 52 tons).
Walschaerts gear, P.V.

| | |
|---|---|
| 60500‡ | Edward Thompson |
| 60501\* | Cock o' the North |
| 60502\* | Earl Marischal |
| 60503\* | Lord President |
| 60504\* | Mons Meg |
| 60505\* | Thane of Fife |
| 60506\* | Wolf of Badenoch |
| 60507† | Highland Chieftain |
| 60508† | Duke of Rothesay |
| 60509† | Waverley |
| 60510† | Robert the Bruce |
| 60511‡ | Airborne |
| 60512‡ | Steady Aim |
| 60513‡ | Dante |
| 60514‡ | Chamossaire |
| 60515‡ | Sun Stream |
| 60516‡ | Hycilla |
| 60517‡ | Ocean Swell |
| 60518‡ | Tehran |
| 60519‡ | Honeyway |
| 60520‡ | Owen Tudor |
| 60521‡ | Watling Street |
| 60522‡ | Straight Deal |
| 60523‡ | Sun Castle |
| 60524‡ | Herringbone |
| 60525§ | A. H. Peppercorn |
| 60526\*\* | Sugar Palm |
| 60527§ | Sun Chariot |
| 60528§ | Tudor Minstrel |
| 60529\*\* | Pearl Diver |
| 60530§ | Sayajirao |
| 60531§ | Bahram |
| 60532\*\* | Blue Peter |
| 60533§ | Happy Knight |
| 60534§ | Irish Elegance |
| 60535§ | Hornet's Beauty |
| 60536§ | Trimbush |

| | | |
|---|---|---|
| 537§ Bachelor's Button | 60812 | |
| 538**Velocity | 60813 | |
| 539§ Bronzino | 60814 | |
| | 60815 | |
| Totals: Class A2 15 | 60816 | |
| Class A2/1 4 | 60817 | |
| Class A2/2 6 | 60818 | |
| Class A2/3 15 | 60819 | |
| | 60820 | |
| | 60821 | |
| ——— | 60822 | |
| | 60823 | |

## 6-4   8P   Class W1

Introduced 1937. Rebuilt from Gresley experimental high-pressure 4-cyl. compound with water-tube boiler, introduced 1929.
Weights: Loco. 107 tons 17 cwt.
        Tender 60 tons 7 cwt.
Pressure: 250 lb. Su.
Cyls.: (3) 20″ × 26″.
Driving Wheels: 6′ 8″. T.E.: 41,435 lb.
Walschaerts gear and derived motion. P.V.

700                 Total 1

———

## 6-2   6MT   Class V2

Introduced 1936. Gresley design.
Weights: Loco. 93 tons 2 cwt.
        Tender 52 tons.
Pressure: 220 lb. Su.
Cyls.: (3) 18½″ × 26″.
Driving Wheels: 6′ 2″. T.E.: 33,730 lb.
Walschaerts gear and derived motion. P.V

800   Green Arrow
801
802
803
804
805
806
807
808
809   The Snapper, The East Yorkshire Regiment, The Duke of York's Own
810
811

| | |
|---|---|
| 60824 | |
| 60825 | |
| 60826 | |
| 60827 | |
| 60828 | |
| 60829 | |
| 60830 | |
| 60831 | |
| 60832 | |
| 60833 | |
| 60834 | |
| 60835 | The Green Howard, Alexandra, Princess of Wales's Own Yorkshire Regiment |
| 60836 | |
| 60837 | |
| 60838 | |
| 60839 | |
| 60840 | |
| 60841 | |
| 60842 | |
| 60843 | |
| 60844 | |
| 60845 | |
| 60846 | |
| 60847 | St. Peter's School, York, A.D. 627 |
| 60848 | |
| 60849 | |
| 60850 | |
| 60851 | |
| 60852 | |
| 60853 | |
| 60854 | |
| 60855 | |

| | | | |
|---|---|---|---|
| 60856 | | | |
| 60857 | | | |
| 60858 | | | |
| 60859 | | | |
| 60860 | Durham School | | |
| 60861 | | | |
| 60862 | | | |
| 60863 | | | |
| 60864 | | | |
| 60865 | | | |
| 60866 | | | |
| 60867 | | | |
| 60868 | | | |
| 60869 | | | |
| 60870 | | | |
| 60871 | | | |
| 60872 | King's Own Yorkshire Light Infantry | | |
| 60873 | Coldstreamer | | |
| 60874 | 60902 | 60930 | 60958 |
| 60875 | 60903 | 60931 | 60959 |
| 60876 | 60904 | 60932 | 60960 |
| 60877 | 60905 | 60933 | 60961 |
| 60878 | 60906 | 60934 | 60962 |
| 60879 | 60907 | 60935 | 60963 |
| 60880 | 60908 | 60936 | 60964 |
| 60881 | 60909 | 60937 | 60965 |
| 60882 | 60910 | 60938 | 60966 |
| 60883 | 60911 | 60939 | 60967 |
| 60884 | 60912 | 60940 | 60968 |
| 60885 | 60913 | 60941 | 60969 |
| 60886 | 60914 | 60942 | 60970 |
| 60887 | 60915 | 60943 | 60971 |
| 60888 | 60916 | 60944 | 60972 |
| 60889 | 60917 | 60945 | 60973 |
| 60890 | 60918 | 60946 | 60974 |
| 60891 | 60919 | 60947 | 60975 |
| 60892 | 60920 | 60948 | 60976 |
| 60893 | 60921 | 60949 | 60977 |
| 60894 | 60922 | 60950 | 60978 |
| 60895 | 60923 | 60951 | 60979 |
| 60896 | 60924 | 60952 | 60980 |
| 60897 | 60925 | 60953 | 60981 |
| 60898 | 60926 | 60954 | 60982 |
| 60899 | 60927 | 60955 | 60983 |
| 60900 | 60928 | 60956 | |
| 60901 | 60929 | 60957 | |

**Total 184**

## 4-6-0   5MT   Class

Introduced 1942. Thompson design.
Weights: Loco.   71 tons 3 cwt.
             Tender 52 tons.
Pressure: 225 lb. Su.
Cyls.: (O) 20″ × 26″.
Driving Wheels: 6′ 2″.  T.E.: 26,880
Walschaerts gear.   P.V.

| | |
|---|---|
| 61000 | Springbok |
| 61001 | Eland |
| 61002 | Impala |
| 61003 | Gazelle |
| 61004 | Oryx |
| 61005 | Bongo |
| 61006 | Blackbuck |
| 61007 | Klipspringer |
| 61008 | Kudu |
| 61009 | Hartebeeste |
| 61010 | Wildebeeste |
| 61011 | Waterbuck |
| 61012 | Puku |
| 61013 | Topi |
| 61014 | Oribi |
| 61015 | Duiker |
| 61016 | Inyala |
| 61017 | Bushbuck |
| 61018 | Gnu |
| 61019 | Nilghai |
| 61020 | Gemsbok |
| 61021 | Reitbok |
| 61022 | Sassaby |
| 61023 | Hirola |
| 61024 | Addax |
| 61025 | Pallah |
| 61026 | Ourebi |
| 61027 | Madoqua |
| 61028 | Umseke |
| 61029 | Chamois |
| 61030 | Nyala |
| 61031 | Reedbuck |
| 61032 | Stembok |
| 61033 | Dibatag |
| 61034 | Chiru |
| 61035 | Pronghorn |
| 61036 | Ralph Assheton |
| 61037 | Jairou |
| 61038 | Blacktail |
| 61039 | Steinbok |
| 61040 | Roedeer |

| | | | | |
|---|---|---|---|---|
| 61041 | 61079 | 61116 | 61153 | 61200 |
| 61042 | 61080 | 61117 | 61154 | 61201 |
| 61043 | 61081 | 61118 | 61155 | 61202 |
| 61044 | 61082 | 61119 | 61156 | 61203 |
| 61045 | 61083 | 61120 | 61157 | 61204 |
| 61046 | 61084 | 61121 | 61158 | 61205 |
| 61047 | 61085 | 61122 | 61159 | 61206 |
| 61048 | 61086 | 61123 | 61160 | 61207 |
| 61049 | 61087 | 61124 | 61161 | 61208 |
| 61050 | 61088 | 61125 | 61162 | 61209 |
| 61051 | 61089 | 61126 | 61163 | 61210 |
| 61052 | 61090 | 61127 | 61164 | 61211 |
| 61053 | 61091 | 61128 | 61165 | 61212 |
| 61054 | 61092 | 61129 | 61166 | 61213 |
| 61055 | 61093 | 61130 | 61167 | 61214 |
| 61056 | 61094 | 61131 | 61168 | 61215 William Henton Carver |
| 61058 | 61095 | 61132 | 61169 | 61216 |
| 61059 | 61096 | 61133 | 61170 | 61217 |
| 61060 | 61097 | 61134 | 61171 | 61218 |
| 61061 | 61098 | 61135 | 61172 | 61219 |
| 61062 | 61099 | 61136 | 61173 | 61220 |
| 61063 | 61100 | 61137 | 61174 | 61221 Sir Alexander Erskine-Hill |
| 61064 | 61101 | 61138 | 61175 | 61222 |
| 61065 | 61102 | 61139 | 61176 | 61223 |
| 61066 | 61103 | 61140 | 61177 | 61224 |
| 61067 | 61104 | 61141 | 61178 | 61225 |
| 61068 | 61105 | 61142 | 61179 | 61226 |
| 61069 | 61106 | 61143 | 61180 | 61227 |
| 61070 | 61107 | 61144 | 61181 | 61228 |
| 61071 | 61108 | 61145 | 61182 | 61229 |
| 61072 | 61109 | 61146 | 61183 | 61230 |
| 61073 | 61110 | 61147 | 61184 | 61231 |
| 61074 | 61111 | 61148 | 61185 | 61232 |
| 61075 | 61112 | 61149 | 61186 | 61233 |
| 61076 | 61113 | 61150 | 61187 | 61234 |
| 61077 | 61114 | 61151 | 61188 | 61235 |
| 61078 | 61115 | 61152 | | 61236 |
| 61189 Sir William Gray | | | | 61237 Geoffrey H. Kitson |
| 61190 | | | | 61238 Leslie Runciman |
| 61191 | | | | 61239 |
| 61192 | | | | 61240 Harry Hinchliffe |
| 61193 | | | | 61241 Viscount Ridley |
| 61194 | | | | 61242 Alexander Reith Gray |
| 61195 | | | | 61243 Sir Harold Mitchell |
| 61196 | | | | 61244 Strang Steel |
| 61197 | | | | 61245 Murray of Elibank |
| 61198 | | | | 61246 Lord Balfour of Burleigh |
| 61199 | | | | |

**61247-61478**

61247 Lord Burghley
61248 Geoffrey Gibbs
61249 FitzHerbert Wright
61250 A. Harold Bibby
61251 Oliver Bury

| | | | |
|---|---|---|---|
| 61252 | 61284 | 61316 | 61348 |
| 61253 | 61285 | 61317 | 61349 |
| 61254 | 61286 | 61318 | 61350 |
| 61255 | 61287 | 61319 | 61351 |
| 61256 | 61288 | 61320 | 61352 |
| 61257 | 61289 | 61321 | 61353 |
| 61258 | 61290 | 61322 | 61354 |
| 61259 | 61291 | 61323 | 61355 |
| 61260 | 61292 | 61324 | 61356 |
| 61261 | 61293 | 61325 | 61357 |
| 61262 | 61294 | 61326 | 61358 |
| 61263 | 61295 | 61327 | 61359 |
| 61264 | 61296 | 61328 | 61360 |
| 61265 | 61297 | 61329 | 61361 |
| 61266 | 61298 | 61330 | 61362 |
| 61267 | 61299 | 61331 | 61363 |
| 61268 | 61300 | 61332 | 61364 |
| 61269 | 61301 | 61333 | 61365 |
| 61270 | 61302 | 61334 | 61366 |
| 61271 | 61303 | 61335 | 61367 |
| 61272 | 61305 | 61336 | 61368 |
| 61273 | 61305 | 61337 | 61369 |
| 61274 | 61306 | 61338 | 61370 |
| 61275 | 61307 | 61339 | 61371 |
| 61276 | 61308 | 61340 | 61372 |
| 61277 | 61309 | 61341 | 61373 |
| 61278 | 61310 | 61342 | 61374 |
| 61279 | 61311 | 61343 | 61375 |
| 61280 | 61312 | 61344 | 61376 |
| 61281 | 61313 | 61345 | 61377 |
| 61282 | 61314 | 61346 | 61378 |
| 61283 | 61315 | 61347 | |

61379 Mayflower

| | | | |
|---|---|---|---|
| 61380 | 61388 | 61396 | 61404 |
| 61381 | 61389 | 61397 | 61405 |
| 61382 | 61390 | 61398 | 61406 |
| 61383 | 61391 | 61399 | 61407 |
| 61384 | 61392 | 61400 | 61408 |
| 61385 | 61393 | 61401 | 61409 |
| 61386 | 61394 | 61402 | |
| 61387 | 61395 | 61403 | |

## 4-6-0   5MT   Class B...

**B16/I** Introduced 1920. Raven ... design with inside Stephenson gea...
**B16/2\*** Introduced 1937. Gresley ... build of B16/I with double W... schaerts gear and derived motion... inside cylinder.
**B16/3†** Introduced 1944. Thompson... build of B16/I with three W... schaerts gears.

Weights: Loco. $\begin{cases} 77 \text{ tons 14 cwt.} \\ 79 \text{ tons 4 cwt.*} \\ 78 \text{ tons 19 cwt.†} \end{cases}$
Tender 46 tons 12 cwt.
Pressure: 180 lb. Su.
Cyls.: (3) $18\frac{1}{2}" \times 26"$.
Driving Wheels: 5' 8". T.E.: 30,030
P.V.

| | | | |
|---|---|---|---|
| 61410 | 61428 | 61446 | 614.. |
| 61411 | 61429 | 61447 | 614 |
| 61412 | 61430 | 61448† | 614 |
| 61413 | 61431 | 61449† | 614 |
| 61414 | 61432 | 61450 | 614 |
| 61415 | 61433 | 61451 | 614 |
| 61416 | 61434† | 61452 | 614 |
| 61417† | 61435* | 61453† | 614 |
| 61418† | 61436 | 61454† | 614 |
| 61419 | 61437* | 61455* | 614 |
| 61420† | 61438* | 61456 | 614 |
| 61421* | 61439† | 61457* | 614 |
| 61422 | 61440 | 61458 | 614 |
| 61423 | 61441 | 61459 | 614 |
| 61424 | 61442 | 61460 | 614 |
| 61425 | 61443 | 61461† | |
| 61426 | 61444† | 61462 | |
| 61427 | 61445 | 61463† | |

Totals : Class B16/I
Class B16/2
Class B16/3

For full details of
ELECTRIC AND DIESEL LOCO...
on the E., N.E. & Scottish Region...
see the
ABC OF B.R. LOCOMOTIV...
Part II, Nos. 10000-39999
For full details of
CLASS "4MT" AND "2MT" 2-6...
Nos. 43000-43161 & 46400-4652...
on the E., N.E. & Scottish Region...
see the
ABC OF B.R. LOCOMOTIV...
Part III, Nos. 40000-59999

**‹-0   4P   Class B12**

**/1\*** Introduced 1911. S. D. Holden
‹.E. design with small Belpaire boiler.
**‹/3** Introduced 1932. Gresley re-
uild of B12/1 with large round-
opped boiler and long-travel valves.
**‹/1†** Introduced 1943. Rebuild of
12/1 with small round-topped boiler,
etaining original valves.
B12/2 was a development of B12/1
ith Lentz valves, since rebuilt to
12/3.)

ights: Loco. { 63 tons.\*†
               { 69 tons 10 cwt.
         Tender  39 tons 6 cwt.
ssure: 180 lb. Su. Cyls.: 20″ × 28″
ving Wheels: 6′ 6″. T.E.: 21,970 lb.

| | | | |
|---|---|---|---|
| ‹01\* | 61535 | 61554 | 61570 |
| ‹02\* | 61537 | 61555 | 61571 |
| ‹08† | 61538 | 61556 | 61572 |
| ‹12 | 61539\* | 61557 | 61573 |
| ‹14 | 61540 | 61558 | 61574 |
| ‹16 | 61541 | 61561 | 61575 |
| ‹19 | 61542 | 61562 | 61576 |
| ‹20 | 61543\* | 61563\* | 61577 |
| ‹23 | 61545 | 61564 | 61578 |
| ‹24† | 61546 | 61565 | 61579 |
| ‹28\* | 61547 | 61566 | 61580 |
| ‹30 | 61549 | 61567 | |
| ‹32† | 61550 | 61568 | |
| ‹33 | 61553 | 61569 | |

Totals : Class B12/1   9
         Class B12/3  44

---

**‹-0   4P   Classes
   (B17/6: 5P)   B2 & B17**

**‹1¹** Introduced 1928. Gresley
esign for G.E. section with G.E.-type
nders.
**‹6³** Introduced 1947. B17/1 fitted
ith 100A (B1 type) boiler.
**‹4²** Introduced 1936. Locos with
N.E.R. 4,200-gallon tenders.
**‹6⁴** Introduced 1943. B17/4 fitted
ith 100A (B1 type) boiler.
**‹6⁵** Introduced 1937. Rebuild of
7/4 with streamlined casing. Classi-
d B17/5. Rebuilt with 100A boiler
d de-streamlined in 1951.
ghts: Loco.  77 tons 5 cwt.
       Tender { 39 tons 6 cwt.¹ ³
              { 52 tons.³ ⁴ ⁵

---

Pressure: { 180 lb.¹
          { 225 lb.²
          { 180 lb.³  } Su.
          { 225 lb.⁴ ⁵
Cyls.: (3) 17½″ × 26″.
Driving Wheels: 6′ 8″.
T.E.: { 22,485 lb.¹
      { 28,555 lb.²
      { 22,485 lb.³
      { 28,555 lb.⁴ ⁵
Walschaerts gear and derived motion.
P.V.

**B2⁶** Introduced 1945. Thompson 2-cyl.
rebuild of B17, with 100A boiler and
N.E. tender.

**B2⁷** Introduced 1945, with L.N.E.R.
tender.
Weights: Loco.   73 tons 10 cwt.
         Tender { 46 tons 12 cwt.⁶
                { 52 tons.⁷
Pressure: 225 lb. Su.
Cyls.: (O) 20″ × 26″.
Driving Wheels: 6′ 8″. T.E.: 24,865 lb.
Walschaerts gear and derived motion.
P.V.

61600² Sandringham
61601¹ Holkham
61602² Walsingham
61603⁶ Framlingham
61604² Elveden
61605² Lincolnshire Regiment
61606² Audley End
61607⁶ Blickling
61608² Gunton
61609² Quidenham
61610¹ Honingham Hall
61611¹ Raynham Hall
61612² Houghton Hall
61613² Woodbastwick Hall
61614⁶ Castle Hedingham
61615⁷ Culford Hall
61616⁶ Fallodon
61617⁶ Ford Castle
61618¹ Wynyard Park
61619¹ Welbeck Abbey
61620⁶ Clumber
61621¹ Hatfield House
61622² Alnwick Castle
61623² Lambton Castle
61625¹ Raby Castle
61626¹ Brancepeth Castle
61627² Aske Hall

| | |
|---|---|
| 61629[1] | Naworth Castle |
| 61630[2] | Tottenham Hotspur |
| 61631[1] | Serlby Hall |
| 61632[7] | Belvoir Castle |
| 61633[2] | Kimbolton Castle |
| 61634[1] | Hinchingbrooke |
| 61635[2] | Milton |
| 61636[2] | Harlaxton Manor |
| 61637[1] | Thorpe Hall |
| 61638[1] | Melton Hall |
| 61639[6] | Norwich City |
| 61640[1] | Somerleyton Hall |
| 61641[2] | Gayton Hall |
| 61642[2] | Kilverstone Hall |
| 61643[1] | Champion Lodge |
| 61644[6] | Earlham Hall |
| 61645[2] | The Suffolk Regiment |
| 61646[2] | Gilwell Park |
| 61647[1] | Helmingham Hall |
| 61648[3] | Arsenal |
| 61649[3] | Sheffield United |
| 61650[3] | Grimsby Town |
| 61651[3] | Derby County |
| 61652[3] | Darlington |
| 61653[3] | Huddersfield Town |
| 61654[4] | Sunderland |
| 61655[4] | Middlesbrough |
| 61656[3] | Leeds United |
| 61657[4] | Doncaster Rovers |
| 61658[4] | The Essex Regiment |
| 61659[5] | East Anglian |
| 61660[3] | Hull City |
| 61661[3] | Sheffield Wednesday |
| 61662[3] | Manchester United |
| 61663[4] | Everton |
| 61664[4] | Liverpool |
| 61665[4] | Leicester City |
| 61666[4] | Nottingham Forest |
| 61667[3] | Bradford |
| 61668[4] | Bradford City |
| 61669[4] | Barnsley |
| 61670[5] | City of London |
| 61671[7] | Royal Sovereign |
| 61672[4] | West Ham United |

Totals :  Class B2    10
Class B17/1    15
Class B17/4    10
Class B17/6    36

## 2-6-2    5MT    Class

Introduced 1941. Gresley design.
Weights: Loco.    70 tons 8 cwt.
Tender 42 tons 15 cwt.
Pressure: 250 lb. Su.
Cyls.: (3) 15″ × 26″.
Driving Wheels: 5′ 8″.  T.E.: 27,420
Walschaerts gear and derived moti
P.V.

61700    Bantam Cock
61701                          Tota

## 2-6-0    4MT    Class

K2/2 Introduced 1914. Gresley G
design.
† K2/2 fitted with side-window cal
Scottish Region.
K2/1* Introduced 1931. Rebuilt fr
small-boilered K1 (introduced 19
‡ K2/1 with side-window cab.
Weights: Loco.    64 tons 8 cwt.
Tender 43 tons 2 cwt.
Pressure: 180 lb. Su.
Cyls.: (O) 20″ × 26″.
Driving Wheels: 5′ 8″.  T.E.: 23,400
Walschaerts gear.    P.V

| | | | |
|---|---|---|---|
| 61720* | 61731 | 61742 | 617 |
| 61721‡ | 61732 | 61743 | 617 |
| 61722‡ | 61733† | 61744 | 617 |
| 61723* | 61734† | 61745 | 617 |
| 61724* | 61735† | 61746 | 617 |
| 61725* | 61736 | 61747 | 617 |
| 61726* | 61737 | 61748 | 617 |
| 61727* | 61738 | 61749 | 617 |
| 61728* | 61739 | 61750 | 617 |
| 61729‡ | 61740 | 61751 | 617 |
| 61730 | 61741† | 61752 | 617 |

| | | | |
|---|---|---|---|
| 61764† | Loch Arkaig | | |
| 61765 | 61767 | 61769† | 617 |
| 61766 | 61768 | 61770† | |
| 61772† | Loch Lochy | | |
| 61773 | | | |
| 61774† | Loch Garry | | |
| 61775† | Loch Treig | | |
| 61776† | 1778 | 61780 | |
| 61777 | 61779† | | |
| 61781† | Loch Morar | | |
| 61782† | Loch Eil | | |
| 61783† | Loch Sheil | | |
| 61784† | 61785† | 61786† | |

| | |
|---|---|
| 87† Loch Quoich | |
| 88† Loch Rannoch | |
| 89† Loch Laidon | |
| 90† Loch Lomond | |
| 91† Loch Laggan | |
| 92† | 61793† | |
| 94† Loch Oich | |

**Totals : Class K2/1  9**
**Class K2/2  66**

**Classes**
**-0    6MT    K3 & K5**

2 Introduced 1924. Development
f Gresley G.N. design, built to
N.E.R. loading gauge.
3* Introduced 1929. Differ in details
nly, such as springs, from K3/2.
3/2 fitted with G.N. tender.
K3/1 were G.N. locos (introduced
920), with G.N. cabs, and K3/4, K3/5
nd K3/6 were variations of K3/2,
iffering in weight and details. These
ocos have now been modified to
3/2.)

ights: Loco.    72 tons 12 cwt.
Tender {52 tons.
{43 tons 2 cwt.‡

ssure: 180 lb. Su.
s.: (3) 18½″ × 26″.
ving Wheels: 5′ 8″.  T.E.: 30,030 lb.
lschaerts gear. and derived motion.
.V.

Introduced 1945.  Thompson
-cyl. rebuild of K3.
ights: Loco.    71 tons 5 cwt.
Tender 52 tons.

ssure: 225 lb. Su.
s.: (O) 20″ × 26″.
ving Wheels: 5′ 8″.  T.E.: 29,250 lb.
lschaerts gear.    P.V.

| | | | |
|---|---|---|---|
| 00 | 61813 | 61826 | 61839 |
| 301 | 61814 | 61827 | 61840 |
| 302 | 61815 | 61828 | 61841‡ |
| 303 | 61816 | 61829 | 61842 |
| 304 | 61817 | 61830 | 61843 |
| 305 | 61818 | 61831 | 61844 |
| 306 | 61819 | 61832 | 61845 |
| 307 | 61820 | 61833 | 61846 |
| 308 | 61821 | 61834 | 61847 |
| 309 | 61822 | 61835 | 61848 |
| 310 | 61823 | 61836 | 61849 |
| 311 | 61824 | 61837 | 61850 |
| 312‡ | 61825 | 61838 | 61851 |

| | | | |
|---|---|---|---|
| 61852 | 61888* | 61924 | 61960 |
| 61853 | 61889* | 61925 | 61961 |
| 61854‡ | 61890 | 61926 | 61962 |
| 61855‡ | 61891 | 61927 | 61963 |
| 61856‡ | 61892 | 61928 | 61964 |
| 61857‡ | 61893 | 61929 | 61965 |
| 61858‡ | 61894 | 61930 | 61966 |
| 61859‡ | 61895 | 61931 | 61967 |
| 61860 | 61896 | 61932 | 61968 |
| 61861 | 61897 | 61933 | 61969 |
| 61862 | 61898 | 61934 | 61970 |
| 61863† | 61899 | 61935 | 61971 |
| 61864 | 61900 | 61936 | 61972 |
| 61865 | 61901 | 61937 | 61973 |
| 61866 | 61902 | 61938 | 61974 |
| 61867 | 61903 | 61939 | 61975 |
| 61868 | 61904 | 61940 | 61976 |
| 61869 | 61905 | 61941 | 61977 |
| 61870* | 61906 | 61942 | 61978 |
| 61871* | 61907 | 61943 | 61979 |
| 61872* | 61908 | 61944 | 61980 |
| 61873* | 61909 | 61945 | 61981 |
| 61874* | 61910 | 61946 | 61982 |
| 61875* | 61911 | 61947 | 61983 |
| 61876* | 61912 | 61948 | 61984 |
| 61877* | 61913 | 61949 | 61985 |
| 61878* | 61914 | 61950 | 61986 |
| 61879* | 61915 | 61951 | 61987 |
| 61880* | 61916 | 61952 | 61988 |
| 61881* | 61917 | 61953 | 61989 |
| 61882* | 61918 | 61954 | 61990 |
| 61883* | 61919 | 61955 | 61991 |
| 61884* | 61920 | 61956 | 61992 |
| 61885* | 61921 | 61957 | |
| 61886* | 61922 | 61958 | |
| 61887* | 61923 | 61959 | |

**Totals : Class K3/2  172**
**Class K3/3  20**
**Class K5  1**

---

**IMPORTANT NOTE**

A careful reading of the notes
on page 2 is essential to
understand the use of
reference marks in this book.

17

## 2-6-0　6MT　K1 & K4

**K4*** Introduced 1937. Gresley loco for West Highland line.

Weights: Loco.　68 tons 8 cwt.
　　　　　Tender 44 tons 4 cwt.

Pressure: 200 lb. Su.

Cyls.: (3) $18\frac{1}{2}'' \times 26''$.

Driving Wheels: 5' 2". T.E.: 36,600 lb.

Walschaerts gear and derived motion. P.V.

**K1/1†** Introduced 1945. Thompson 2-cyl. loco. Rebuilt from K4.

**K1** Introduced 1949. Peppercorn development of Thompson K1/1 (No. 61997) for new construction, with increased length.

Weights: Loco.　66 tons 17 cwt.
　　　　　Tender 44 tons 4 cwt.

Pressure: 225 lb. Su.

Cyls.: (O) $20'' \times 26''$.

Driving Wheels: 5' 2". T.E.: 32,080 lb

Walschaerts gear.　P.V.

61993* Loch Long
61994* The Great Marquess
61995* Cameron of Lochiel
61996* Lord of the Isles
61997† MacCailinMor
61998* MacLeod of MacLeod

| | | | |
|---|---|---|---|
| 62001 | 62019 | 62037 | 62055 |
| 62002 | 62020 | 62038 | 62056 |
| 62003 | 62021 | 62039 | 62057 |
| 62004 | 62022 | 62040 | 62058 |
| 62005 | 62023 | 62041 | 62059 |
| 62006 | 62024 | 62042 | 62060 |
| 62007 | 62025 | 62043 | 62061 |
| 62008 | 62026 | 62044 | 62062 |
| 62009 | 62027 | 62045 | 62063 |
| 62010 | 62028 | 62046 | 62064 |
| 62011 | 62029 | 62047 | 62065 |
| 62012 | 62030 | 62048 | 62066 |
| 62013 | 62031 | 62049 | 62067 |
| 62014 | 62032 | 62050 | 62068 |
| 62015 | 62033 | 62051 | 62069 |
| 62016 | 62034 | 62052 | 62070 |
| 62017 | 62035 | 62053 | |
| 62018 | 62036 | 62054 | |

Totals :　Class K1　　70
　　　　　Class K1/1　　1
　　　　　Class K4　　　5

## 4-4-0　2P　Class D

Introduced 1899. Pickersgill G.N. design.

* Introduced 1920. Heywood superheated locos.

Weights: Loco. $\begin{cases} 46 \text{ tons } 7 \text{ cwt.} \\ 48 \text{ tons } 13 \text{ cwt.} \end{cases}$
　　　　　Tender 37 tons 8 cwt.

Pressure: 165 lb. SS.　Cyls.: 18" ×

Driving Wheels: 6' 1". T.E.: 16,18

| | | | |
|---|---|---|---|
| 62260 | 62265 | 62269 | 622 |
| 62262 | 62267 | 62270 | |
| 62264 | 62268 | 62271 | |

62273* George Davidson
62274* Benachie
62275* Sir David Stewart
62276* Andrew Bain
62277* Gordon Highlander
62278* Hatton Castle
62279* Glen Grant

Total

## 4-4-0　2P　Class D

**D20/1** Introduced 1899. W. Worsdell N.E. design. Since superheated.

**D20/2*** Introduced 1936. D20/1 rebuilt with long-travel valves.

† Locos with tender rebuilt from J39-type tank.

Weights: Loco. $\begin{cases} 54 \text{ tons } 2 \text{ cwt.} \\ 55 \text{ tons } 9 \text{ cwt.*} \end{cases}$
　　　　　Tender $\begin{cases} 41 \text{ tons } 4 \text{ cwt.} \\ 43 \text{ tons.*} \end{cases}$

Pressure: 175 lb. Su.　Cyls.: 19" ×

Driving Wheels: 6' 10". T.E.: 17,02 P.V.

| | | | |
|---|---|---|---|
| 62343 | 62358† | 62378 | 623 |
| 62345 | 62359 | 62380 | 623 |
| 62347 | 62360* | 62381 | 623 |
| 62349* | 62371* | 62383 | 62. |
| 62351 | 62372 | 62384 | 62. |
| 62352 | 62374 | 62386† | 623 |
| 62355 | 62375* | 62387 | |

Totals :　Class D20/1
　　　　　Class D20/2

18

## 0   3P   Class D30

Introduced 1914. Development
D30/1, introduced 1912 (Reid N.B.
"Scott" class) with detail differences.
Weights: Loco.   57 tons 16 cwt.
            Tender 46 tons 13 cwt.
Pressure: 165 lb. Su. Cyls.: 20" × 26".
Driving Wheels: 6' 6". T.E.: 18,700 lb.

8 The Pirate
9 Meg Dods
0 Dominie Sampson
1 Laird o' Monkbarns
2 Caleb Balderstone
3 Dugald Dalgetty
4 Claverhouse
5 Ellangowan
6 Cuddie Headrigg
7 Dumbledykes
8 The Talisman
9 The Abbot
0 Jingling Geordie
1 Kenilworth
2 Quentin Durward
4 Kettledrummle
5 Norna
6 Lord Glenvarloch
7 Adam Woodcock
8 Peter Poundtext
9 Father Ambrose
0 Wandering Willie
1 Black Duncan
2 Simon Glover

Total 24

## 0   3P   Class D33

duced 1909. Later Reid N.B.
intermediate " class. Since super-
seded.
Weights: Loco.   54 tons 3 cwt.
            Tender 44 tons 11 cwt.
Pressure: 180 lb. Su. Cyls.: 19" × 26".
Driving Wheels: 6' 0". T.E.: 19,945 lb.

4               Total 1

## 4-4-0   3P   Class D34

Introduced 1913. Reid N.B. "Glen" class.
Weights: Loco.   57 tons 14 cwt.
            Tender 46 tons 13 cwt.
Pressure: 165 lb. Su. Cyls : 20" × 26".
Driving Wheels: 6' 0". T.E.: 20,260 lb.
P.V

62467 Glenfinnan
62468 Glen Orchy
62469 Glen Douglas
62470 Glen Roy
62471 Glen Falloch
62472 Glen Nevis
62474 Glen Croe
62475 Glen Beasdale
62477 Glen Dochart
62478 Glen Quoich
62479 Glen Sheil
62480 Glen Fruin
62482 Glen Mamie
62483 Glen Garry
62484 Glen Lyon
62485 Glen Murran
62487 Glen Arklet
62488 Glen Aladale
62489 Glen Dessary
62490 Glen Fintaig
62492 Glen Garvin
62493 Glen Gloy
62494 Glen Gour
62495 Glen Luss
62496 Glen Loy
62497 Glen Mallie
62498 Glen Moidart

Total 27

## Classes
## 4-4-0   2P   D15 & D16

D16/3[1] Introduced 1933. Gresley rebuild of D15 with larger round-topped
boiler and modified footplating. D15
was Belpaire boiler development of
original J. Holden (G.E.) "Claud
Hamilton " Class.

D16/3[2] Introduced 1933. Rebuild of
D15 with larger round-topped boiler,
modified footplating and 8" piston
valves.

19

**D16/3³** Introduced 1936. Rebuild of D15 with larger round-topped boiler, modified footplating and 9½″ piston valves.

**D16/3⁴** Introduced 1938. Rebuild of D16/2 with round-topped boiler, but retaining original footplating and slide valves.

**D16/3⁵** Introduced 1939. Rebuild of D16/2 with round-topped boiler and modified footplating, retaining slide valves.

(At grouping the remaining locos of the " Claud Hamilton " class retaining small round-topped boilers were classified D14. Saturated locos of D15 were originally classified D15, super-heated locos with short smokeboxes D15/1 and superheated locos with extended smokeboxes D15/2. All the remaining locos were converted to D15/2 and then known simply as D15. D16/1 were the original D16 locos with short smokeboxes.)

Weights : Loco. 55 tons 18 cwt.
Tender 39 tons 5 cwt.
Pressure: 180 lb. Su. Cyls.: 19″ × 26″.
Driving Wheels: 7′ 0″. T.E.: 17,095 lb.

| | | | |
|---|---|---|---|
| 62510¹ | 62539¹ | 62566¹ | 62593¹ |
| 62511¹ | 62540¹ | 62567¹ | 62596⁴ |
| 62513¹ | 62541¹ | 62568² | 62597¹ |
| 62514¹ | 62542⁴ | 62569⁴ | 62599³ |
| 62515¹ | 62543⁴ | 62570⁴ | 62601⁴ |
| 62516¹ | 62544⁴ | 62571¹ | 62604¹ |
| 62517¹ | 62545¹ | 62572¹ | 62605⁴ |
| 62518¹ | 62546²* | 62573⁴ | 62606⁴ |
| 62519¹ | 62548¹ | 62574¹ | 62607⁴ |
| 62521¹ | 62549¹ | 62575⁴ | 62608¹ |
| 62522¹ | 62551¹ | 62576³ | 62609² |
| 62523¹ | 62552¹ | 62577⁴ | 62610¹ |
| 62524¹ | 62553⁴ | 62578¹ | 62611⁴ |
| 62525¹ | 62554⁴ | 62579¹ | 62612⁴ |
| 62526¹ | 62555¹ | 62580⁴ | 62613⁴ |
| 62529¹ | 62556⁴ | 62582¹ | 62614⁵ |
| 62530¹ | 62557⁴ | 62584⁴ | 62615⁴ |
| 62531¹ | 62558⁴ | 62585¹ | 62617⁴ |
| 62532³ | 62559¹ | 62586¹ | 62618⁴ |
| 62533¹ | 62561¹ | 62587² | 62619⁴ |
| 62534¹ | 62562⁴ | 62588² | 62620⁴ |
| 62535³ | 62564⁴ | 62589⁴ | |
| 62536³ | 62565⁴ | 62592⁴ | |

**Total : 90**

* Named *Claud Hamilton*.

---

## 4-4-0   3P   Class D

Introduced 1913. Robinson " Director " class.
Weights: Loco. 61 tons.
Tender 48 tons 6 cwt.
Pressure: 180 lb. Su. Cyls.: 20″ ×
Driving Wheels: 6′ 9″. T.E.: 19,64
P.V.

| 62650 | Prince Henry |
|---|---|
| 62652 | Edwin A. Beazley |
| 62653 | Sir Edward Fraser |
| 62654 | Walter Burgh Gair |
| 62655 | The Earl of Kerry |
| 62656 | Sir Clement Royds |
| 62658 | Prince George |
| 62659 | Worsley-Taylor |

**Total**

---

## 4-4-0   3P   Class D

**D11/1*** Introduced 1920. Robinson " Large Director," developmen D10.

**D11/2** Introduced 1924. Post-gro locos built to Scottish loading g From 1938 the class has been re with long-travel valves.
Weights: Loco. 61 tons 3 cwt.
Tender 48 tons 6 cwt.
Pressure: 180 lb. Su. Cyls.: 20″ ×
Driving Wheels: 6′ 9″. T.E.: 19,6
P.V.

| 62660* | Butler-Henderson |
|---|---|
| 62661* | Gerard Powys Dewh |
| 62662* | Prince of Wales |
| 62663* | Prince Albert |
| 62664* | Princess Mary |
| 62665* | Mons |
| 62666* | Zeebrugge |
| 62667* | Somme |
| 62668* | Jutland |
| 62669* | Ypres |
| 62670* | Marne |
| 62671 | Bailie MacWheeble |
| 62672 | Baron of Bradwardi |
| 62673 | Evan Dhu |
| 62674 | Flora MacIvor |
| 62675 | Colonel Gardiner |
| 62676 | Jonathan Oldbuck |
| 62677 | Edie Ochiltree |

*to bottom :* Class
4-6-0 No. 61419 ;
B16/3 4-6-0 No.
0 ; Class D49/! 4-4-0
2703 *Hertfordshire ;*
D20/1 4-4-0 No.
62397.

*Ord, J. H. West-
od, J. Cupit, K.
ld*

21

Top left : Class B17/6 4-6-0 No. 61657 Doncaster Rovers. Top right : Class B12/3 4-6-0 No. 61538. Bottom left : Class V2 2-6-2 No. 60907
Bottom right : Class B12/1 4-6-0 No. 61502.
[R. E. Vincent, J. R. Eagles, J. F. Henton, J. F. Aylord

22

Top left: Class K1 2-6-0 No. 62063. Top right: Class K4 2-6-0 No. 61995 Cameron of Lochiel. Bottom left: Class K3/2 2-6-0 No. 61973. Bottom right: Class K2/2 2-6-0 No. 61737.
[R. E. Vincent, J. F. Aylard (2), E. D. Briton.

23

*Top to bottom :*
*D30 4-4-0 No.*
*The Talisman ;*
*D34 4-4-0 No. 6248*
*Dessary ; Class*
*4-4-0 No. 62662 Pri*
*Wales ; Class*
*4-4-0 No. 6258*

*[J. Robertson (2*
*Ransome-Wallis,*
*Casserley*

24

Top to bottom : Class E4
2-4-0's Nos. 62794 (with
ex-D15 tender) and
62795 (with side window
cab) ; Class D40 4-4-0
No. 62262 ; Class Q6
0-8-0 No. 63362

[P. L. Melvill, P.
Ransome-Wallis, C. L.
Kerr, G. Oates.

25

**FACING PAGE**
Top to bottom : Class
O2/1 2-8-0 No. 63928 ;
Class O1 2-8-0 No.
63777 ; Class O4/3
2-8-0 No. 63666 ; Class
WD 2-10-0 No. 90765.
[P. H. Wells, H. C.
Casserley (2), F. F. Moss

**THIS PAGE**
Top to bottom : Class
J38 0-6-0 No. 65918
(with J39 boiler);Class
J39/2 0-6-0 No. 64926;
Class J20 0-6-0 No.
64692 ; Class J19 0-6-0
No. 64647.
[H. C. Casserley, J.
Robertson, P. H. Wells
B. C. Lockey.

Left : Class A2/2 4
No. 60501 Cock o'
North.
[J. C. W

Below : Class A2 4
No. 60536 Trimb
[J. Rober

Above: Class A1 4-6
No. 60140 Balmor

Left: Class A2/3 4-6
No. 60511 Airborn
[E. Trea

| | |
|---|---|
| 62678 | Luckie Mucklebackit |
| 62679 | Lord Glenallan |
| 62680 | Lucy Ashton |
| 62681 | Captain Craigengelt |
| 62682 | Haystoun of Bucklaw |
| 62683 | Hobbie Elliott |
| 62684 | Wizard of the Moor |
| 62685 | Malcolm Graeme |
| 62686 | The Fiery Cross |
| 62687 | Lord James of Douglas |
| 62688 | Ellen Douglas |
| 62689 | Maid of Lorn |
| 62690 | The Lady of the Lake |
| 62691 | Laird of Balmawhapple |
| 62692 | Allan-Bane |
| 62693 | Roderick Dhu |
| 62694 | James Fitzjames |

**Totals : Class D11/1 11**
**Class D11/2 24**

---

**4-0**    **4P**    **Class D49**

D49/1 *†  Introduced 1927. Gresley design with piston valves, Walschaerts gear and derived motion.
D49/2‡  Introduced 1928. Development of D49/1 with Lentz Rotary Cam poppet valves.
(D49/3 comprised locos 62720-4 as built with Lentz Oscillating Cam poppet valves. From 1938 these locos were converted to D49/1. 62751-75 have larger valves than the earlier D49/2, and were at first classified D49/4.)
* Fitted with G.C. tender.
§Fitted with N.E. tender.
The remainder have L.N.E.R. tenders.

Weights: Loco.   { 66 tons.*†
              { 64 tons 10 cwt.‡§
              { 48 tons 6 cwt.*
      Tender { 44 tons 2 cwt.†§
              { 52 tons.‡

Pressure: 180 lb. Su.
Cyls.: (3) 17″ × 26″*†‡§
Driving Wheels: 6′ 8″
T.E.: 21,555 lb.*†§

| | |
|---|---|
| 62700* | Yorkshire |
| 62701* | Derbyshire |
| 62702* | Oxfordshire |
| 62703† | Hertfordshire |
| 62704* | Stirlingshire |
| 62705* | Lanarkshire |
| 62706* | Forfarshire |

| | |
|---|---|
| 62707* | Lancashire |
| 62708* | Argyllshire |
| 62709* | Berwickshire |
| 62710* | Lincolnshire |
| 62711* | Dumbartonshire |
| 62712* | Morayshire |
| 62713* | Aberdeenshire |
| 62714* | Perthshire |
| 62715* | Roxburghshire |
| 62716* | Kincardineshire |
| 62717* | Banffshire |
| 62718* | Kinross-shire |
| 62719* | Peebles-shire |
| 62720† | Cambridgeshire |
| 62721* | Warwickshire |
| 62722† | Huntingdonshire |
| 62723† | Nottinghamshire |
| 62724† | Bedfordshire |
| 62725* | Inverness-shire |
| 62726‡ | The Meynell |
| 62727§ | The Quorn |
| 62728* | Cheshire |
| 62729* | Rutlandshire |
| 62730* | Berkshire |
| 62731* | Selkirkshire |
| 62732* | Dumfries-shire |
| 62733* | Northumberland |
| 62734* | Cumberland |
| 62735* | Westmorland |
| 62736‡ | The Bramham Moor |
| 62737‡ | The York and Ainsty |
| 62738‡ | The Zetland |
| 62739‡ | The Badsworth |
| 62740‡ | The Bedale |
| 62741‡ | The Blankney |
| 62742‡ | The Braes of Derwent |
| 62743‡ | The Cleveland |
| 62744‡ | The Holderness |
| 62745‡ | The Hurworth |
| 62746‡ | The Middleton |
| 62747‡ | The Percy |
| 62748‡ | The Southwold |
| 62749‡ | The Cottesmore |
| 62750‡ | The Pytchley |
| 62751‡ | The Albrighton |
| 62752‡ | The Atherstone |
| 62753‡ | The Belvoir |
| 62754‡ | The Berkeley |

| | | | |
|---|---|---|---|
| 62755‡ | The Bilsdale | | |
| 62756‡ | The Brocklesby | | |
| 62757‡ | The Burton | | |
| 62758‡ | The Cattistock | | |
| 62759‡ | The Craven | | |
| 62760‡ | The Cotswold | | |
| 62761‡ | The Derwent | | |
| 62762‡ | The Fernie | | |
| 62763‡ | The Fitzwilliam | | |
| 62764‡ | The Garth | | |
| 62765‡ | The Goathland | | |
| 62766‡ | The Grafton | | |
| 62767‡ | The Grove | | |
| 62769‡ | The Oakley | | |
| 62770‡ | The Puckeridge | | |
| 62771‡ | The Rufford | | |
| 62772‡ | The Sinnington | | |
| 62773‡ | The South Durham | | |
| 62774‡ | The Staintondale | | |
| 62775‡ | The Tynedale | | |

Totals : Class D49/1 34
Class D49/2 41

## 2-4-0 1MT Class E4

Introduced 1891. J Holden G.E. design.
* Fitted with side-window cab.
Weights: Loco. 40 tons 6 cwt.
Tender 30 tons 13 cwt.
Pressure: 160 lb. Cyls.: 17½″ × 24″.
Driving Wheels· 5′ 8″. T.E.: 14,700 lb.

| | | | |
|---|---|---|---|
| 62780 | 62785 | 62790 | 62795* |
| 62781* | 62786 | 62791 | 62796 |
| 62782 | 62787 | 62792 | 62797* |
| 62783 | 62788* | 62793* | |
| 62784* | 62789 | 62794 | |

Total 18

## 0-8-0 6F Class Q6

Introduced 1913. Raven N.E. design.
* Some locos are fitted with tenders from withdrawn B15 locos.
Weights: Loco. 65 tons 18 cwt.
Tender { 44 tons 2 cwt.
44 tons.*
Pressure: 180 lb. Su.
Cyls.: (O) 20″ × 26″.
Driving Wheels: 4′ 7½″. T.E.: 28,800 lb. P.V.

| | | | |
|---|---|---|---|
| 63340 | 63341 | 63342 | 63343 |

| | | | |
|---|---|---|---|
| 63344 | 63373 | 63402 | 6343 |
| 63345 | 63374 | 63403 | 6343 |
| 63346 | 63375 | 63404 | 6343 |
| 63347 | 63376 | 63405 | 6343 |
| 63348 | 63377 | 63406 | 6343 |
| 63349 | 63378 | 63407 | 6343 |
| 63350 | 63379 | 63408 | 6343 |
| 63351 | 63380 | 63409 | 6343 |
| 63352 | 63381 | 63410 | 6343 |
| 63353 | 63382 | 63411 | 6344 |
| 63354 | 63383 | 63412 | 6344 |
| 63355 | 63384 | 63413 | 6344 |
| 63356 | 63385 | 63414 | 6344 |
| 63357 | 63386 | 63415 | 6344 |
| 63358 | 63387 | 63416 | 6344 |
| 63359 | 63388 | 63417 | 6344 |
| 63360 | 63389 | 63418 | 6344 |
| 63361 | 63390 | 63419 | 6344 |
| 63362 | 63391 | 63420 | 6344 |
| 63363 | 63392 | 63421 | 6345 |
| 63364 | 63393 | 63422 | 6345 |
| 63365 | 63394 | 63423 | 6345 |
| 63366 | 63395 | 63424 | 6345 |
| 63367 | 63396 | 63425 | 6345 |
| 63368 | 63397 | 63426 | 6345 |
| 63369 | 63398 | 63427 | 6345 |
| 63370 | 63399 | 63428 | 6345 |
| 63371 | 63400 | 63429 | 6345 |
| 63372 | 63401 | 63430 | 6345 |

Total 12

## 0-8-0 8F Class Q

Introduced 1919. Raven N.E. desig
Weights: Loco. 71 tons 12 cwt.
Tender 44 tons 2 cwt.
Pressure: 180 lb. Su.
Cyls.: (3) 18½″ × 26″.
Driving Wheels: 4′ 7½″. T.E.: 36,965
P.V.

| | | | |
|---|---|---|---|
| 63460 | 63464 | 63468 | 63472 |
| 63461 | 63465 | 63469 | 63473 |
| 63462 | 63466 | 63470 | 63474 |
| 63463 | 63467 | 63471 | |

Total

## Classes
## 0-0  8F (O1)  O1 & O4
##      7F (O4)

*1*[1] Introduced 1911. Robinson
G.C. design with small Belpaire
boiler, steam and vacuum brakes and
water scoop.

*3*[2] Introduced 1917. R.O.D. locos
with steam brake only and no scoop.
Taken into L.N.E.R. stock from 1924.

*2*[3] Introduced 1925. O4/3 with
cab and boiler mountings reduced to
Scottish loading gauge.

*5*[4] Introduced 1932. Rebuilt with
shortened O2-type boiler and separate
smokebox saddle.

*6*[5] Introduced 1924. Rebuilt from
O5, retaining higher cab (63912-20
with side-windows).

*7*[6] Introduced 1939. Rebuilt with
shortened O2-type boiler, retaining
G.C. smokebox.

*8*[7] Introduced 1944. Rebuilt with
100A(B1) boiler, retaining original
cylinders.

(O4/4 were rebuilds with O2 boilers,
once rebuilt again ; O5 was a G.C.
development of O4 with larger
Belpaire boilers.)

Weights: Loco. { 73 tons 4 cwt.[1]
73 tons 4 cwt.[2]
73 tons 4 cwt.[3]
74 tons 13 cwt.[4]
73 tons 4 cwt.[5]
73 tons 17 cwt.[6]
72 tons 10 cwt.[7]

Tender { 48 tons 6 cwt. (with scoop)
47 tons 6 cwt. (without
scoop)

Pressure: 180 lb. Su.
Cyls.: (O) 21″ × 26″.
Driving Wheels: 4′ 8″. T.E.: 31,325 lb.
P.V.

*8*[8] Introduced 1944. Thompson re-
build with 100A boiler, Walschaerts
valve gear and new cylinders.
Weights: Loco.  73 tons 6 cwt.
Tender as O4.
Pressure: 225 lb. Su.
Cyls.: (O) 20″ × 26″.
Driving Wheels: 4′ 8″. T.E.: 35,520 lb
Walschaerts gear.  P.V.

| | | | |
|---|---|---|---|
| 570[6] | 63579[8] | 63589[8] | 63598[1] |
| 571[8] | 63581[1] | 63590[8] | 63599[1] |
| 572[1] | 63582[6] | 63591[8] | 63600[8] |
| 573[1] | 63583[8] | 63592[8] | 63601[1] |
| 574[1] | 63584[1] | 63593[1] | 63602[1] |
| 575[7] | 63585[1] | 63594[8] | 63603[6] |
| 576[1] | 63586[1] | 63595[6] | 63604[1] |
| 577[1] | 63587[1] | 63596[8] | 63605[2] |
| 578[8] | 63588[6] | 63597[1] | 63606[1] |

| | | | |
|---|---|---|---|
| 63607[1] | 63656[2] | 63704[8] | 63752[8] |
| 63608[1] | 63657[2] | 63705[6] | 63753[2] |
| 63609[1] | 63658[1] | 63706[6] | 63754[2] |
| 63610[8] | 63659[2] | 63707[1] | 63755[8] |
| 63611[1] | 63660[1] | 63708[8] | 63756[2] |
| 63612[1] | 63661[6] | 63709[8] | 63757[1] |
| 63613[7] | 63662[6] | 63710[1] | 63758[8] |
| 63614[1] | 63663[8] | 63711[8] | 63759[2] |
| 63615[6] | 63664[1] | 63712[8] | 63760[8] |
| 63616[6] | 63665[2] | 63713[2] | 63761[6] |
| 63617[1] | 63666[2] | 63714[2] | 63762[1] |
| 63618[1] | 63667[2] | 63715[2] | 63763[2] |
| 63619[8] | 63668[2] | 63716[2] | 63764[2] |
| 63620[1] | 63669[6] | 63717[2] | 63765[2] |
| 63621[1] | 63670[8] | 63718[2] | 63766[2] |
| 63622[1] | 63671[1] | 63719[1] | 63767[2] |
| 63623[1] | 63672[2] | 63720[2] | 63768[8] |
| 63624[1] | 63673[6] | 63721[2] | 63769[2] |
| 63625[1] | 63674[8] | 63722[1] | 63770[6] |
| 63626[1] | 63675[6] | 63723[1] | 63771[2] |
| 63628[4] | 63676[8] | 63724[2] | 63772[6] |
| 63629[2] | 63677[1] | 63725[8] | 63773[8] |
| 63630[8] | 63678[8] | 63726[4] | 63774[2] |
| 63631[1] | 63679[2] | 63727[1] | 63775[6] |
| 63632[1] | 63680[8] | 63728[2] | 63776[2] |
| 63633[7] | 63681[2] | 63729[2] | 63777[8] |
| 63634[6] | 63682[8] | 63730[8] | 63779[2] |
| 63635[1] | 63683[1] | 63731[2] | 63780[8] |
| 63636[2] | 63684[1] | 63732[2] | 63781[2] |
| 63637[2] | 63685[2] | 63733[2] | 63782[2] |
| 63638[2] | 63686[2] | 63734[2] | 63783[2] |
| 63639[2] | 63687[8] | 63735[2] | 63784[8] |
| 63640[1] | 63688[2] | 63736[1] | 63785[7] |
| 63641[2] | 63689[8] | 63737[2] | 63786[8] |
| 63642[2] | 63690[8] | 63738[7] | 63787[8] |
| 63643[6] | 63691[2] | 63739[2] | 63788[4] |
| 63644[3] | 63692[1] | 63740[8] | 63789[8] |
| 63645[2] | 63693[1] | 63741[2] | 63790[2] |
| 63646[8] | 63694[2] | 63742[2] | 63791[8] |
| 63647[3] | 63695[2] | 63743[1] | 63792[8] |
| 63648[3] | 63696[2] | 63744[2] | 63793[2] |
| 63649[2] | 63697[2] | 63745[4] | 63794[6] |
| 63650[8] | 63698[1] | 63746[8] | 63795[8] |
| 63651[7] | 63699[6] | 63747[6] | 63796[8] |
| 63652[8] | 63700[1] | 63748[6] | 63797[1] |
| 63653[7] | 63701[2] | 63749[6] | 63798[2] |
| 63654[1] | 63702[2] | 63750[7] | 63799[1] |
| 63655[1] | 63703[2] | 63751[2] | 63800[3] |

| | | | |
|---|---|---|---|
| 63801[2] | 63836[7] | 63862[2] | 63889[3] |
| 63802[7] | 63837[2] | 63863[6] | 63890[8] |
| 63803[8] | 63838[8] | 63864[2] | 63891[6] |
| 63804[2] | 63839[4] | 63865[8] | 63893[7] |
| 63805[1] | 63840[2] | 63867[2] | 63894[6] |
| 63806[8] | 63841[2] | 63868[8] | 63895[2] |
| 63807[7] | 63842[2] | 63869[8] | 63897[7] |
| 63808[8] | 63843[5] | 63870[2] | 63898[3] |
| 63812[2] | 63845[2] | 63872[8] | 63899[2] |
| 63813[2] | 63846[2] | 63873[2] | 63900[2] |
| 63816[4] | 63847[3] | 63874[3] | 63901[8] |
| 63817[8] | 63848[4] | 63876[8] | 63902[6] |
| 63818[7] | 63850[2] | 63877[2] | 63904[5] |
| 63819[7] | 63851[4] | 63878[8] | 63905[5] |
| 63821[2] | 63852[2] | 63879[8] | 63906[5] |
| 63822[4] | 63853[7] | 63880[6] | 63907[6] |
| 63823[2] | 63854[8] | 63881[2] | 63908[5] |
| 63824[6] | 63855[7] | 63882[7] | 63911[6] |
| 63827[2] | 63856[8] | 63883[2] | 63912[5] |
| 63828[7] | 63857[6] | 63884[6] | 63913[6] |
| 63829[2] | 63858[2] | 63885[2] | 63914[5] |
| 63832[2] | 63859[2] | 63886[8] | 63915[5] |
| 63833[2] | 63860[6] | 63887[8] | 63917[5] |
| 63835[2] | 63861[2] | 63888[3] | 63920[5] |

Totals : Class O1   58
          Class O4/1   65
          Class O4/2   11
          Class O4/3   113
          Class O4/5   6
          Class O4/6   13
          Class O4/7   40
          Class O4/8   18

For full details of
ELECTRIC AND DIESEL LOCOS
on the E., N.E. & Scottish Regions
see the
ABC OF B.R. LOCOMOTIVES
Part II, Nos. 10000-39999

For full details of
CLASS "4MT" AND "2MT" 2-6-0s
Nos. 43000-43161 & 46400-46527
on the E., N.E. & Scottish Regions
see the
ABC OF B.R. LOCOMOTIVES
Part III, Nos. 40000-59999

## 2-8-0   8F   Class O

O2/1* Introduced 1921. Development of experimental Gresley G.N. 3-cylinder loco (L.N.E.R. 3921). Subsequently rebuilt with side-window cab, and reduced boiler mountings.

O2/2† Introduced 1924. Development of O2/1 with detail differences.

O2/3 Introduced 1932. Development of O2/2 with side-window cab and reduced boiler mountings.

O2/4‡ Introduced 1943. Rebuilt with 100A (B1 type) boiler and smokebox extended backwards (63924 retaining G.N. tender).

Weights: Loco. $\begin{cases} 75 \text{ tons } 16 \text{ cwt.*†} \\ 78 \text{ tons } 13 \text{ cwt.} \\ 74 \text{ tons } 2 \text{ cwt.‡} \end{cases}$

Tender $\begin{cases} 43 \text{ tons } 2 \text{ cwt. (63922-46)} \\ 52 \text{ tons (63947-87)} \end{cases}$

Pressure: 180 lb. Su.
Cyls.: (3) 18½" × 26".
Driving Wheels: 4' 8". T.E.: 36,470 lb
Walschaerts gear and derived motion. P.V.

| | | | |
|---|---|---|---|
| 63922* | 63939† | 63956 | 63973 |
| 63923* | 63940† | 63957 | 63974 |
| 63924‡ | 63941† | 63958 | 63975 |
| 63925* | 63942† | 63959 | 63976 |
| 63926* | 63943† | 63960 | 63977 |
| 63927* | 63944† | 63961 | 63978 |
| 63928* | 63945† | 63962‡ | 63979 |
| 63929* | 63946† | 63963 | 63980 |
| 63930* | 63947 | 63964 | 63981 |
| 63931* | 63948 | 63965 | 63982 |
| 63932‡ | 63949 | 63966 | 63983 |
| 63933† | 63950‡ | 63967 | 63984 |
| 63934† | 63951 | 63968 | 63985 |
| 63935† | 63952 | 63969 | 63986 |
| 63936† | 63953 | 63970 | 63987 |
| 63937† | 63954 | 63971 | |
| 63938† | 63955 | 63972 | |

Totals : Class O2/1
          Class O2/2   1
          Class O2/3   3
          Class O2/4

**IMPORTANT NOTE**

A careful reading of the notes on page 2 is essential to understand the use of reference marks in this book.

## 6-0 2F Class J3

Introduced 1912. Larger-boilered rebuild of J4.
Weights: Loco. 42 tons 12 cwt.
Tender 38 tons 10 cwt.
Pressure: 175 lb. Cyls.: $17\frac{1}{2}'' \times 26''$.
Driving Wheels: 5' 2". T.E.: 19,105 lb.

| | | | |
|---|---|---|---|
| 64122 | 64131 | 64140 | 64141 |
| 64125 | 64132 | | |

**Total 6**

## 6-0 3F Class J6

Introduced 1911. Gresley G.N. design.
Weights: Loco. 50 tons 10 cwt.
Tender 43 tons 2 cwt.
Pressure: 170 lb. Su. Cyls.: $19'' \times 26''$.
Driving Wheels: 5' 2". T.E.: 21,875 lb.
V.

| | | | |
|---|---|---|---|
| 64170 | 64198 | 64226 | 64254 |
| 64171 | 64199 | 64227 | 64255 |
| 64172 | 64200 | 64228 | 64256 |
| 64173 | 64201 | 64229 | 64257 |
| 64174 | 64202 | 64230 | 64258 |
| 64175 | 64203 | 64231 | 64259 |
| 64176 | 64204 | 64232 | 64260 |
| 64177 | 64205 | 64233 | 64261 |
| 64178 | 64206 | 64234 | 64262 |
| 64179 | 64207 | 64235 | 64263 |
| 64180 | 64208 | 64236 | 64264 |
| 64181 | 64209 | 64237 | 64265 |
| 64182 | 64210 | 64238 | 64266 |
| 64183 | 64211 | 64239 | 64267 |
| 64184 | 64212 | 64240 | 64268 |
| 64185 | 64213 | 64241 | 64269 |
| 64186 | 64214 | 64242 | 64270 |
| 64187 | 64215 | 64243 | 64271 |
| 64188 | 64216 | 64244 | 64272 |
| 64189 | 64217 | 64245 | 64273 |
| 64190 | 64218 | 64246 | 64274 |
| 64191 | 64219 | 64247 | 64275 |
| 64192 | 64220 | 64248 | 64276 |
| 64193 | 64221 | 64249 | 64277 |
| 64194 | 64222 | 64250 | 64278 |
| 64195 | 64223 | 64251 | 64279 |
| 64196 | 64224 | 64252 | |
| 64197 | 64225 | 64253 | |

**Total 110**

## 0-6-0 3F Class J11

Introduced 1901. Robinson G.C. design. Parts 1 and 4 have 3,250 gallon tenders; Parts 2 and 5, 4,000 gallon. Parts 1 and 2 have high boiler mountings; Parts 4 and 5 low. All Parts 4 and 5 are superheated, and some of Parts 1 and 2. There are frequent changes between these parts.
J11/3* Introduced 1942. Rebuilt with long-travel piston valves and boiler higher pitched.
Weights: Loco. { 51 tons 19 cwt. (Sat.) 52 tons 2 cwt (Su.) 53 tons 6 cwt.*
Tender { 44 tons 3 cwt. (3,250 gall.) 48 tons 6 cwt. (4,000 gall.)
Pressure: 180 lb. SS. Cyls.: $18\frac{1}{2}'' \times 26''$.
Driving Wheels: 5' 2". T.E.: 21,960 lb.

| | | | |
|---|---|---|---|
| 64280 | 64312 | 64344 | 64376 |
| 64281 | 64313 | 64345 | 64377 |
| 64282 | 64314* | 64346* | 64378 |
| 64283* | 64315 | 64347 | 64379* |
| 64284* | 64316* | 64348 | 64380 |
| 64285 | 64317* | 64349 | 64381 |
| 64286 | 64318* | 64350 | 64382 |
| 64287 | 64319 | 64351 | 64383 |
| 64288 | 64320 | 64352* | 64384 |
| 64289 | 64321 | 64353 | 64385 |
| 64290 | 64322 | 64354* | 64386* |
| 64291 | 64323 | 64355 | 64387 |
| 64292 | 64324* | 64356 | 64388 |
| 64293 | 64325 | 64357 | 64389 |
| 64294 | 64326 | 64358 | 64390 |
| 64295 | 64327 | 64359* | 64391 |
| 64296 | 64328 | 64360 | 64392 |
| 64297 | 64329 | 64361 | 64393* |
| 64298 | 64330 | 64362* | 64394 |
| 64299 | 64331 | 64363 | 64395 |
| 64300 | 64332* | 64364* | 64396 |
| 64301 | 64333* | 64365 | 64397 |
| 64302 | 64334 | 64366 | 64398 |
| 64303 | 64335 | 64367 | 64399 |
| 64304* | 64336 | 64368 | 64400 |
| 64305 | 64337 | 64369 | 64401 |
| 64306 | 64338 | 64370 | 64402* |
| 64307 | 64339 | 64371 | 64403 |
| 64308 | 64340 | 64372 | 64404 |
| 64309 | 64341 | 64373* | 64405 |
| 64310 | 64342 | 64374 | 64406* |
| 64311 | 64343 | 64375* | 64407 |

| | | | |
|---|---|---|---|
| 64408 | 64420* | 64432 | 64444 |
| 64409 | 64421 | 64433 | 64445 |
| 64410 | 64422 | 64434 | 64446 |
| 64411 | 64423 | 64435 | 64447 |
| 64412 | 64424 | 64436 | 64448 |
| 64413 | 64425 | 64437 | 64449 |
| 64414 | 64426 | 64438 | 64450* |
| 64415 | 64427* | 64439* | 64451 |
| 64416 | 64428 | 64440 | 64452 |
| 64417* | 64429 | 64441* | 64453 |
| 64418* | 64430 | 64442* | |
| 64419 | 64431 | 64443 | |

Totals : Class J11/3　31
Class J11 (other parts) 143

---

## 0-6-0　　3F　　Class J35

J35/5* Introduced 1906. Reid N.B.
design with piston valves.
J35/4 Introduced 1908. Slide valves.
(Parts 1, 2 and 3 were variations of
Parts 4 and 5 before superheating.)
Weights: Loco. $\begin{cases} 51 \text{ tons.*} \\ 50 \text{ tons 15 cwt.} \end{cases}$
Tender $\begin{cases} 38 \text{ tons 1 cwt.*} \\ 37 \text{ tons 15 cwt.} \end{cases}$
Pressure: 180 lb. Su. Cyls.: $18\frac{1}{2}'' \times 26''$.
Driving Wheels: 5' 0". T.E.: 22,080 lb.

| | | | |
|---|---|---|---|
| 64460* | 64482 | 64500 | 64520 |
| 64461* | 64483 | 64501 | 64521 |
| 64462* | 64484 | 64502 | 64522 |
| 64463* | 64485 | 64504 | 64523 |
| 64464* | 64486 | 64505 | 64524 |
| 64466* | 64487 | 64506 | 64525 |
| 64468* | 64488 | 64507 | 64526 |
| 64470* | 64489 | 64509 | 64527 |
| 64471* | 64490 | 64510 | 64528 |
| 64472* | 64491 | 64511 | 64529 |
| 64473* | 64492 | 64512 | 64530 |
| 64474* | 64493 | 64513 | 64531 |
| 64475* | 64494 | 64514 | 64532 |
| 64476* | 64495 | 64515 | 64533 |
| 64477* | 64496 | 64516 | 64534 |
| 64478 | 64497 | 64517 | 64535 |
| 64479 | 64498 | 64518 | |
| 64480 | 64499 | 64519 | |

Totals : Class J35/4　55
Class J35/5　15

---

## 0-6-0　　4F　　Class J3?

Introduced 1914. Reid N.B. design.
Superheated development of J35.
Weights: Loco. 54 tons 14 cwt.
Tender 40 tons 19 cwt.
Pressure: 180 lb. Su. Cyls.: $19\frac{1}{2}'' \times 26''$.
Driving Wheels: 5' 0". T.E.: 25,210 lb.
P.V.

| | | | |
|---|---|---|---|
| 64536 | 64562 | 64588 | 64614 |
| 64537 | 64563 | 64589 | 64615 |
| 64538 | 64564 | 64590 | 64616 |
| 64539 | 64565 | 64591 | 64617 |
| 64540 | 64566 | 64592 | 64618 |
| 64541 | 64567 | 64593 | 64619 |
| 64542 | 64568 | 64594 | 64620 |
| 64543 | 64569 | 64595 | 64621 |
| 64544 | 64570 | 64596 | 64622 |
| 64545 | 64571 | 64597 | 64623 |
| 64546 | 64572 | 64598 | 64624 |
| 64547 | 64573 | 64599 | 64625 |
| 64548 | 64574 | 64600 | 64626 |
| 64549 | 64575 | 64601 | 64627 |
| 64550 | 64576 | 64602 | 64628 |
| 64551 | 64577 | 64603 | 64629 |
| 64552 | 64578 | 64604 | 64630 |
| 64553 | 64579 | 64605 | 64631 |
| 64554 | 64580 | 64606 | 64632 |
| 64555 | 64581 | 64607 | 64633 |
| 64556 | 64582 | 64608 | 64634 |
| 64557 | 64583 | 64609 | 64635 |
| 64558 | 64584 | 64610 | 64636 |
| 64559 | 64585 | 64611 | 64637 |
| 64560 | 64586 | 64612 | 64638 |
| 64561 | 64587 | 64613 | 64639 |

Total 104

---

## 0-6-0　　4F　　Class J19

Introduced 1912. S. Holden G.E.
design rebuilt with round-topped
boiler from 1934.
* Rebuilt with 19" cyls. and 180 lb.
pressure.
† Rebuilt with 19" cyls. and 160 lb.
pressure.
Weights: Loco. 50 tons 7 cwt.
Tender 38 tons 5 cwt.
Pressure $\begin{cases} 170 \text{ lb. Su.} \\ 180 \text{ lb. Su.*} \\ 160 \text{ lb. Su.†} \end{cases}$

Cyls.: $\begin{cases} 20'' \times 26''. \\ 19'' \times 26''.*† \end{cases}$
Driving Wheels: 4' 11".
T.E.: $\begin{cases} 27,430 \text{ lb.} \\ 26,215 \text{ lb.}* \\ 23,300 \text{ lb.}† \end{cases}$
P.V.

| | | | |
|---|---|---|---|
| 64640 | 64649 | 64658 | 64667 |
| 64641 | 64650 | 64659 | 64668 |
| 64642 | 64651 | 64660 | 64669 |
| 64643 | 64652 | 64661 | 64670 |
| 64644 | 64653 | 64662 | 64671* |
| 64645 | 64654 | 64663 | 64672† |
| 64646 | 64655 | 64664* | 64673 |
| 64647 | 64656 | 64665 | 64674 |
| 64648 | 64657 | 64666 | |

**Total 35**

## 0-6-0    6F    Class J20

**J20*** Introduced 1920. Hill G.E. design with Belpaire boiler.
**J20/1** Introduced 1943. Rebuilt with B12/1 type round-topped boiler.
Weights: Loco. 54 tons 15 cwt.
Tender 38 tons 5 cwt.
Pressure: 180 lb. Su. Cyls.: 20" × 28".
Driving Wheels: 4' 11". T.E.: 29,045 lb.
P.V.

| | | | |
|---|---|---|---|
| 64675* | 64682 | 64688 | 64694 |
| 64676* | 64683 | 64689 | 64695 |
| 64677 | 64684 | 64690 | 64696* |
| 64678 | 64685 | 64691 | 64697 |
| 64679 | 64686 | 64692 | 64698* |
| 64680 | 64687* | 64693 | 64699 |
| 64681 | | | |

**Totals : Class J20    5**
**Class J20/1    20**

## 0-6-0    5F    Class J39

Introduced 1926. Gresley design.
**J39/1** Standard 3,500 gallon tender.
**J39/2*** Standard 4,200 gallon tender.
**J39/3†** Various N.E. tenders (3,940 gallon on 64843-5, 4,125 gallon on 64855-9).
Weights: Loco. 57 tons 17 cwt.
Tender $\begin{cases} 44 \text{ tons } 4 \text{ cwt.} \\ 52 \text{ tons } 13 \text{ cwt.}* \end{cases}$ and others
Pressure: 180 lb. Su. Cyls.: 20" × 26".
Driving Wheels: 5' 2". T.E.: 25,665 lb.
P.V.

| | | | |
|---|---|---|---|
| 64700 | 64703 | 64706 | 64709 |
| 64701 | 64704 | 64707 | 64710 |
| 64702 | 64705 | 64708 | 64711 |

| | | | |
|---|---|---|---|
| 64712 | 64760 | 64808 | 64856† |
| 64713 | 64761 | 64809 | 64857† |
| 64714 | 64762 | 64810 | 64858† |
| 64715 | 64763 | 64811 | 64859† |
| 64716 | 64764 | 64812 | 64860 |
| 64717 | 64765 | 64813 | 64861 |
| 64718 | 64766 | 64814 | 64862 |
| 64719 | 64767 | 64815 | 64863 |
| 64720 | 64768 | 64816 | 64864 |
| 64721 | 64769 | 64817 | 64865 |
| 64722 | 64770 | 64818 | 64866 |
| 64723 | 64771 | 64819 | 64867 |
| 64724 | 64772 | 64820* | 64868 |
| 64725 | 64773 | 64821* | 64869 |
| 64726 | 64774 | 64822* | 64870 |
| 64727 | 64775 | 64823 | 64871 |
| 64728 | 64776 | 64824 | 64872* |
| 64729 | 64777 | 64825 | 64873* |
| 64730 | 64778 | 64826 | 64874* |
| 64731 | 64779 | 64827 | 64875* |
| 64732 | 64780 | 64828 | 64876* |
| 64733 | 64781 | 64829 | 64877* |
| 64734 | 64782 | 64830 | 64878* |
| 64735 | 64783 | 64831 | 64879* |
| 64736 | 64784* | 64832 | 64880* |
| 64737 | 64785* | 64833 | 64881* |
| 64738 | 64786* | 64834 | 64882* |
| 64739 | 64787* | 64835 | 64883* |
| 64740 | 64788* | 64836 | 64884* |
| 64741 | 64789* | 64837 | 64885* |
| 64742 | 64790* | 64838* | 64886* |
| 64743 | 64791* | 64839* | 64887* |
| 64744 | 64792* | 64840* | 64888* |
| 64745 | 64793* | 64841* | 64889* |
| 64746 | 64794* | 64842† | 64890* |
| 64747 | 64795* | 64843† | 64891* |
| 64748 | 64796 | 64844† | 64892* |
| 64749 | 64797 | 64845† | 64893* |
| 64750 | 64798 | 64846 | 64894* |
| 64751 | 64799 | 64847 | 64895* |
| 64752 | 64800 | 64848 | 64896* |
| 64753 | 64801 | 64849 | 64897* |
| 64754 | 64802 | 64850 | 64898* |
| 64755 | 64803 | 64851 | 64899* |
| 64756 | 64804 | 64852 | 64900* |
| 64757 | 64805 | 64853 | 64901* |
| 64758 | 64806 | 64854 | 64902* |
| 64759 | 64807 | 64855† | 64903* |

| | | | |
|---|---|---|---|
| 64904* | 64926* | 64948* | 64970* |
| 64905* | 64927* | 64949* | 64971† |
| 64906* | 64928* | 64950* | 64972† |
| 64907* | 64929* | 64951* | 64973† |
| 64908* | 64930* | 64952* | 64974† |
| 64909* | 64931* | 64953* | 64975† |
| 64910* | 64932* | 64954* | 64976† |
| 64911* | 64933 | 64955* | 64977† |
| 64912* | 64934 | 64956* | 64978† |
| 64913* | 64935 | 64957* | 64979† |
| 64914* | 64936 | 64958* | 64980† |
| 64915* | 64937 | 64959* | 64981† |
| 64916* | 64938 | 64960* | 64982† |
| 64917* | 64939 | 64961* | 64983† |
| 64918* | 64940 | 64962* | 64984† |
| 64919* | 64941 | 64963* | 64985† |
| 64920* | 64942 | 64964* | 64986† |
| 64921* | 64943 | 64965* | 64987† |
| 64922* | 64944 | 64966* | 64988† |
| 64923* | 64945* | 64967* | |
| 64924* | 64946* | 64968* | |
| 64925* | 64947* | 64969* | |

Totals : Class J39/1  156
Class J39/2  106
Class J39/3  27

## 0-6-0  2MT  Class J1

Introduced 1908. Ivatt G.N. design.
Weights: Loco.  46 tons 14 cwt.
Tender 43 tons 2 cwt.
Pressure: 175 lb.  Cyls.: 18" × 26".
Driving Wheels: 5' 8". T.E.: 18,430 lb.

65002 | 65013 | 65014

Total 3

## 0-6-0  2MT  Class J2

Introduced 1912. Ivatt/Gresley G.N. design.
Weights: Loco.  50 tons 10 cwt.
Tender 43 tons 2 cwt.
Pressure: 170 lb. Su.  Cyls.: 19" × 26".
Driving Wheels: 5' 8". T.E.: 19,945 lb. P.V.

65015 | 65017 | 65020 | 65023
65016 | 65018 | 65022

Total 7

## 0-6-0  2F  Class J

Introduced 1886. T. W. Worsdell design. Majority built as 2-... compounds and later rebuilt... simple locos.
* Rebuilt with superheater, Stephen... gear and piston valves.
† Rebuilt with piston valves, su... heater removed.
Weights: Loco. { 43 tons 15 cwt.* / 42 tons 9 cwt.†
Tender  36 tons 19 cwt.
Pressure: 160 lb. SS.
Cyls.: 19" × 24"
T.E.: 19,240 lb.
Driving Wheels: 5' 1¼".

| | | | |
|---|---|---|---|
| 65033* | 65062* | 65082* | 650.. |
| 65035† | 65064* | 65088* | 650.. |
| 65038* | 65068* | 65089* | 651.. |
| 65039† | 65070† | 65090* | 651.. |
| 65042† | 65075* | 65091* | 651.. |
| 65047* | 65077* | 65092* | 651.. |
| 65061* | 65078* | 65097* | 651.. |

Total

## 0-6-0  2F  Class J

J10/4* Introduced 1896. Pollitt... velopment of J10/2 with lar... bearings and larger tenders.
J10/6 Introduced 1901. Robin... locos with larger bearings and sm... tenders.
Weights: Loco.  41 tons 6 cwt.
Tender { 37 tons 6 cwt. / 43 tons.*
Pressure: 160 lb.  Cyls.: 18" × 2..
Driving Wheels: 5' 1". T.E.: 18,780

| | | | |
|---|---|---|---|
| 65131 | 65143* | 65157* | 6516.. |
| 65132 | 65144* | 65158* | 6517.. |
| 65133 | 65145* | 65159* | 6517.. |
| 65134* | 65146* | 65160* | 6517.. |
| 65135* | 65147* | 65162 | 6517.. |
| 65138 | 65148* | 65164* | 6517.. |
| 65139 | 65153* | 65165* | 6517.. |
| 65140* | 65154* | 65166* | 6517.. |
| 65142* | 65156* | 65167* | 6518.. |

| | | | |
|---|---|---|---|
| 181 | 65187 | 65197 | 65203 |
| 182 | 65191 | 65198 | 65205 |
| 184 | 65192 | 65199 | 65208 |
| 185 | 65194 | 65200 | 65209 |
| 186 | 65196 | 65202 | |

Totals : Class J10/4   28

Class J10/6   27

## 6-0    2F      Class J36

roduced 1888. Holmes N.B. design.
eights: Loco. 41 tons 19 cwt.
         Tender 33 tons 9 cwt.
essure: 165 lb.   Cyls.: $18\frac{1}{4}'' \times 26''$.
iving Wheels: 5' 0".   T.E.: 19,690 lb.

| | | | |
|---|---|---|---|
| 210 | 65244 | 65282 | 65318 |
| 211 | 65246 | 65285 | 65319 |
| 213 | 65247 | 65287 | 65320 |
| 216* | 65249 | 65290 | 65323 |
| 217* | 65250 | 65293 | 65324 |
| 218 | 65251 | 65295 | 65325 |
| 221 | 65252 | 65296 | 65327 |
| 222* | 65253* | 65297 | 65329 |
| 224* | 65257 | 65300 | 65330 |
| 225 | 65258 | 65303 | 65331 |
| 227 | 65259 | 65304 | 65333 |
| 228 | 65260 | 65305 | 65334 |
| 229 | 65261 | 65306 | 65335 |
| 230 | 65265 | 65307 | 65338 |
| 233* | 65267 | 65310 | 65341 |
| 234 | 65268* | 65311 | 65342 |
| 235* | 65270 | 65312 | 65343 |
| 236* | 65273 | 65313 | 65344 |
| 237 | 65275 | 65314 | 65345 |
| 239 | 65276 | 65315 | 65346 |
| 241 | 65277 | 65316 | |
| 242 | 65280 | 65317 | |
| 243* | 65281 | | Total 96 |

ames

| | |
|---|---|
| 65216 Byng | 65235 Gough |
| 65217 French | 65236 Horne |
| 65222 Somme | 65243 Maude |
| 65224 Mons | 65253 Joffre |
| 65233 Plumer | 65268 Allenby |

## 0-6-0    2F      Class J15

Introduced 1883. Worsdell G.E. design, modified by J. Holden.
* Fitted with side-window cab for Colne Valley line.
Weights: Loco. 37 tons 2 cwt.
         Tender 30 tons 13 cwt.
Pressure: 160 lb.   Cyls.: $17\frac{1}{2}'' \times 24''$.
Driving Wheels: 4' 11".   T.E.: 16,940 lb.

| | | | |
|---|---|---|---|
| 65356 | 65430 | 65450 | 65466 |
| 65359 | 65432* | 65451 | 65467 |
| 65361 | 65433 | 65452 | 65468 |
| 65370 | 65434 | 65453 | 65469 |
| 65384 | 65435 | 65454 | 65470 |
| 65388 | 65438* | 65455 | 65471 |
| 65389 | 65440 | 65456 | 65472 |
| 65390 | 65441 | 65457 | 65473 |
| 65391* | 65442 | 65458 | 65474 |
| 65404 | 65443 | 65459 | 65475 |
| 65405* | 65444 | 65460 | 65476 |
| 65417 | 65445 | 65461 | 65477 |
| 65420 | 65446 | 65462 | 65478 |
| 65422 | 65447 | 65463 | 65479 |
| 65424* | 65448 | 65464 | |
| 65425 | 65449 | 65465 | |

Total 62

## 0-6-0    3F      Class J5

Introduced 1909. Ivatt G.N. design.
* Rebuilt with superheater.
Weights: Loco. 47 tons 2 cwt.
         Tender 43 tons 2 cwt.
Pressure: $\begin{cases} 175 \text{ lb} \\ 170 \text{ lb. Su.*} \end{cases}$
Cyls.: $18'' \times 26''$.
Driving Wheels: 5' 2".
T.E.: $\begin{cases} 20,210 \text{ lb.} \\ 19,630 \text{ lb.} \end{cases}$

| | | | |
|---|---|---|---|
| 65480* | 65486 | 65491 | 65496 |
| 65481 | 65487 | 65492 | 65497 |
| 65482 | 65488 | 65493 | 65498 |
| 65483 | 65489* | 65494 | 65499 |
| 65485 | 65490 | 65495 | |

Total 19

### IMPORTANT NOTE

A careful reading of the notes on page 2 is essential to understand the use of reference marks in this book.

## 0-6-0  4F  Class J17

Introduced 1901. J. Holden G.E. design. Many rebuilt from round-top boiler J16, introduced 1900.

\* Fitted with small tender.

Weights: Loco.  45 tons 8 cwt.
Tender { 30 tons 12 cwt.*
{ 38 tons 5 cwt.

Pressure: 180 lb. Su.  Cyls.: 19" × 26".
Driving Wheels: 4' 11".  T.E.: 24,340 lb.

| | | | |
|---|---|---|---|
| 65500* | 65523 | 65545 | 65568 |
| 65501* | 65524 | 65546 | 65569 |
| 65502* | 65525 | 65547 | 65570 |
| 65503* | 65526 | 65548 | 65571* |
| 65504* | 65527 | 65549 | 65572 |
| 65505* | 65528* | 65551 | 65573 |
| 65506* | 65529 | 65552 | 65574 |
| 65507* | 65530 | 65553 | 65575 |
| 65508* | 65531 | 65554 | 65576 |
| 65509 | 65532 | 65555 | 65577 |
| 65510* | 65533 | 65556 | 65578 |
| 65511* | 65534 | 65557 | 65579 |
| 65512* | 65535 | 65558 | 65580 |
| 65513* | 65536 | 65559 | 65581 |
| 65514* | 65537 | 65560 | 65582 |
| 65515* | 65538 | 65561 | 65583 |
| 65516* | 65539 | 65562 | 65584 |
| 65517* | 65540 | 65563 | 65585 |
| 65518* | 65541 | 65564 | 65586 |
| 65519* | 65542 | 65565 | 65587 |
| 65520 | 65543 | 65566 | 65588 |
| 65521 | 65544 | 65567 | 65589 |
| 65522 | | | |

Total 89

## 0-6-0  3F  Class J25

Introduced 1898. W. Worsdell N.E. design.

\* Original design, Saturated, with slide valves.
† Rebuilt with superheater and piston valves.
‡ Rebuilt with piston valves, superheater removed.

Weights: Loco. { 39 tons 11 cwt.*
{ 41 tons 14 cwt.†
{ 40 tons 17 cwt.‡
Tender 36 tons 19 cwt.

Pressure: 160 lb. SS.  Cyls.: 18½" × 26".
Driving Wheels: 4' 7½".  T.E.: 21,905 lb.

| | | | |
|---|---|---|---|
| 65645† | 65650* | 65656* | 65662† |
| 65647* | 65654‡ | 65657* | 65663* |
| 65648* | 65655* | 65661* | 65666* |

| | | | |
|---|---|---|---|
| 65667* | 65686* | 65696* | 657 |
| 65670* | 65687* | 65697* | 657 |
| 65671* | 65688* | 65698* | 657 |
| 65673‡ | 65689* | 65699* | 657 |
| 65675* | 65690* | 65700* | 657 |
| 65676* | 65691* | 65702‡ | 657 |
| 65677‡ | 65692‡ | 65705* | 657 |
| 65680* | 65693* | 65706† | 657 |
| 65683‡ | 65694* | 65708* | 657 |
| 65685* | 65695* | 65710* | 657 |

Total

## 0-6-0  5F  Class

Introduced 1904. W. Worsdell design.

Weights: Loco.  46 tons 16 cwt.
Tender 36 tons 19 cwt.

Pressure: 180 lb.  Cyls.: 18½" ×
Driving Wheels: 4' 7½".  T.E.: 24,64

| | | | |
|---|---|---|---|
| 65730 | 65743 | 65756 | 657 |
| 65731 | 65744 | 65757 | 657 |
| 65732 | 65745 | 65758 | 657 |
| 65733 | 65746 | 65759 | 657 |
| 65734 | 65747 | 65760 | 657 |
| 65735 | 65748 | 65761 | 657 |
| 65736 | 65749 | 65762 | 657 |
| 65737 | 65750 | 65763 | 657 |
| 65738 | 65751 | 65764 | 657 |
| 65739 | 65752 | 65765 | 657 |
| 65740 | 65753 | 65766 | 657 |
| 65741 | 65754 | 65767 | |
| 65742 | 65755 | 65768 | |

Total

## 0-6-0  5F  Class

Introduced 1906. W. Worsdell design developed from J26.

\* Introduced 1921. Raven locos. S heated, with piston valves.
† Introduced 1943. Piston va superheater removed.

Weights: Loco. { 47 tons Sat.
{ 49 tons 10 cwt
Tender 36 tons 19 cwt

Pressure: 180 lb. SS.  Cyls.: 18½" ×
Driving Wheels: 4' 7½".  T.E.: 24,6

| | | | |
|---|---|---|---|
| 65780 | 65782 | 65784 | 65 |
| 65781 | 65783 | 65785 | 65 |

| | | | |
|---|---|---|---|
| 38 | 65815 | 65842 | 65869* |
| 49 | 65816 | 65843 | 65870† |
| 90 | 65817 | 65844 | 65871* |
| 91 | 65818 | 65845 | 65872* |
| 92 | 65819 | 65846 | 65873† |
| 93 | 65820 | 65847 | 65874* |
| 94 | 65821 | 65848 | 65875† |
| 95 | 65822 | 65849 | 65876† |
| 96 | 65823 | 65850 | 65877† |
| 97 | 65824 | 65851 | 65878* |
| 98 | 65825 | 65852 | 65879† |
| 99 | 65826 | 65853 | 65880* |
| 00 | 65827 | 65854 | 65881* |
| 01 | 65828 | 65855 | 65882† |
| 02 | 65829 | 65856 | 65883* |
| 03 | 65830 | 65857 | 65884† |
| 04 | 65831 | 65858 | 65885* |
| 05 | 65832 | 65859 | 65886* |
| 06 | 65833 | 65860† | 65887* |
| 07 | 65834 | 65861† | 65888† |
| 08 | 65835 | 65862† | 65889* |
| 09 | 65836 | 65863* | 65890* |
| 10 | 65837 | 65864† | 65891† |
| 11 | 65838 | 65865† | 65892* |
| 12 | 65839 | 65866* | 65893* |
| 13 | 65840 | 65867† | 65894* |
| 14 | 65841 | 65868† | |

Total 115

## -0    6F    Class J38

...duced 1926. Gresley design.
...edecessor of J39, with 4' 8" wheels,
...iler 6" longer than J39 and smoke-
...ox 6" shorter.
...built with J39 boiler.
...ghts: Loco.    58 tons 19 cwt.
                Tender 44 tons 4 cwt.
...sure: 180 lb. Su. Cyls.: 20" × 26".
...ing Wheels: 4' 8". T.E.: 28,415 lb.

| | | | |
|---|---|---|---|
| 00 | 65909 | 65918* | 65927* |
| 01 | 65910 | 65919 | 65928 |
| 02 | 65911 | 65920 | 65929 |
| 03* | 65912 | 65921 | 65930 |
| 04 | 65913 | 65922 | 65931 |
| 05 | 65914 | 65923 | 65932 |
| 06* | 65915 | 65924 | 65933 |
| 07 | 65916 | 65925 | 65934 |
| 08* | 65917* | 65926* | |

Total 35

## 2-4-2T    1P    Class F4

Introduced 1884. Worsdell G.E. design, modified by J. Holden.
Weight: 53 tons 19 cwt.
Pressure: 160 lb.  Cyls.: 17½" × 24".
Driving Wheels: 5' 4". T.E.: 15,620 lb.

| | | | |
|---|---|---|---|
| 67157 | 67174 | 67186 | 67187 |
| 67162 | 67176 | | |

Total 6

## 2-4-2T    2P    Class F5

Introduced 1911. S. D. Holden design. (Rebuilt from F4.)
* Introduced 1949. Push-and-pull fitted.
Weight: 53 tons 19 cwt.
Pressure: 180 lb.  Cyls.: 17½" × 24".
Driving Wheels: 5' 4"  T.E.: 17,570 lb.

| | | | |
|---|---|---|---|
| 67188 | 67196 | 67204 | 67212 |
| 67189 | 67197 | 67205 | 67213 |
| 67190 | 67198 | 67206 | 67214 |
| 67191 | 67199 | 67207 | 67215 |
| 67192 | 67200* | 67208 | 67216 |
| 67193* | 67201 | 67209 | 67217 |
| 67194 | 67202* | 67210 | 67218 |
| 67195 | 67203* | 67211 | 67219 |

Total 32

## 2-4-2T    2P    Class F6

Introduced 1911. S. D Holden design, development of F4 with higher pressure and larger tanks.
Weight: 56 tons 9 cwt.
Pressure: 180 lb.  Cyls.: 17½" × 24".
Driving Wheels: 5' 4". T.E.: 17,570 lb.

| | | | |
|---|---|---|---|
| 67220 | 67225 | 67230 | 67235 |
| 67221 | 67226 | 67231 | 67236 |
| 67222 | 67227 | 67232 | 67237 |
| 67223 | 67228 | 67233 | 67238 |
| 67224 | 67229 | 67234 | 67239 |

Total 20

IMPORTANT NOTE

A careful reading of the notes on page 2 is essential to understand the use of reference marks in this book.

## 0-4-4T IP Class G5

Introduced 1894. W. Worsdell N.E. design.
● Push-and-pull fitted.
† Push-and-pull fitted and rebuilt with larger tanks.
Weight: 54 tons 4 cwt.
Pressure: 160 lb. Cyls.: 18″ × 24″.
Driving Wheels: 5′ 1¼″. T.E.: 17,265 lb.

| | | | |
|---|---|---|---|
| 67240 | 67270 | 67298 | 67326 |
| 67241 | 67271 | 67300 | 67327 |
| 67243 | 67272 | 67301 | 67328 |
| 67246 | 67273* | 67302 | 67329 |
| 67247 | 67274 | 67304 | 67332 |
| 67248 | 67277 | 67305* | 67333 |
| 67249 | 67278 | 67307 | 67334 |
| 67250* | 67279* | 67308 | 67335 |
| 67251 | 67280* | 67309 | 67336 |
| 67253* | 67281* | 67310 | 67337* |
| 67254 | 67282* | 67311* | 67338 |
| 67256 | 67283 | 67312 | 67339* |
| 67257 | 67284 | 67314 | 67340† |
| 67258 | 67286* | 67315 | 67341 |
| 67259 | 67287 | 67316 | 67342 |
| 67261* | 67288 | 67318 | 67343 |
| 67262 | 67289 | 67319 | 67344 |
| 67263 | 67290 | 67320 | 67345 |
| 67265 | 67293 | 67321 | 67346 |
| 67266 | 67294 | 67322* | 67347 |
| 67267 | 67295 | 67323* | 67349 |
| 67268 | 67296 | 67324 | |
| 67269* | 67297* | 67325 | |

Total 90

## 4-4-2T IP Class C12

Introduced 1898. Ivatt G.N. design.
*†Boiler pressure reduced to 170 lb
††Push-and-pull fitted.
Weight: 62 tons 6 cwt.
Pressure: { 175 lb.
{ 170 lb.*†
Cyls.: 18″ × 26″.
Driving Wheels: 5′ 8″.
T.E.: { 18,425 lb.
{ 17,900 lb.*†

| | | | |
|---|---|---|---|
| 67350 | 67354* | 67361 | 67364 |
| 67352 | 67357 | 67362 | 67365 |
| 67353 | 67360 | 67363† | 67366 |

| | | | |
|---|---|---|---|
| 67367 | 67376 | 67386‡ | 673 |
| 67368 | 67379 | 67387‡ | 673 |
| 67369 | 67380 | 67389 | 673 |
| 67371 | 67382 | 67390 | 673 |
| 67372 | 67383 | 67391 | |
| 67374† | 67384 | 67392 | |
| 67375 | 67385 | 67393 | |

Total

## 4-4-2T 2P Class C

Introduced 1903. Robinson G design, later rebuilt with superhea
● Push-and-pull fitted.
Weight: 66 tons 13 cwt.
Pressure: 160 lb. Su. Cyls.: 18″ ×
Driving Wheels: 5′ 7″. T.E.: 17,100

| | | | |
|---|---|---|---|
| 67400 | 67412 | 67421* | 674. |
| 67401 | 67413 | 67422 | 674 |
| 67402 | 67414 | 67423 | 674 |
| 67403 | 67415 | 67424 | 674 |
| 67405 | 67416* | 67425 | 674 |
| 67407 | 67417* | 67426 | 674 |
| 67408 | 67418* | 67427 | 674 |
| 67409 | 67419 | 67428 | 674 |
| 67411 | 67420* | 67429 | 674 |

Total

## 4-4-2T 2P Class C

Introduced 1907. Robinson G.C. des
later superheated, development
C13. With detail differences.
Weight: 71 tons.
Pressure: 160 lb. Su. Cyls.: 18″ × 2
Driving Wheels: 5′ 7″. T.E.: 17,100

| | | | |
|---|---|---|---|
| 67440 | 67443 | 67446 | 6744 |
| 67441 | 67444 | 67447 | 6745 |
| 67442 | 67445 | 67448 | 6745 |

Total

## 4-4-2T 2P Class C

Introduced 1911. Reid N.B. design.
* Push-and-pull fitted.
Weight: 68 tons 15 cwt.
Pressure: 175 lb. Cyls.: 18″ × 2
Driving Wheels: 5′ 9″. T.E.: 18,160

| | | | |
|---|---|---|---|
| 67452 | 67455 | 67458 | 6746 |
| 67453 | 67456 | 67459 | 6746 |
| 67454 | 67457 | 67460* | 6746 |

| 64 | 67469 | 67475 | 67480 |
|----|-------|-------|-------|
| 65 | 67470 | 67476 | 67481 |
| 66 | 67472 | 67477 | |
| 67 | 67473 | 67478 | |
| 68 | 67474 | 67479 | |

**Total 29**

## -2T  2P  Class C16

...duced 1915. Reid N.B. design,
...perheated development of C15.
...perheater removed.
ght: 72 tons 10 cwt.
sure: 165 lb. SS. Cyls.: 19″ × 26″.
...ing Wheels: 5′ 9″. T.E.: 19,080 lb.

| 82 | 67488 | 67493 | 67498 |
|----|-------|-------|-------|
| 83* | 67489 | 67494 | 67499 |
| 84 | 67490 | 67495 | 67500 |
| 85 | 67491 | 67496 | 67501 |
| 86 | 67492 | 67497 | 67502 |
| 87 | | | |

**Total 21**

## Classes
## -2T  VI (3MT) / V3 (4MT)  VI & V3

Introduced 1930. Gresley design.
Introduced 1939. Development of
... with higher pressure (locos num...ered below 67682 rebuilt from VI).
...ghts: { 84 tons. / 86 tons 16 cwt.*
...sure: { 180 lb. Su. / 200 lb. Su.*
..: (3) 16″ × 26″.
...ing Wheels: 5′ 8″.
.. { 22,465 lb. / 24,960 lb.
...schaerts gear, derived motion. P.V.

| 00 | 67613 | 67626 | 67639 |
|----|-------|-------|-------|
| 01 | 67614 | 67627 | 67640 |
| 02 | 67615 | 67628 | 67641 |
| 03 | 67616 | 67629 | 67642 |
| 04* | 67617 | 67630 | 67643 |
| 05 | 67618 | 67631 | 67644 |
| 06* | 67619 | 67632 | 67645 |
| 07 | 67620 | 67633 | 67646 |
| 08 | 67621 | 67634* | 67647 |
| 09 | 67622 | 67635 | 67648 |
| 10 | 67623 | 67636* | 67649 |
| 11 | 67624* | 67637 | 67650 |
| 12 | 67625 | 67638 | 67651 |

| 67652* | 67662 | 67672* | 67682* |
|--------|-------|--------|--------|
| 67653 | 67663 | 67673 | 67683* |
| 67654 | 67664 | 67674 | 67684* |
| 67655 | 67665 | 67675* | 67685* |
| 67656* | 67666 | 67676 | 67686* |
| 67657 | 67667 | 67677 | 67687* |
| 67658 | 67668 | 67678 | 67688* |
| 67659 | 67669* | 67679 | 67689* |
| 67660 | 67670 | 67680 | 67690* |
| 67661 | 67671 | 67681 | 67691* |

**Totals : Class VI  72**
**Class V3  20**

## 2-6-4T  4MT  Class LI

Introduced 1945. Thompson design.
Weight: 89 tons 9 cwt.
Pressure: 225 lb. Cyls.: (O) 20″ × 26″.
Driving Wheels: 5′ 2″. T.E.: 32,080 lb.
Walschaerts gear.  P.V.

| 67701 | 67726 | 67751 | 67776 |
|-------|-------|-------|-------|
| 67702 | 67727 | 67752 | 67777 |
| 67703 | 67728 | 67753 | 67778 |
| 67704 | 67729 | 67754 | 67779 |
| 67705 | 67730 | 67755 | 67780 |
| 67706 | 67731 | 67756 | 67781 |
| 67707 | 67732 | 67757 | 67782 |
| 67708 | 67733 | 67758 | 67783 |
| 67709 | 67734 | 67759 | 67784 |
| 67710 | 67735 | 67760 | 67785 |
| 67711 | 67736 | 67761 | 67786 |
| 67712 | 67737 | 67762 | 67787 |
| 67713 | 67738 | 67763 | 67788 |
| 67714 | 67739 | 67764 | 67789 |
| 67715 | 67740 | 67765 | 67790 |
| 67716 | 67741 | 67766 | 67791 |
| 67717 | 67742 | 67767 | 67792 |
| 67718 | 67743 | 67768 | 67793 |
| 67719 | 67744 | 67769 | 67794 |
| 67720 | 67745 | 67770 | 67795 |
| 67721 | 67746 | 67771 | 67796 |
| 67722 | 67747 | 67772 | 67797 |
| 67723 | 67748 | 67773 | 67798 |
| 67724 | 67749 | 67774 | 67799 |
| 67725 | 67750 | 67775 | 67800 |

**Total 100**

## 0-6-0ST  4F  Class J94

Introduced 1943. Riddles M.o.S. design.
(Bought from M.o.S. 1946.)
Weight: 48 tons 5 cwt.
Pressure: 170 lb.     Cyls.: 18″ × 26″.
Driving Wheels: 4′ 3″.  T.E.: 23,870 lb.

| | | | |
|---|---|---|---|
| 68006 | 68025 | 68044 | 68063 |
| 68007 | 68026 | 68045 | 68064 |
| 68008 | 68027 | 68046 | 68065 |
| 68009 | 68028 | 68047 | 68066 |
| 68010 | 68029 | 68048 | 68067 |
| 68011 | 68030 | 68049 | 68068 |
| 68012 | 68031 | 68050 | 68069 |
| 68013 | 68032 | 68051 | 68070 |
| 68014 | 68033 | 68052 | 68071 |
| 68015 | 68034 | 68053 | 68072 |
| 68016 | 68035 | 68054 | 68073 |
| 68017 | 68036 | 68055 | 68074 |
| 68018 | 68037 | 68056 | 68075 |
| 68019 | 68038 | 68057 | 68076 |
| 68020 | 68039 | 68058 | 68077 |
| 68021 | 68040 | 68059 | 68078 |
| 68022 | 68041 | 68060 | 68079 |
| 68023 | 68042 | 68061 | 68080 |
| 68024 | 68043 | 68062 | |

Total 75

## 0-4-0ST  0F  Class Y9

Introduced 1882. Holmes N.B. design.
* Locos running permanently attached
to wooden tenders.
Weights: Loco.   27 tons 16 cwt.
          Tender   6 tons.*
Pressure: 130 lb. Cyls.: (O) 14″ × 20″.
Driving Wheels: 3′ 8″.  T.E.: 9,845 lb.

| | | | |
|---|---|---|---|
| 68093* | 68101 | 68109* | 68118* |
| 68094* | 68102 | 68110 | 68119* |
| 68095* | 68103* | 68112* | 68120* |
| 68096* | 68104 | 68113 | 68121* |
| 68097* | 68105 | 68114* | 68122* |
| 68098 | 68106* | 68115 | 68123 |
| 68099* | 68107* | 68116* | 68124 |
| 68100 | 68108* | 68117* | |

Total 31

## 0-4-0T  0F  Class

Introduced 1913.  Hill G.E. design.
Weight: 38 tons 1 cwt.
Pressure: 180 lb.  Cyls.: (O) 17″ ×
Driving Wheels: 3′ 10″. T.E.: 19,225
Walschaerts gear.

| | | | |
|---|---|---|---|
| 68125 | 68126 | 68127 | 681 |

Tota

(See also page 43)

## 0-4-0T  Unclass  Class

Sentinel Wagon Works design.  Sin
speed Geared Sentinel Locomoti
The parts of this class differ in det
including size of boiler and
capacity.
Y1/1* Introduced 1925.
Y1/2† Introduced 1927.
§ Sprocket gear ratio 9 : 25 (remaind
11 : 25).
Weights: { 20 tons 17 cwt.*
          { 19 tons 16 cwt.†
Pressure: 275 lb. Su. Cyls.: 6⅞″ ×
Driving Wheels: 2′ 6″.
T.E.: { 7,260 lb.
      { 8,870 lb.§
Poppet valves.

| | | |
|---|---|---|
| 68130S* | 68142† | 6814 |
| 68131S* | 68143†§ | 6815 |
| 68133S* | 68144†§ | 6815 |
| 68137† | 68145†§ | 6815 |
| 68138† | 68146†§ | 6815 |
| 68140† | 68148†§ | |

Totals : Class Y1/1
         Class Y1/2

(See also page 43)

## 0-4-0T  Dock Tank  Class

Introduced 1890. T. W. Worsdell
design.
Weight: 15 tons 10 cwt.
Pressure: 140 lb.   Cyls.: 11″ ×
Driving Wheels: 3′ 0″. T.E.: 6,000

| |
|---|
| 68091 |

Tota

**-0T** Unclass **Class Y3**

inel Wagon Works design. Two-
eed Geared Sentinel Locos.
iduced 1927.

rocket gear ratio 15 : 19 (re-
ainder 19 : 19).

ght: 20 tons 16 cwt.
sure: 275 lb. Su. Cyls.: 6¾" × 9".
ing Wheels: 2' 6".

> { Low Gear: 12,600 lb.
> High Gear: 4,705 lb.
> { Low Gear: 15,960 lb.*
> High Gear: 5,960 lb.*

>et valves.

| 54 | 68161 | 68169 | 68183* |
|----|-------|-------|--------|
| | 68162 | 68176 | 68184 |
| 56 | 68164 | 68177S | 68185 |
| 58 | 68165S | 68178S | |
| 59 | 68166S | 68180* | |
| 60 | 68168S | 68182* | |

*(See also below)* **Total 21**

---

**0-4-2T** 0F **Class Z4**

Introduced 1915. Manning-Wardle
design for G.N. of S.
Weight: 25 tons 17 cwt.
Pressure: 160 lb. Cyls.: (O) 13" × 20".
Driving Wheels: 3' 6". T.E.: 10,945 lb.

68190 | 68191 **Total 2**

---

**0-4-2T** 0F **Class Z5**

Introduced 1915. Manning-Wardle
design of G.N. of S.
Weight: 30 tons 18 cwt.
Pressure: 160 lb. Cyls.: (O) 14" × 20".
Driving Wheels: 4' 0". T.E.: 11,105 10t

68192 | 68193 **Total 2**

---

# DEPARTMENTAL LOCOMOTIVES

In additional to service locomotives (denoted by a bold
" S " in these pages) that are still shown with numbers in
the British Railways series, a number of E. & N.E. Region
departmental locomotives have been renumbered between
I and 100. These are shown below, with their former B.R.
numbers in brackets.

**0-6-ST** 3F **Class J52/2**
*(For dimensions see page 54)*
I (68845)　　2 (68816)

**0-4-0T** Unclass **Class Y3**
*(For dimensions—15:19 gear ratio—
see above).*
3 (68181)

**0-4-0T** Unclass **Class Y1/1**
*(For dimensions see page 42)*
4 (68132)

**0-4-0T** 0F **Class Y7**
Introduced 1888. T. W. Worsdell
N.E. design.
Weight: 22 tons 14 cwt.
Pressure: 140 lb. Cyls.: 14" × 20".
Driving Wheels: 3' 6¼".
T.E.: 11,040 lb.

34 (68088)

**0-6-0T** 2F **Class J66**
*(For dimensions see page 53)*
31 (68382)　　32 (68370)
36 (68378)

**0-4-0T** 0F **Class Y4**
*(For dimensions see page 42)*
33 (68129)

**0-4-0T** Unclass **Class Y1/4**
Sentinel Wagon Works design.
(This part introduced 1927).
Single-speed Geared Sentinel
Locomotives. The three parts of
this class differ in details, includ-
ing size of boiler and fuel
capacity.
Sprocket gear ratio 11:25.
Weight: 19 tons 7 cwt.
Pressure: 275 lb. Su.
Cyls.: 6¾" × 9 ".
Driving Wheels: 2' 6".
T.E.: 7,260 lb. Poppet valves.
51 (68136)

## 0-6-0T   0F   Class J63

Introduced 1906. Robinson G.C. design.
Weight: 37 tons 9 cwt.
Pressure: 150 lb. Cyls.: (O) 13″ × 20″.
Driving Wheels: 3′ 6″. T.E.: 10,260 lb.

| 68204 | 68206 | 68208 | 68210 |
| 68205 | 68207 | 68209 | |

**Total 7**

## 0-6-0T   0F   Class J65

Introduced 1889. J. Holden G.E. design.
Weight: 36 tons 11 cwt.
Pressure: 160 lb.   Cyls.: 14″ × 20″.
Driving Wheels: 4′ 0″. T.E.: 11,105 lb.

| 68211 | | 68214 | **Total 2** |

## 0-6-0T (Tram Locos)
### 0F   Class J70

Introduced 1903. J. Holden G.E. design.
Weight: 27 tons 1 cwt.
Pressure: 180 lb. Cyls.: (O) 12″ × 15″.
Driving Wheels: 3′ 1″. T.E.: 8,930 lb.
Walschaerts gear.

| 68216 | 68222 | 68225 | 68226 |
| 68219 | 68223 | | |

**Total 6**

## 0-6-0T   Unclass.   Class J71

Introduced 1886. T. W. Worsdell N.E. design.
*†Altered cylinder dimensions.
Weight: 37 tons 12 cwt.
Pressure: 140 lb. Dr. Wheels: 4′ 7¼″
Cyls.: { 16″ × 22″ { 12,130 lb.
{ 16⅜″ × 22″* T.E.: { 13,300 lb.*
{ 18″ × 22″† { 15,355 lb.†

| 68230* | 68250* | 68266 | 68282 |
| 68232 | 68251 | 68267 | 68283 |
| 68233 | 68252* | 68269 | 68284 |
| 68234* | 68253* | 68270 | 68287* |
| 68235 | 68254 | 68271 | 68289* |
| 68236 | 68256 | 68272 | 68290 |
| 68238 | 68258* | 68273 | 68291 |
| 68239 | 68259* | 68275 | 68292 |
| 68240 | 68260 | 68276 | 68293* |
| 68242 | 68262 | 68278 | 68294 |
| 68244 | 68263 | 68279 | 68295 |
| 68245 | 68264 | 68280* | 68296 |
| 68246 | 68265 | 68281 | 68297 |

| 68298 | 68304* | 68308* | 683 |
| 68300 | 68305* | 68309* | 683 |
| 68301 | 68306* | 68312† | |
| 68303* | 68307* | 68313* | |

**Total**

## 0-6-0T   0F   Class

Introduced 1904. Reid N.B. d
with short wheelbase.
Weight: 38 tons 14 cwt
Pressure: 130 lb. Cyls.: (O) 15″ ×
Driving Wheels: 3′ 9″. T.E.: 12,15

| 68320 | 68329 | 68338 | 68? |
| 68321 | 68330 | 68339 | 68. |
| 68322 | 68331 | 68340 | 68? |
| 68323 | 68332 | 68341 | 68 |
| 68324 | 68333 | 68342 | 68. |
| 68325 | 68334 | 68343 | 68? |
| 68326 | 68335 | 68344 | 68. |
| 68327 | 68336 | 68345 | 68? |
| 68328 | 68337 | 68346 | |

**Tota**

## 0-6-0T   3F   Class

Introduced 1891. W. Worsdell design.
Weight: 46 tons 15 cwt.
Pressure: 160 lb.   Cyls.: 19″ ×
Driving Wheels: 4′ 7½″. T.E.: 21,3

| 68355 | 68358 | 68361 | 68? |
| 68356 | 68359 | 68362 | 68? |
| 68357 | 68360 | | |

**Tota**

*For full details of*
ELECTRIC AND DIESEL LOC
on the E., N.E. & Scottish Regio
*see the*
ABC OF B.R. LOCOMOTIV
Part II, Nos. 10000-39999

*For full details of*
CLASS "4MT" AND "2MT" 2-6
Nos. 43000-43161 & 46400-4652
on the E., N.E. & Scottish Regio
*see the*
ABC OF B.R. LOCOMOTIV
Part III, Nos. 40000-59999

Above : Class 6MT
4-6-2 No. 72004 *Clan Macdonald.*
[*J. Robertson*

Below : Class 7MT
4-6-2 No. 70025 *Western Star.*
[*J. E. Wilkinson*

Above : Class A3
4-6-2 No. 60098 *Spion Kop.*
[*J. Robertson*

Below : Class A4
4-6-2 No. 60015
*Quicksilver.*
[*J. R. Eagles*

Top left : Class J25 0-6-0 No. 65717. Top right : Class J21 0-6-0
No. 65089. Bottom left : Class J3 0-6-0 No. 64132. Bottom right :
Class J6 0-6-0 No. 64277.
[R. E. Vincent, J. F. Aylord (2), N. Fields

46

Top left: Class J26 0-6-0 No. 65749. Top right: Class J10 0-6-0 No. 65143.
Bottom left: Class J11/3 0-6-0 No. 64332. Bottom right: Class J36 0-6-0
No. 65216 Byng.
[H. C. Casserley, F. W. Day, P. Ransome-Wallis, J. F. Aylard

47

Top left: Class Y4 0-4-0T No. 68125. Top right: Class F6 2-4-2T
No. 67225. Bottom left: Class Z4 0-4-2T No. 68190. Bottom right:
Class F5 2-4-2T No. 67194.

[R. E. Vincent (3), H. C. Casseley

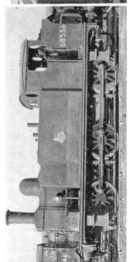

*Top left :* Class J67/I 0-6-0T No. 68594.
*Bottom left :* Class J69/I 0-6-0T No. 68556.

*Top right :* Class J68 0-6-0T No. 68664.
*Bottom right :* Class Y9 0-4-0ST No. 68098.

[*R. E. Vincent* (2), *P. H. Wells, J. Robertson*

49

Top left: Class J83 0-6-0T No. 68472. Top right: Class J94 0-6-0ST
No. 68044. Bottom left: Class G5 0-4-4T No. 67286. Bottom
right: Class J88 0-6-0T No. 68327.
[J. Robertson, Dr. G. D. Parkes, R. E. Vincent, R. S. Potts

50

Above : Class N1 0-6-2T No. 69481.
Below : Class N5/2 0-6-2T No. 69299.

[H. C. Casserley
[C. C. B. Herbert

Above : Class N2/3 0-6-2T No. 69567.
Below : Class N7/3 0-6-2T No. 69721.

[J. P. Wilson
[R. E. Vincent

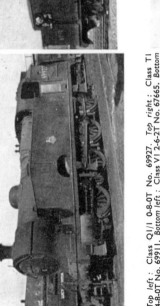

Top left: Class QI/I 0-8-0T No. 69927. Top right: Class TI
4-8-0T No. 69911. Bottom left: Class VI 2-6-2T No. 67665. Bottom
right: Class SI/I 0-8-4T No. 69900.

[D. R. A. Coan, H. C. Casserley (2), E. D. Briton

## 0-6-0T 2F Class J66

oduced 1886. J. Holden G.E. design·
ight: 40 tons 6 cwt.
ssure: 160 lb. Cyls.: 16½″ × 22″.
ving Wheels: 4′ 0″. T.E.: 16,970 lb.

| | | |
|---|---|---|
| 371 | 68374 | 68383 |

**Total 3**

(See also page 43)

## 0-6-0T 2F Class J77

oduced 1899. W. Worsdell N.E.
ebuild of Fletcher 0-4-4T originally
uilt 1874-84.
Darlington rebuilds with square-
:ornered cab roof (remainder York
ebuilds with rounded cab).
eight: 43 tons.
essure: 160 lb. Cyls.: 17″ × 22″.
iving Wheels: 4′ 1½″. T.E.: 17,560 lb.

| | | | |
|---|---|---|---|
| 391 | 68407 | 68422 | 68432* |
| 392* | 68408 | 68423 | 68434 |
| 393* | 68409 | 68424 | 68435 |
| 395* | 68410 | 68425 | 68436 |
| 397* | 68412* | 68426 | 68437 |
| 399 | 68413 | 68427 | 68438 |
| 401 | 68414 | 68428 | 68440* |
| 402 | 68417 | 68429 | |
| 405* | 68420* | 68430 | |
| 406 | 68421 | 68431 | |

**Total 37**

## 0-6-0T 2F Class J83

:roduced 1900. Holmes N.B. design.
Veight: 45 tons 5 cwt.
·essure: 150 lb. Cyls.: 17″ × 26″.
riving Wheels: 4′ 6″. T.E.: 17,745 lb.

| | | | |
|---|---|---|---|
| 3442 | 68452 | 68463 | 68473 |
| 3443 | 68453 | 68464 | 68474 |
| 3444 | 68454 | 68465 | 68475 |
| 3445 | 68455 | 68466 | 68476 |
| 3446 | 68456 | 68467 | 68477 |
| 3447 | 68457 | 68468 | 68478 |
| 3448 | 68458 | 68469 | 68479 |
| 3449 | 68459 | 68470 | 68480 |
| 3450 | 68460 | 68471 | 68481 |
| 3451 | 68461 | 68472 | |

**Total 39**

## 0-6-0T 2F Classes J67 & J69

J67/1* Introduced 1890. J. Holden
G.E. design with 160 lb. pressure.
J69/1† Introduced 1902. Development
of J67 with 180 lb. pressure, larger
tanks and larger firebox (some
rebuilt from J67).
J67/2‡ Introduced 1937. Rebuild of
J69 with 160 lb. boiler and small
firebox.
J69/2§ Introduced 1950. J67/1 rebuilt
with 180 lb. boiler and large firebox.

Weights: { 40 tons.*‡
{ 40 tons 9 cwt.†§
Pressure: { 160 lb.*‡
{ 180 lb.†§
Cyls.: 16½″ × 22″.
Driving Wheels: 4′ 0″.
T.E.: { 16,970 lb.*‡
{ 19,090 lb.†§

| | | | |
|---|---|---|---|
| 68490§ | 68521* | 68552† | 68585† |
| 68491† | 68522§ | 68553† | 68586* |
| 68492* | 68523* | 68554† | 68587† |
| 68493* | 68524† | 68555† | 68588* |
| 68494† | 68525† | 68556† | 68589* |
| 68495† | 68526† | 68557† | 68590* |
| 68496* | 68527† | 68558† | 68591† |
| 68497† | 68528† | 68559† | 68592* |
| 68498§ | 68529† | 68560† | 68593* |
| 68499† | 68530† | 68561† | 68594* |
| 68500† | 68531† | 68562† | 68595* |
| 68501† | 68532† | 68563† | 68596† |
| 68502† | 68533† | 68565† | 68597‡ |
| 68503† | 68534† | 68566† | 68598† |
| 68504† | 68535† | 68567† | 68599† |
| 68505† | 68536† | 68568† | 68600† |
| 68507† | 68537† | 68569† | 68601† |
| 68508† | 68538† | 68570† | 68602† |
| 68509† | 68540† | 68571† | 68603† |
| 68510§ | 68541† | 68572‡ | 68605† |
| 68511* | 68542† | 68573† | 68606* |
| 68512§ | 68543† | 68574† | 68607† |
| 68513§ | 68544† | 68575† | 68608* |
| 68514* | 68545† | 68576† | 68609† |
| 68515* | 68546† | 68577† | 68610‡ |
| 68516* | 68547† | 68578† | 68611† |
| 68517§ | 68548† | 68579† | 68612† |
| 68518* | 68549† | 68581† | 68613† |
| 68519§ | 68550† | 68583† | 68616* |
| 68520§ | 68551† | 68584* | 68617† |

53

## 68618-68834

| | | | |
|---|---|---|---|
| 68618† | 68625† | 68630† | 68635† |
| 68619† | 68626† | 68631† | 68636† |
| 68621† | 68628‡ | 68632† | |
| 68623† | 68629† | 68633† | |

Totals : Class J67/1   27
           Class J67/2   10
           Class J69/1   90
           Class J69/2   7

## 0-6-0T   3F   Class J68

Introduced 1912. Hill G.E. development of J69 with side-window cab.
Weight: 42 tons 9 cwt.
Pressure: 180 lb.    Cyls.: 16½″ × 22″.
Driving Wheels: 4′ 0″. T.E.: 19,090 lb.

| | | | |
|---|---|---|---|
| 68638 | 68646 | 68654 | 68662 |
| 68639 | 68647 | 68655 | 68663 |
| 68640 | 68648 | 68656 | 68664 |
| 68641 | 68649 | 68657 | 68665 |
| 68642 | 68650 | 68658 | 68666 |
| 68643 | 68651 | 68659 | |
| 68644 | 68652 | 68660 | |
| 68645 | 68653 | 68661 | |

Total 29

## 0-6-0T   2F   Class J72

Introduced 1898. W. Worsdell N.E. design.
* Altered cylinder dimensions.
Weight: 38 tons 12 cwt.
Pressure: 140 lb.   Cyls.: $\begin{cases} 17″ × 24″ \\ 18″ × 24″* \end{cases}$
Driving Wheels: 4′ 1¼″
T.E.: $\begin{cases} 16,760 \text{ lb.} \\ 18,790 \text{ lb.}* \end{cases}$

| | | | |
|---|---|---|---|
| 68670 | 68675 | 68680 | 68685* |
| 68671 | 68676 | 68681 | 68686 |
| 68672 | 68677 | 68682 | 68687 |
| 68673 | 68678 | 68683 | 68688 |
| 68674 | 68679 | 68684 | 68689 |

---

**IMPORTANT NOTE**

A careful reading of the notes on page 2 is essential to understand the use of reference marks in this book.

---

| | | | |
|---|---|---|---|
| 68690 | 68707 | 68723 | 68739 |
| 68691 | 68708 | 68724 | 68740 |
| 68692 | 68709 | 68725 | 68741 |
| 68693 | 68710 | 68726 | 68742 |
| 68694 | 68711 | 68727 | 68743 |
| 68695 | 68712 | 68728 | 68744 |
| 68696 | 68713 | 68729 | 68745 |
| 68697 | 68714 | 68730 | 68746 |
| 68698 | 68715 | 68731 | 68747 |
| 68699 | 68716 | 68732 | 68748 |
| 68700 | 68717 | 68733 | 68749 |
| 68701 | 68718 | 68734 | 68750 |
| 68702 | 68719 | 68735 | 68751 |
| 68703 | 68720 | 68736 | 68752 |
| 68704 | 68721 | 68737 | 68753 |
| 68705 | 68722 | 68738 | 68754 |
| 68706 | | | |

(Class continued with No. 69001)

## 0-6-0ST   3F   Class J52

J52/2 Introduced 1897. Ivatt standard G.N. saddletank with domed boiler.
J52/1* Introduced 1922. Rebuild of Stirling domeless saddletank (introduced 1892)—non-condensing.
J52/1† Introduced 1922. Condensing rebuild of Stirling locos.
‡ J52/2 with boiler pressure raised to 175 lb.
Weight: 51 tons 14 cwt.
Pressure: $\begin{cases} 170 \text{ lb.} \\ 175 \text{ lb.}‡ \end{cases}$ Cyls.: 18″ × 26″.
Driving Wheels: 4′ 8″. T.E.: $\begin{cases} 21,735 \text{ lb.} \\ 22,370 \text{ lb.} \end{cases}$

| | | | |
|---|---|---|---|
| 68757† | 68779* | 68799* | 68818 |
| 68758† | 68780* | 68800* | 68819 |
| 68759† | 68781† | 68802* | 68820 |
| 68760† | 68783* | 68803* | 68821 |
| 68761† | 68784† | 68804* | 68822 |
| 68764* | 68785* | 68805 | 68823 |
| 68765* | 68786* | 68806 | 68824 |
| 68768* | 68787* | 68807 | 68825 |
| 68769* | 68788† | 68808 | 68826 |
| 68770* | 68790* | 68809 | 68827 |
| 68771* | 68791† | 68810 | 68828 |
| 68772* | 68793† | 68811 | 68829 |
| 68773† | 68794† | 68812 | 68830 |
| 68774† | 68795† | 68813 | 68831 |
| 68776† | 68796† | 68814 | 68832 |
| 68777† | 68797* | 68815 | 68833 |
| 68778† | 68798* | 68817 | 68834 |

54

| | | | | | | | |
|---|---|---|---|---|---|---|---|
| 335 | 68850 | 68864 | 68878 | 68954† | 68964† | 68974† | 68984§ |
| 336 | 68851 | 68865 | 68879 | 68955† | 68965† | 68975† | 68985§ |
| 337 | 68852 | 68866 | 68880 | 68956† | 68966† | 68976† | 68986§ |
| 338 | 68853 | 68867 | 68881 | 68957† | 68967† | 68977† | 68987§ |
| 339 | 68854 | 68868 | 68882 | 68958† | 68968† | 68978§ | 68988§ |
| 340‡ | 68855 | 68869 | 68883 | 68959† | 68969† | 68979§ | 68989§ |
| 341 | 68856 | 68870 | 68884 | 68960† | 68970† | 68980§ | 68990§ |
| 342 | 68857 | 68871 | 68885 | 68961† | 68971† | 68981§ | 68991§ |
| 343 | 68858 | 68872 | 68886 | 68962† | 68972† | 68982§ | |
| 344 | 68859 | 68873 | 68887 | 68963† | 68973† | 68983§ | |
| 346 | 68860‡ | 68874 | 68888 | | | | |
| 347 | 68861 | 68875 | 68889 | | | | |
| 348 | 68862 | 68876‡ | | | | | |
| 349 | 68863 | 68877 | | | | | |

Totals : Class J52/1  39
Class J52/2  83

(See also page 43)

Totals : Class J50/1  10
Class J50/2  40
Class J50/3  38
Class J50/4  14

---

**6-0T**   **4F**   **Class J50**

J/2* Introduced 1922. Gresley G.N.
design (68900-19 rebuilt from smaller
J51, built 1915-22).
J/3† Introduced 1926. Post-grouping
development with detail differences.
J/1‡ Introduced 1929. Rebuilt from
smaller J51, built 1913-4.
J/4§ Introduced 1937. Development
of J50/3 with larger bunker.

Weights: $\begin{cases} 56 \text{ tons } 6 \text{ cwt.‡} \\ 58 \text{ tons } 3 \text{ cwt.†§} \\ 57 \text{ tons.*} \end{cases}$

Pressure: 175 lb.   Cyls.: 18½" × 26".
Driving Wheels: 4' 8".   T.E.: 23,635 lb.

| | | | |
|---|---|---|---|
| 890‡ | 68906* | 68922* | 68938* |
| 891‡ | 68907* | 68923* | 68939* |
| 892‡ | 68908* | 68924* | 68940† |
| 893‡ | 68909* | 68925* | 68941† |
| 894‡ | 68910* | 68926* | 68942† |
| 895‡ | 68911* | 68927* | 68943† |
| 896‡ | 68912* | 68928* | 68944† |
| 897‡ | 68913* | 68929* | 68945† |
| 898‡ | 68914* | 68930* | 68946† |
| 899‡ | 68915* | 68931* | 68947† |
| 900* | 68916* | 68932* | 68948† |
| 901* | 68917* | 68933* | 68949† |
| 902* | 68918* | 68934* | 68950† |
| 903* | 68919* | 68935* | 68951† |
| 904* | 68920* | 68936* | 68952† |
| 905* | 68921* | 68937* | 68953† |

---

**0-6-0T**   **2F**   **Class J72**
(Continued from 68754)

| | | | |
|---|---|---|---|
| 69001 | 69008 | 69015 | 69022 |
| 69002 | 69009 | 69016 | 69023 |
| 69003 | 69010 | 69017 | 69024 |
| 69004 | 69011 | 69018 | 69025 |
| 69005 | 69012 | 69019 | 69026 |
| 69006 | 69013 | 69020 | 69027 |
| 69007 | 69014 | 69021 | 69028 |

---

**2-6-4T**   **5F**   **Class L3**
Introduced 1914. Robinson G.C.
design.
Weight: 97 tons 9 cwt.
Pressure: 180 lb. Su.   Cyls.: 21" × 26".
Driving Wheels: 5' 1".   T.E.: 28,760 lb.

| | | | |
|---|---|---|---|
| 69050 | 69060 | 69065 | 69069 |
| 69052 | 69064 | | Total 6 |

---

**0-6-2T**   **3F**   **Class N10**
Introduced 1902. W. Worsdell N.E.
design.
Weight: 57 tons 14 cwt.
Pressure: 160 lb.   Cyls.: 18½" × 26".
Driving Wheels: 4' 7½".   T.E.: 21,905 lb.

| | | | |
|---|---|---|---|
| 69090 | 69095 | 69100 | 69106 |
| 69091 | 69096 | 69101 | 69107 |
| 69092 | 69097 | 69102 | 69108 |
| 69093 | 69098 | 69104 | 69109 |
| 69094 | 69099 | 69105 | |
| | | | Total 19 |

## 0-6-2T 3F Class N13

Introduced 1913. Stirling H. & B. design.
Pressure: 175 lb. Cyls.: 18" × 26".
Driving Wheels: 4' 6". T.E.: 23,205 lb.

| | | | |
|---|---|---|---|
| 69113 | 69115 | 69117 | 69119 |
| 69114 | 69116 | | |

Total 6

## 0-6-2T 4MT Class N14

Introduced 1909. Reid N.B. design.
Pressure: 175 lb. Cyls.: 18" × 26".
Driving Wheels: 4' 6". T.E.: 23,205 lb.

| | |
|---|---|
| 69120 | 69125 |

Total 2

## 0-6-2T 4MT Class N15

N15/2* Introduced 1910. Reid N.B. design developed from N14. Cowlairs incline banking locos.
N15/1 Introduced 1910. Development of N15/2 with smaller bunker for normal duties.
Weights: 62 tons 1 cwt.* / 60 tons 18 cwt.
Pressure: 175 lb. Cyls.: 18" × 26".
Driving Wheels: 4' 6". T.E.: 23,205 lb.

| | | | |
|---|---|---|---|
| 69126* | 69147 | 69168 | 69189 |
| 69127* | 69148 | 69169 | 69190 |
| 69128* | 69149 | 69170 | 69191 |
| 69129* | 69150 | 69171 | 69192 |
| 69130* | 69151 | 69172 | 69193 |
| 69131* | 69152 | 69173 | 69194 |
| 69132 | 69153 | 69174 | 69195 |
| 69133 | 69154 | 69175 | 69196 |
| 69134 | 69155 | 69176 | 69197 |
| 69135 | 69156 | 69177 | 69198 |
| 69136 | 69157 | 69178 | 69199 |
| 69137 | 69158 | 69179 | 69200 |
| 69138 | 69159 | 69180 | 69201 |
| 69139 | 69160 | 69181 | 69202 |
| 69140 | 69161 | 69182 | 69203 |
| 69141 | 69162 | 69183 | 69204 |
| 69142 | 69163 | 69184 | 69205 |
| 69143 | 69164 | 69185 | 69206 |
| 69144 | 69165 | 69186 | 69207 |
| 69145 | 69166 | 69187 | 69208 |
| 69146 | 69167 | 69188 | 69209 |
| 69210 | 69214 | 69218 | 6922 |
| 69211 | 69215 | 69219 | 6922 |
| 69212 | 69216 | 69220 | 6922 |
| 69213 | 69217 | 69221 | |

Totals : Class N15/1
Class N15/2

## 0-6-2T 2MT Class N4

N4/2 Introduced 1889. Parker M & L. design.
(N4/1 was N4/2 with longer chimne(y))
Weights: 61 tons 10 cwt.
Pressure: 160 lb. Cyls.: 18" × 2(6")
Driving Wheels: 5' 1". T.E.: 18,780
Joy gear.

| | | | |
|---|---|---|---|
| 69225 | 69230 | 69233 | 6923 |
| 69227 | 69231 | 69235 | |
| 69228 | 69232 | 69236 | |

Total :

## 0-6-2T 2MT Class N5

N5/2 Introduced 1891. Parker M & L. design developed from N4.
Weight: 62 tons 7 cwt.
Pressure: 160 lb. Cyls.: 18" × 2(6")
Driving Wheels: 5' 1". T.E.: 18,780

| | | | |
|---|---|---|---|
| 69250 | 69270 | 69288 | 6930 |
| 69253 | 69271 | 69289 | 6930 |
| 69254 | 69272 | 69290 | 6930 |
| 69255 | 69273 | 69291 | 6930 |
| 69256 | 69274 | 69292 | 6931 |
| 69257 | 69275 | 69293 | 6931 |
| 69258 | 69276 | 69294 | 6931 |
| 69259 | 69277 | 69295 | 6931 |
| 69260 | 69278 | 69296 | 6931 |
| 69261 | 69279 | 69297 | 6931 |
| 69262 | 69280 | 69298 | 6931 |
| 69263 | 69281 | 69299 | 6931 |
| 69264 | 69282 | 69300 | 6931 |
| 69265 | 69283 | 69301 | 6932 |
| 69266 | 69284 | 69302 | 6932 |
| 69267 | 69285 | 69303 | 6932 |
| 69268 | 69286 | 69304 | 6932 |
| 69269 | 69287 | 69305 | 6932 |

| | | | |
|---|---|---|---|
| 9325 | 69337 | 69349 | 69361 |
| 9326 | 69338 | 69350 | 69362 |
| 9327 | 69339 | 69351 | 69363 |
| 9328 | 69340 | 69352 | 69364 |
| 9329 | 69341 | 69353 | 69365 |
| 9330 | 69342 | 69354 | 69366 |
| 9331 | 69343 | 69355 | 69367 |
| 9332 | 69344 | 69356 | 69368 |
| 9333 | 69345 | 69357 | 69369 |
| 9334 | 69346 | 69358 | 69370 |
| 9335 | 69347 | 69359 | |
| 9336 | 69348 | 69360 | |

**Totals : Class N5/2 118**

---

## -6-2T 2MT Class N8

ntroduced 1886. T. W. Worsdell
N.E. design, saturated, with Joy's gear
and slide valves (majority rebuilt
from compounds).
Rebuilt with superheater, Stephenson
gear and piston valves, 24″ piston
stroke.
As † but with 26″ stroke.
Rebuilt with Stephenson gear and
piston valves, superheater removed,
24″ stroke.
As § but with 26″ piston stroke.
Weights: $\begin{cases} 56 \text{ tons } 5 \text{ cwt.}*§¶ \\ 58 \text{ tons } 14 \text{ cwt.}†‡ \end{cases}$
Pressure: 160 lb. SS.
Cyls.: $\begin{cases} 18″ \times 24″.* \\ 19″ \times 24″.†§ \\ 19″ \times 26″.‡¶ \end{cases}$
Driving Wheels: 5′ 1¼″.
T.E.: $\begin{cases} 17,265 \text{ lb.}* \\ 19,235 \text{ lb.}†§ \\ 20,840 \text{ lb.}‡¶ \end{cases}$

| | | | |
|---|---|---|---|
| 9377† | 69381¶ | 69386‡ | 69392* |
| 9378§ | 69385¶ | 69390† | 69394† |

**Total 8**

---

## -6-2T 3MT Class N9

troduced 1893. T. W. Worsdell N E.
design.
Weight: 56 tons 10 cwt.
Pressure: 160 lb.    Cyls.: 19″ × 26′.
Driving Wheels: 5′ 1¼″.   T.E.: 20,840 lb.

| | | |
|---|---|---|
| 424 | 69427 | 69429 |

**Total 3**

---

## 0-6-2T 2MT Class N1

* Introduced 1907. Ivatt G.N. design, prototype of class.
†‡§¶ Introduced 1907. Standard design with shorter tanks and detail differences.
§¶ Rebuilt with superheater and reduced pressure.
‡¶ Fitted with condensing gear.
Weights: $\begin{cases} 64 \text{ tons } 14 \text{ cwt.}* \\ 65 \text{ tons } 17 \text{ cwt.} \end{cases}$
Pressure: $\begin{cases} 175 \text{ lb.} \\ 170 \text{ lb. Su.}§¶ \end{cases}$
Cyls.: 18″ × 16″.
Driving Wheels: 5′ 8″.
T.E.: $\begin{cases} 18,430 \text{ lb.} \\ 17,900 \text{ lb. Su.}§¶ \end{cases}$

| | | | |
|---|---|---|---|
| 69430* | 69444† | 69458† | 69471‡ |
| 69431‡ | 69445† | 69459† | 69472§ |
| 69432‡ | 69446† | 69460† | 69474‡ |
| 69433‡ | 69447† | 69461† | 69475‡ |
| 69434‡ | 69449† | 69462† | 69476‡ |
| 69435¶ | 69450‡ | 69463† | 69477‡ |
| 69436§ | 69451† | 69464¶ | 69478¶ |
| 69437‡ | 69452§ | 69465‡ | 69481‡ |
| 69439¶ | 69453‡ | 69466‡ | 69482¶ |
| 69440† | 69454† | 69467‡ | 69483§ |
| 69441‡ | 69455† | 69468‡ | 69484‡ |
| 69442‡ | 69456‡ | 69469‡ | 69485‡ |
| 69443† | 69457‡ | 69470‡ | |

**Total 51**

---

For full details of
ELECTRIC AND DIESEL LOCOS
on the E., N.E. & Scottish Regions
see the
ABC OF B.R. LOCOMOTIVES
Part II, Nos. 10000–39999

For full details of
CLASS "4MT" AND "2MT" 2-6-0s
Nos. 43000–43161 & 46400–46527
on the E., N.E. & Scottish Regions
see the
ABC OF B.R. LOCOMOTIVES
Part III, Nos. 40000–59999

## 0-6-2T 3MT Class N2

**N2/1*** Introduced 1925. Post-grouping development of Gresley G.N. N2/1, introduced 1920, which class is now included in N2/2. Condensing gear and small chimney.

**N2/2†** Condensing gear removed.

**N2/3‡** Introduced 1925. Locos built non-condensing, originally fitted with large chimney. Some now with small chimney.

**N2/4§** Introduced 1928. Development of N2/2, slightly heavier. Condensing gear and small chimney.
(The small chimneys are to suit the Metropolitan loading gauge, for working to Moorgate St. Condensing gear has been removed from or added to certain locos transferred from or to the London area.)

Weights: { 70 tons 5 cwt.*†
{ 70 tons 8 cwt.‡
{ 71 tons 9 cwt.§

Pressure: 170 lb. Su. Cyls.: 19″ × 26″. Driving Wheels: 5′ 8″. T.E.: 19,945 lb. P.V.

| | | | |
|---|---|---|---|
| 69490* | 69515† | 69540* | 69565‡ |
| 69491* | 69516† | 69541* | 69566‡ |
| 69492* | 69517* | 69542* | 69567‡ |
| 69493* | 69518† | 69543* | 69568§ |
| 69494* | 69519* | 69544* | 69569§ |
| 69495* | 69520* | 69545* | 69570§ |
| 69496* | 69521* | 69546* | 69571§ |
| 69497* | 69522* | 69547* | 69572§ |
| 69498* | 69523* | 69548* | 69573§ |
| 69499* | 69524* | 69549* | 69574§ |
| 69500† | 69525† | 69550† | 69575§ |
| 69501† | 69526* | 69551† | 69576§ |
| 69502† | 69527* | 69552† | 69577§ |
| 69503† | 69528* | 69553† | 69578§ |
| 69504† | 69529* | 69554† | 69579§ |
| 69505† | 69530* | 69555† | 69580§ |
| 69506* | 69531* | 69556§ | 69581§ |
| 69507† | 69532* | 69557† | 69582§ |
| 69508† | 69533* | 69558† | 69583§ |
| 69509† | 69534* | 69559† | 69584§ |
| 69510† | 69535* | 69560† | 69585§ |
| 69511† | 69536* | 69561† | 69586§ |
| 69512* | 69537* | 69562† | 69587§ |
| 69513* | 69538* | 69563‡ | 69588§ |
| 69514† | 69539* | 69564‡ | 69589§ |

| | | | |
|---|---|---|---|
| 69590§ | 69592§ | 69594‡ | 695 |
| 69591§ | 69593§ | 69595‡ | |

**Totals : Class N2/2**
**Class N2/3**
**Class N2/4**

## 0-6-2T 3MT Class N7

**N7/1¹** Introduced 1925. Post-grouping development of Hill G.E. design with detail differences.

**N7/2²** Introduced 1926. Development of N7/1 with long-travel valves.

**N7/3³** Introduced 1927. Doncaster built version of N7/2 with round-topped boiler.

**N7/4⁴** Introduced 1940. Pre-grouping N7 (G.E.) rebuilt with round-topped boiler, retaining short-travel valves.

**N7/5⁵** Introduced 1943. N7/1 rebuilt with round-topped boiler, retaining short-travel valves.

**N7/3⁶** Introduced 1943. N7/2 rebuilt with round-topped boiler.

Weights: { 63 tons 13 cwt.¹
{ 64 tons 17 cwt.²
{ 64 tons.³
{ 61 tons 16 cwt.⁴
{ 64 tons.⁵
{ 64 tons.⁶

Pressure: 180 lb. Su. Cyls.: 18″ × 2
Driving Wheels: 4′ 10″. T.E.: 20,515
Walschaerts gear, P.V.

| | | | |
|---|---|---|---|
| 69600⁴ | 69618⁴ | 69636⁵ | 696 |
| 69601⁴ | 69619⁴ | 69637¹ | 696 |
| 69602⁴ | 69620⁴ | 69638⁵ | 696 |
| 69603³ | 69621⁴ | 69639⁵ | 696 |
| 69604⁴ | 69622⁵ | 69640⁵ | 696 |
| 69605⁴ | 69623⁵ | 69641⁵ | 696 |
| 69606⁴ | 69624¹ | 69642⁵ | 696 |
| 69607⁴ | 69625⁵ | 69643⁵ | 696 |
| 69608⁴ | 69626¹ | 69644⁵ | 696 |
| 69609⁴ | 69627¹ | 69645¹ | 696 |
| 69610⁴ | 69628⁵ | 69646¹ | 696 |
| 69611⁴ | 69629¹ | 69647⁵ | 696 |
| 69612⁴ | 69630⁵ | 69648⁵ | 696 |
| 69613⁴ | 69631¹ | 69649⁵ | 696 |
| 69614⁴ | 69632⁵ | 69650⁵ | 696 |
| 69615⁴ | 69633⁵ | 69651⁵ | 696 |
| 69616⁴ | 69634⁵ | 69652⁵ | 6967 |
| 69617⁴ | 69635⁵ | 69653⁵ | 6967 |

| | | | |
|---|---|---|---|
| 672[6] | 69688[6] | 69704[3] | 69720[3] |
| 673[6] | 69689[2] | 69705[3] | 69721[3] |
| 674[6] | 69690[2] | 69706[3] | 69722[3] |
| 675[6] | 69691[6] | 69707[3] | 69723[3] |
| 676[6] | 69692[6] | 69708[3] | 69724[3] |
| 677[6] | 69693[6] | 69709[3] | 69725[3] |
| 678[6] | 69694[2] | 69710[3] | 69726[3] |
| 679[6] | 69695[2] | 69711[3] | 69727[3] |
| 680[6] | 69696[6] | 69712[3] | 69728[3] |
| 681[6] | 69697[6] | 69713[3] | 69729[3] |
| 682[6] | 69698[6] | 69714[3] | 69730[3] |
| 683[2] | 69699[6] | 69715[3] | 69731[3] |
| 684[6] | 69700[6] | 69716[3] | 69732[3] |
| 685[6] | 69701[6] | 69717[3] | 69733[3] |
| 686[6] | 69702[3] | 69718[3] | |
| 687[6] | 69703[3] | 69719[3] | |

Totals :  Class N7/1    9
          Class N7/2    5
          Class N7/3   57
          Class N7/4   22
          Class N7/5   41

---

## -6-2T    3F    Class A7

troduced 1910. Raven N.E. design,
later rebuilt with superheater and
reduced pressure.
Saturated.
eight: 87 tons 10 cwt.
essure: { 160 lb. Su.
        { 180 lb.*
yls.: (3) $16\frac{1}{2}''$ × 26″.
riving Wheels: 4' 7¼″.
E.: { 26,140 lb.
   { 29,405 lb.*
V.

| | | | |
|---|---|---|---|
| 9770 | 69776 | 69782 | 69787* |
| 9771 | 69778* | 69783 | 69788 |
| 9772 | 69779 | 69784 | |
| 9773 | 69780 | 69785 | |
| 9774 | 69781 | 69786 | |

Total 17

---

### IMPORTANT NOTE

A careful reading of the notes
on page 2 is essential to
underst and the use of
reference marks in this book.

---

## 4-6-2T    3P    Class A5

A5/1 Introduced 1911. Robinson G.C.
design.
A5/2* Introduced 1925. Post-grouping
development of A5/1 with reduced
boiler mountings and detail differ-
ences.
Weights: { 85 tons 18 cwt.
        { 90 tons 11 cwt.*
Pressure: 180 lb. Su. Cyls.: 20″ × 26″.
Driving Wheels: 5' 7″. T.E.: 23,750 lb.
P.V.

| | | | |
|---|---|---|---|
| 69800 | 69811 | 69822 | 69833* |
| 69801 | 69812 | 69823 | 69834* |
| 69802 | 69813 | 69824 | 69835* |
| 69803 | 69814 | 69825 | 69836* |
| 69804 | 69815 | 69826 | 69837* |
| 69805 | 69816 | 69827 | 69838* |
| 69806 | 69817 | 69828 | 69839* |
| 69807 | 69818 | 69829 | 69840* |
| 69808 | 69819 | 69830* | 69841* |
| 69809 | 69820 | 69831* | 69842* |
| 69810 | 69821 | 69832* | |

Totals :  Class A5/1   30
          Class A5/2   13

---

## 4-6-2T    3P    Class A8

Introduced 1931. Gresley rebuild of
Raven Class " D " 4-4-4T (intro-
duced 1913).
Weight: 86 tons 18 cwt.
Pressure: 175 lb. Su.
Cyls.: (3) $16\frac{1}{2}''$ × 26″.
Driving Wheels: 5' 9″. T.E.: 22,940 lb.
P.V.

| | | | |
|---|---|---|---|
| 69850 | 69862 | 69874 | 69885 |
| 69851 | 69863 | 69875 | 69886 |
| 69852 | 69864 | 69876 | 69887 |
| 69853 | 69865 | 69877 | 69888 |
| 69854 | 69866 | 69878 | 69889 |
| 69855 | 69867 | 69879 | 69890 |
| 69856 | 69868 | 69880 | 69891 |
| 69857 | 69869 | 69881 | 69892 |
| 69858 | 69870 | 69882 | 69893 |
| 69859 | 69871 | 69883 | 69894 |
| 69860 | 69872 | 69884 | |
| 69861 | 69873 | | |

Total 45

## 0-8-4T  7F  Class S1

S1/1* Introduced 1907. Robinson G.C. design, since rebuilt with superheater.

S1/2† Introduced 1932. S1/1 rebuilt with booster and superheater, booster since removed.

S1/3‡ Introduced 1932. New locos built with booster, booster later removed.

Weights: { 99 tons 6 cwt.*
{ 99 tons 2 cwt.†
{ 99 tons 1 cwt.‡

Pressure: 180 lb. Su.
Cyls.: (3) 18″ × 26″.
Driving Wheels: 4′ 8″. T.E.: 34,525 lb.

| | | | |
|---|---|---|---|
| 69900* | 69902* | 69904‡ | 69905‡ |
| 69901† | 69903* | | |

Totals : Class S1/1  3
Class S1/2  1
Class S1/3  2

## 4-8-0T  5F  Class T1

Introduced 1909. W. Worsdell N.E. design.
* Rebuilt with superheater.
Weight: 85 tons 8 cwt.
Pressure: 175 lb. SS.
Cyls.: (3) 18″ × 26″.
Driving Wheels: 4′ 7¼″. T.E.: 34,080 lb. P.V.

| | | | |
|---|---|---|---|
| 69910 | 69912 | 69914* | 69916 |
| 69911 | 69913 | 69915 | 69917 |

| | | | |
|---|---|---|---|
| 69918 | 69920 | 69921 | 69922 |
| 69919 | | | Total 1 |

## 0-8-0T  5F  Class Q1

Thompson rebuild of Robinson G.C. Q4 0-8-0, introduced 1902.

Q1/1* Introduced 1942. 1,500 gallon tanks.

Q1/2 Introduced 1943. 2,000 gallon tanks.

Weights: { 69 tons 18 cwt.*
{ 73 tons 13 cwt.

Pressure: 180 lb. Cyls.: (O) 19″ × 26″.
Driving Wheels: 4′ 8″. T.E.: 25,645 lb.

| | | | |
|---|---|---|---|
| 69925* | 69929 | 69932 | 69935 |
| 69926* | 69930 | 69933 | 69936 |
| 69927* | 69931 | 69934 | 69937 |
| 69928* | | | |

Total 1

## 2-8-8-2T  Unclass  Class U1
### (Beyer-Garratt loco)

Introduced 1925 Gresley/Beyer Peacock design.
Weight: 178 tons 1 cwt.
Pressure: 180 lb. Su.
Cyls.: (6) 18½″ × 26″.
Driving Wheels: 4′ 8″. T.E.: 72,940 lb.
Walschaerts gear, derived motion. P.V.

69999  Total 1

# BRITISH RAILWAYS STANDARD LOCOMOTIVES
### Railway Executive member for Mechanical Engineering :
### R. A. RIDDLES, C.B.E.

## 4-6-2  Class 7MT

Introduced 1951. Designed at Derby.
Weights: Loco.  94 tons 0 cwt.
Tender  47 tons 4 cwt.
Pressure: 250 lb.
Cyls.: (O) 20″ × 28″.
Driving Wheels: 6′ 2″. T.E.: 32,150 lb.
Walschaerts gear.  P.V.

| | |
|---|---|
| 70000 | Britannia |
| 70001 | Lord Hurcomb |
| 70002 | Geoffrey Chaucer |
| 70003 | John Bunyan |
| 70004 | William Shakespeare |
| 70005 | John Milton |
| 70006 | Robert Burns |
| 70007 | Coeur-de-Lion |
| 70008 | Black Prince |
| 70009 | Alfred the Great |
| 70010 | Owen Glendower |
| 70011 | Hotspur |
| 70012 | John of Gaunt |
| 70013 | Oliver Cromwell |
| 70014 | Iron Duke |
| 70015 | Apollo |
| 70016 | Ariel |
| 70017 | Arrow |
| 70018 | Flying Dutchman |
| 70019 | Lightning |
| 70020 | Mercury |
| 70021 | Morning Star |
| 70022 | Tornado |

| | |
|---|---|
| )23 | Venus |
| )24 | Vulcan |
| )25 | Western Star |
| )26 | Polar Star |
| )27 | Rising Star |
| )28 | Royal Star |
| )29 | Shooting Star |
| 030 | William Wordsworth |
| 031 | Byron |
| 032 | Tennyson |
| 033 | Charles Dickens |
| 034 | Thomas Hardy |
| 035 | Rudyard Kipling |
| 036 | Boadicea |
| 037 | Hereward the Wake |
| 038 | Robin Hood |
| 039 | Sir Christopher Wren |
| 040 | Clive of India |
| 041 | Sir John Moore |
| 042 | Lord Roberts |
| 043 | Earl Kitchener |
| 044 | Earl Haig |
| 045 | |
| 046 | |
| 047 | |
| 048 | |
| 049 | |
| 050 | |
| 051 | |
| 052 | |
| 053 | |
| 054 | |

gines of this class are still being
delivered. The names of Nos.
70043/4 are provisional and
subject to variation.

### 6-2      Class 6MT

roduced 1952. Designed at Derby.
eights: Loco. 86 tons 19 cwt.
        Tender 47 tons 4 cwt.
essure: 225 lb.
ls.: (O) 19½″ × 28″.
iving Wheels: 6′ 2″. T.E.: 27,520 lb.
alschaerts gear. P.V.

| | |
|---|---|
| ,000 | Clan Buchanan |
| 001 | Clan Cameron |
| 002 | Clan Campbell |
| 003 | Clan Fraser |
| 004 | Clan Macdonald |

| | |
|---|---|
| 72005 | Clan Macgregor |
| 72006 | Clan Mackenzie |
| 72007 | Clan Mackintosh |
| 72008 | Clan Macleod |
| 72009 | Clan Stewart |

**Total 10**

### 4-6-0      Class 5MT

Introduced 1951. Designed at Doncaster.
Weights: Loco. 76 tons 4 cwt.
        Tender 47 tons 4 cwt.
Pressure: 225 lb.
Cyls.: (O) 19″ × 28″. T.E.: 26,120 lb.
Driving Wheels: 6′ 2″.   P.V.
Walschaerts gear.   P.V.

| | | | |
|---|---|---|---|
| 73000 | 73019 | 73038 | 73057 |
| 73001 | 73020 | 73039 | 73058 |
| 73002 | 73021 | 73040 | 73059 |
| 73003 | 73022 | 73041 | 73060 |
| 73004 | 73023 | 73042 | 73061 |
| 73005 | 73024 | 73043 | 73062 |
| 73006 | 73025 | 73044 | 73063 |
| 73007 | 73026 | 73045 | 73064 |
| 73008 | 73027 | 73046 | 73065 |
| 73009 | 73028 | 73047 | 73066 |
| 73010 | 73029 | 73048 | 73067 |
| 73011 | 73030 | 73049 | 73068 |
| 73012 | 73031 | 73050 | 73069 |
| 73013 | 73032 | 73051 | 73070 |
| 73014 | 73033 | 73052 | 73071 |
| 73015 | 73034 | 73053 | 73072 |
| 73016 | 73035 | 73054 | 73073 |
| 73017 | 73036 | 73055 | 73074 |
| 73018 | 73037 | 73056 | |

Engines of this class are still being
delivered.

### 4-6-0      Class 4MT

Introduced 1951. Designed at Brighton.
Weights: Loco. 69 tons 0 cwt.
        Tender 43 tons 3 cwt.
Pressure: 225 lb.
Cyls.: (O) 18″ × 28″.
Driving Wheels: 5′ 8″. T.E.: 25,100 !b.
Walschaerts gear.   P.V.

| | | | |
|---|---|---|---|
| 75000 | 75005 | 75010 | 75015 |
| 75001 | 75006 | 75011 | 75016 |
| 75002 | 75007 | 75012 | 75017 |
| 75003 | 75008 | 75013 | 75018 |
| 75004 | 75009 | 75014 | 75019 |

| | | | |
|---|---|---|---|
| 75020 | 75035 | 75050 | 75065 |
| 75021 | 75036 | 75051 | 75066 |
| 75022 | 75037 | 75052 | 75067 |
| 75023 | 75038 | 75053 | 75068 |
| 75024 | 75039 | 75054 | 75069 |
| 75025 | 75040 | 75055 | 75070 |
| 75026 | 75041 | 75056 | 75071 |
| 75027 | 75042 | 75057 | 75072 |
| 75028 | 75043 | 75058 | 75073 |
| 75029 | 75044 | 75059 | 75074 |
| 75030 | 75045 | 75060 | 75075 |
| 75031 | 75046 | 75061 | 75076 |
| 75032 | 75047 | 75062 | 75077 |
| 75033 | 75048 | 75063 | 75078 |
| 75034 | 75049 | 75064 | 75079 |

**Engines of this class are still being delivered.**

## 2-6-0     Class 4MT

Introduced 1953. Designed at Doncaster
Weights: Loco 59 tons 2 cwt.
      Tender 42 tons 3 cwt.
Pressure: 225 lb.
Cyls.: (O) $17\frac{1}{2}'' \times 26''$
Driving Wheels: 5′ 3″ T.E.: 24,170 lb.
Walschaerts gear. P.V.

| | | | |
|---|---|---|---|
| 76000 | 76012 | 76024 | 76036 |
| 76001 | 76013 | 76025 | 76037 |
| 76002 | 76014 | 76026 | 76038 |
| 76003 | 76015 | 76027 | 76039 |
| 76004 | 76016 | 76028 | 76040 |
| 76005 | 76017 | 76029 | 76041 |
| 76006 | 76018 | 76030 | 76042 |
| 76007 | 76019 | 76031 | 76043 |
| 76008 | 76020 | 76032 | 76044 |
| 76009 | 76021 | 76033 | |
| 76010 | 76022 | 76034 | |
| 76011 | 76023 | 76035 | |

**Engines of this class are still being delivered.**

## 2-6-0     Class 3MT

To be introduced 1953.
Weights: Loco.
      Tender
Pressure:
Cyls.: (O)
Driving Wheels:     T.E.:
Walschaerts gear. P.V.

| | | | |
|---|---|---|---|
| 77000 | 77003 | 77006 | 77009 |
| 77001 | 77004 | 77007 | 77010 |
| 77002 | 77005 | 77008 | 77011 |

| | | | |
|---|---|---|---|
| 77012 | 77014 | 77016 | 770 |
| 77013 | 77015 | 77017 | 770 |

## 2-6-0     Class 2M

Introduced 1953. Designed at Derb
Weights: Loco 49 tons 5 cwt.
      Tender 36 tons 17 cwt.
Pressure: 200 lb.
Cyls.: (O) $16\frac{1}{2}'' \times 24''$
Driving Wheels: 5′ 0″ T.E.: 15,515
Walschaerts gear. P.V.

| | | | |
|---|---|---|---|
| 78000 | 78012 | 78024 | 780. |
| 78001 | 78013 | 78025 | 7802 |
| 78002 | 78014 | 78026 | 7803 |
| 78003 | 78015 | 78027 | 7803 |
| 78004 | 78016 | 78028 | 780 |
| 78005 | 78017 | 78029 | 7 |
| 78006 | 78018 | 78030 | 780 |
| 78007 | 78019 | 78031 | 780 |
| 78008 | 78020 | 78032 | 780 |
| 78009 | 78021 | 78033 | |
| 78010 | 78022 | 78034 | |
| 78011 | 78023 | 78035 | |

**Engines of this class are still be delivered.**

## 2-6-4T     Class 4M

Introduced 1951. Designed at Bright
Weight: 88 tons 10 cwt.
Pressure: 225 lb.
Cyls.: (O) $18'' \times 28''$
Driving Wheels: 5′ 8″. T.E.: 25,100
Walschaerts gear. P.V.

| | | | |
|---|---|---|---|
| 80000 | 80019 | 80038 | 8005 |
| 80001 | 80020 | 80039 | 8005 |
| 80002 | 80021 | 80040 | 8005 |
| 80003 | 80022 | 80041 | 8006 |
| 80004 | 80023 | 80042 | 8006 |
| 80005 | 80024 | 80043 | 8006 |
| 80006 | 80025 | 80044 | 8006 |
| 80007 | 80026 | 80045 | 8006 |
| 80008 | 80027 | 80046 | 8006 |
| 80009 | 80028 | 80047 | 8006 |
| 80010 | 80029 | 80048 | 8006 |
| 80011 | 80030 | 80049 | 8006 |
| 80012 | 80031 | 80050 | 8007 |
| 80013 | 80032 | 80051 | 8007 |
| 80014 | 80033 | 80052 | 8007 |
| 80015 | 80034 | 80053 | 8007 |
| 80016 | 80035 | 80054 | 8007 |
| 80017 | 80036 | 80055 | 8007 |
| 80018 | 80037 | 80056 | 8007 |

| 80076 | 80086 | 80096 | 80106 |
|-------|-------|-------|-------|
| 80077 | 80087 | 80097 | 80107 |
| 80078 | 80088 | 80098 | 80108 |
| 80079 | 80089 | 80099 | 80109 |
| 80080 | 80090 | 80100 | 80110 |
| 80081 | 80091 | 80101 | 80111 |
| 80082 | 80092 | 80102 | 80112 |
| 80083 | 80093 | 80103 | 80113 |
| 80084 | 80094 | 80104 | 80114 |
| 80085 | 80095 | 80105 | 80115 |

gines of this class are still being delivered.

---

## 6-2T    Class 3MT

roduced 1952. Designed at Swindon.
eight: 73 tons 10 cwt.
essure: 200 lb.
ls.: (O) 17½" × 26".
iving Wheels: 5' 3". T.E.: 21,490 lb.
alschaerts gear. P.V.

| 82000 | 82012 | 82024 | 82036 |
|-------|-------|-------|-------|
| 82001 | 82013 | 82025 | 82037 |
| 82002 | 82014 | 82026 | 82038 |
| 82003 | 82015 | 82027 | 82039 |
| 82004 | 82016 | 82028 | 82040 |
| 82005 | 82017 | 82029 | 82041 |
| 82006 | 82018 | 82030 | 82042 |
| 82007 | 82019 | 82031 | 82043 |
| 82008 | 82020 | 82032 | 82044 |
| 82009 | 82021 | 82033 |       |
| 82010 | 82022 | 82034 |       |
| 82011 | 82023 | 82035 |       |

gines of this class are still being delivered.

---

## 6-2T    Class 2MT

be introduced 1953.
eights: Loco.
        Tender
essure:
ls.: (O)
iving Wheels:     T.E.:
alschaerts gear. P.V.

| 84000 | 84008 | 84016 | 84024 |
|-------|-------|-------|-------|
| 84001 | 84009 | 84017 | 84025 |
| 84002 | 84010 | 84018 | 84026 |
| 84003 | 84011 | 84019 | 84027 |
| 84004 | 84012 | 84020 | 84028 |
| 84005 | 84013 | 84021 | 84029 |
| 84006 | 84014 | 84022 |       |
| 84007 | 84015 | 84023 |       |

## 2-8-0    8F    Class WD

Ministry of Supply "Austerity" 2-8-0 locomotives purchased by British Railways, 1948.
Introduced 1943. Riddles M.o.S. design.
Weights: Loco.    70 tons 5 cwt.
           Tender 55 tons 10 cwt.
Pressure: 225 lb. Cyls.: (O) 19" × 28".
Driving Wheels: 4' 8½". T.E.: 34,215 lb.
Walschaerts gear.   P.V.

| 90000 | 90039 | 90078 | 90117 |
|-------|-------|-------|-------|
| 90001 | 90040 | 90079 | 90118 |
| 90002 | 90041 | 90080 | 90119 |
| 90003 | 90042 | 90081 | 90120 |
| 90004 | 90043 | 90082 | 90121 |
| 90005 | 90044 | 90083 | 90122 |
| 90006 | 90045 | 90084 | 90123 |
| 90007 | 90046 | 90085 | 90124 |
| 90008 | 90047 | 90086 | 90125 |
| 90009 | 90048 | 90087 | 90126 |
| 90010 | 90049 | 90088 | 90127 |
| 90011 | 90050 | 90089 | 90128 |
| 90012 | 90051 | 90090 | 90129 |
| 90013 | 90052 | 90091 | 90130 |
| 90014 | 90053 | 90092 | 90131 |
| 90015 | 90054 | 90093 | 90132 |
| 90016 | 90055 | 90094 | 90133 |
| 90017 | 90056 | 90095 | 90134 |
| 90018 | 90057 | 90096 | 90135 |
| 90019 | 90058 | 90097 | 90136 |
| 90020 | 90059 | 90098 | 90137 |
| 90021 | 90060 | 90099 | 90138 |
| 90022 | 90061 | 90100 | 90139 |
| 90023 | 90062 | 90101 | 90140 |
| 90024 | 90063 | 90102 | 90141 |
| 90025 | 90064 | 90103 | 90142 |
| 90026 | 90065 | 90104 | 90143 |
| 90027 | 90066 | 90105 | 90144 |
| 90028 | 90067 | 90106 | 90145 |
| 90029 | 90068 | 90107 | 90146 |
| 90030 | 90069 | 90108 | 90147 |
| 90031 | 90070 | 90109 | 90148 |
| 90032 | 90071 | 90110 | 90149 |
| 90033 | 90072 | 90111 | 90150 |
| 90034 | 90073 | 90112 | 90151 |
| 90035 | 90074 | 90113 | 90152 |
| 90036 | 90075 | 90114 | 90153 |
| 90037 | 90076 | 90115 | 90154 |
| 90038 | 90077 | 90116 | 90155 |

| | | | | | | | |
|---|---|---|---|---|---|---|---|
| 90156 | 90204 | 90252 | 90300 | 90348 | 90396 | 90444 | 9049 |
| 90157 | 90205 | 90253 | 90301 | 90349 | 90397 | 90445 | 9049. |
| 90158 | 90206 | 90254 | 90302 | 90350 | 90398 | 90446 | 9049- |
| 90159 | 90207 | 90255 | 90303 | 90351 | 90399 | 90447 | 9049! |
| 90160 | 90208 | 90256 | 90304 | 90352 | 90400 | 90448 | 9049( |
| 90161 | 90209 | 90257 | 90305 | 90353 | 90401 | 90449 | 90497 |
| 90162 | 90210 | 90258 | 90306 | 90354 | 90402 | 90450 | 90498 |
| 90163 | 90211 | 90259 | 90307 | 90355 | 90403 | 90451 | 9049' |
| 90164 | 90212 | 90260 | 90308 | 90356 | 90404 | 90452 | 9050 |
| 90165 | 90213 | 90261 | 90309 | 90357 | 90405 | 90453 | 9050 |
| 90166 | 90214 | 90262 | 90310 | 90358 | 90406 | 90454 | 9050: |
| 90167 | 90215 | 90263 | 90311 | 90359 | 90407 | 90455 | 9050: |
| 90168 | 90216 | 90264 | 90312 | 90360 | 90408 | 90456 | 9050- |
| 90169 | 90217 | 90265 | 90313 | 90361 | 90409 | 90457 | 9050! |
| 90170 | 90218 | 90266 | 90314 | 90362 | 90410 | 90458 | 90506 |
| 90171 | 90219 | 90267 | 90315 | 90363 | 90411 | 90459 | 90507 |
| 90172 | 90220 | 90268 | 90316 | 90364 | 90412 | 90460 | 90508 |
| 90173 | 90221 | 90269 | 90317 | 90365 | 90413 | 90461 | 90509 |
| 90174 | 90222 | 90270 | 90318 | 90366 | 90414 | 90462 | 9051( |
| 90175 | 90223 | 90271 | 90319 | 90367 | 90415 | 90463 | 9051 |
| 90176 | 90224 | 90272 | 90320 | 90368 | 90416 | 90464 | 9051: |
| 90177 | 90225 | 90273 | 90321 | 90369 | 90417 | 90465 | 9051: |
| 90178 | 90226 | 90274 | 90322 | 90370 | 90418 | 90466 | 9051- |
| 90179 | 90227 | 90275 | 90323 | 90371 | 90419 | 90467 | 9051! |
| 90180 | 90228 | 90276 | 90324 | 90372 | 90420 | 90468 | 9051( |
| 90181 | 90229 | 90277 | 90325 | 90373 | 90421 | 90469 | 9051? |
| 90182 | 90230 | 90278 | 90326 | 90374 | 90422 | 90470 | 9051 |
| 90183 | 90231 | 90279 | 90327 | 90375 | 90423 | 90471 | 9051 |
| 90184 | 90232 | 90280 | 90328 | 90376 | 90424 | 90472 | 9052( |
| 90185 | 90233 | 90281 | 90329 | 90377 | 90425 | 90473 | 9052 |
| 90186 | 90234 | 90282 | 90330 | 90378 | 90426 | 90474 | 90522 |
| 90187 | 90235 | 90283 | 90331 | 90379 | 90427 | 90475 | 90523 |
| 90188 | 90236 | 90284 | 90332 | 90380 | 90428 | 90476 | 9052- |
| 90189 | 90237 | 90285 | 90333 | 90381 | 90429 | 90477 | 9052! |
| 90190 | 90238 | 90286 | 90334 | 90382 | 90430 | 90478 | 9052( |
| 90191 | 90239 | 90287 | 90335 | 90383 | 90431 | 90479 | 9052? |
| 90192 | 90240 | 90288 | 90336 | 90384 | 90432 | 90480 | 9052 |
| 90193 | 90241 | 90289 | 90337 | 90385 | 90433 | 90481 | 9052 |
| 90194 | 90242 | 90290 | 90338 | 90386 | 90434 | 90482 | 9053( |
| 90195 | 90243 | 90291 | 90339 | 90387 | 90435 | 90483 | 9053 |
| 90196 | 90244 | 90292 | 90340 | 90388 | 90436 | 90484 | 9053? |
| 90197 | 90245 | 90293 | 90341 | 90389 | 90437 | 90485 | 9053: |
| 90198 | 90246 | 90294 | 90342 | 90390 | 90438 | 90486 | 9053- |
| 90199 | 90247 | 90295 | 90343 | 90391 | 90439 | 90487 | 9053! |
| 90200 | 90248 | 90296 | 90344 | 90392 | 90440 | 90488 | 9053( |
| 90201 | 90249 | 90297 | 90345 | 90393 | 90441 | 90489 | 90537 |
| 90202 | 90250 | 90298 | 90346 | 90394 | 90442 | 90490 | 90538 |
| 90203 | 90251 | 90299 | 90347 | 90395 | 90443 | 90491 | 9053' |

| | | | |
|---|---|---|---|
| 540 | 90582 | 90624 | 90666 |
| 541 | 90583 | 90625 | 90667 |
| 542 | 90584 | 90626 | 90668 |
| 543 | 90585 | 90627 | 90669 |
| 544 | 90586 | 90628 | 90670 |
| 545 | 90587 | 90629 | 90671 |
| 546 | 90588 | 90630 | 90672 |
| 547 | 90589 | 90631 | 90673 |
| 548 | 90590 | 90632 | 90674 |
| 549 | 90591 | 90633 | 90675 |
| 550 | 90592 | 90634 | 90676 |
| 551 | 90593 | 90635 | 90677 |
| 552 | 90594 | 90636 | 90678 |
| 553 | 90595 | 90637 | 90679 |
| 554 | 90596 | 90638 | 90680 |
| 555 | 90597 | 90639 | 90681 |
| 556 | 90598 | 90640 | 90682 |
| 557 | 90599 | 90641 | 90683 |
| 558 | 90600 | 90642 | 90684 |
| 559 | 90601 | 90643 | 90685 |
| 560 | 90602 | 90644 | 90686 |
| 561 | 90603 | 90645 | 90687 |
| 562 | 90604 | 90646 | 90688 |
| 563 | 90605 | 90647 | 90689 |
| 564 | 90606 | 90648 | 90690 |
| 565 | 90607 | 90649 | 90691 |
| 566 | 90608 | 90650 | 90692 |
| 567 | 90609 | 90651 | 90693 |
| 568 | 90610 | 90652 | 90694 |
| 569 | 90611 | 90653 | 90695 |
| 570 | 90612 | 90654 | 90696 |
| 571 | 90613 | 90655 | 90697 |
| 572 | 90614 | 90656 | 90698 |
| 573 | 90615 | 90657 | 90699 |
| 574 | 90616 | 90658 | 90700 |
| 575 | 90617 | 90659 | 90701 |
| 576 | 90618 | 90660 | 90702 |
| 577 | 90619 | 90661 | 90703 |
| 578 | 90620 | 90662 | 90704 |
| 579 | 90621 | 90663 | 90705 |
| 580 | 90622 | 90664 | 90706 |
| 581 | 90623 | 90665 | 90707 |

| | | | |
|---|---|---|---|
| 90708 | 90715 | 90722 | 90729 |
| 90709 | 90716 | 90723 | 90730 |
| 90710 | 90717 | 90724 | 90731 |
| 90711 | 90718 | 90725 | 90732 |
| 90712 | 90719 | 90726 | Vulcan |
| 90713 | 90720 | 90727 | |
| 90714 | 90721 | 90728 | |

---

## 2-10-0 8F Class WD

**Ministry of Supply "Austerity" 2-10-0 locomotives purchased by British Railways, 1948.**

Introduced 1943. Riddles M.o.S. design.
Weights: Loco. 78 tons 6 cwt.
Tender 55 tons 10 cwt.
Pressure: 225 lb. Cyls.: (O) 19" × 28"
Driving Wheels: 4' 8½". T.E.: 34,215 lb.
Walschaerts gear. P.V.

| | | | |
|---|---|---|---|
| 90750 | 90757 | 90764 | 90771 |
| 90751 | 90758 | 90765 | 90772 |
| 90752 | 90759 | 90766 | 90773 |
| 90753 | 90760 | 90767 | North |
| 90754 | 90761 | 90768 | British |
| 90755 | 90762 | 90769 | 90774 |
| 90756 | 90763 | 90770 | |

---

## 2-10-0 Class 9F

To be introduced 1953.
Weights: Loco.
Tender
Pressure:
Cyls.: (O)
Driving Wheels: T.E.:
Walschaerts gear. P.V.

| | | | |
|---|---|---|---|
| 92000 | 92008 | 92016 | 92024 |
| 92001 | 92009 | 92017 | 92025 |
| 92002 | 92010 | 92018 | 92026 |
| 92003 | 92011 | 92019 | 92027 |
| 92004 | 92012 | 92020 | 92028 |
| 92005 | 92013 | 92021 | 92029 |
| 92006 | 92014 | 92022 | |
| 92007 | 92015 | 92023 | |

# ELECTRIC UNIT NUMBERS

## LIVERPOOL ST.—SHENFIELD 3-CAR ELECTRIC TRAIN UNIT

| | | | | | | | | | |
|---|---|---|---|---|---|---|---|---|---|
| 01 | 11 | 21 | 31 | 41 | 51 | 61 | 71 | 81 | 9 |
| 02 | 12 | 22 | 32 | 42 | 52 | 62 | 72 | 82 | 9 |
| 03 | 13 | 23 | 33 | 43 | 53 | 63 | 73 | 83 | |
| 04 | 14 | 24 | 34 | 44 | 54 | 64 | 74 | 84 | |
| 05 | 15 | 25 | 35 | 45 | 55 | 65 | 75 | 85 | |
| 06 | 16 | 26 | 36 | 46 | 56 | 66 | 76 | 86 | |
| 07 | 17 | 27 | 37 | 47 | 57 | 67 | 77 | 87 | |
| 08 | 18 | 28 | 38 | 48 | 58 | 68 | 78 | 88 | |
| 09 | 19 | 29 | 39 | 49 | 59 | 69 | 79 | 89 | |
| 10 | 20 | 30 | 40 | 50 | 60 | 70 | 80 | 90 | |

## GRIMSBY—IMMINGHAM ELECTRIC TRAMS

| | | | | | | | |
|---|---|---|---|---|---|---|---|
| 1 | 3 | 5 | 7 | 9 | 11 | 13 | 15 |
| 2 | 4 | 6 | 8 | 10 | 12 | 14 | 16 |

## SOUTH TYNESIDE ELECTRIC MOTOR COACHES

| | | | | | |
|---|---|---|---|---|---|
| E.29175E | E.29178E | E.29181E | E.29184E | E.29187E | E.2919 |
| E.29176E | E.29179E | E.29182E | E.29185E | E.29189E | E.2919 |
| E.29177E | E.29180E | E.29183E | E.29186E | E.29190E | |

Motor Parcels Van   E.29493E

## NORTH TYNESIDE ELECTRIC TWIN-UNIT MOTOR COACHE

| | | | | | |
|---|---|---|---|---|---|
| E.29101E | E.29113E | E.29124E | E.29135E | E.29147E | E.2915 |
| E.29102E | E.29114E | E.29125E | E.29136E | E.29148E | E.2915 |
| E.29103E | E.29115E | E.29126E | E.29137E | E.29149E | E.2916 |
| E.29104E | E.29116E | E.29127E | E.29138E | E.29150E | E.2916 |
| E.29105E | E.29117E | E.29128E | E.29139E | E.29151E | E.2916 |
| E.29106E | E.29118E | E.29129E | E.29140E | E.29152E | E.2916 |
| E.29107E | E.29119E | E.29130E | E.29141E | E.29153E | E.2916 |
| E.29108E | E.29120E | E.29131E | E.29142E | E.29154E | |
| E.29109E | E.29121E | E.29132E | E.29144E | E.29155E | |
| E.29110E | E.29122E | E.29133E | E.29145E | E.29156E | |
| E.29111E | E.29123E | E.29134E | E.29146E | E.29157E | |

| Motor Parcels Vans | | Motor Coaches | |
|---|---|---|---|
| E.29467E | E.29468E | E.29165E | E.29166E |

## MANCHESTER — SHEFFIELD ELECTRIC MOTOR COACH

| | | | |
|---|---|---|---|
| E29401 | 29403 | 29405 | 29407 |
| 29402 | 29404 | 29406 | 29408 |

# ROUTE AVAILABILITY OF LOCOMOTIVES

Restrictions on the working of locomotives over the routes of the former L.N.E.R. are denoted by Route Availability numbers. In general a locomotive is not permitted to work over a line of lower R.A. number than itself. The scheme is as follows :

**R.A.1 :** J15, J63, J65, J71, Y1, Y3, Y7, Y8, Y10, Z4.

**R.A.2 :** E4, J67/1, J70, J72, J77, Y9, Z5.

**R.A.3 :** B12/1, F4, F5, J3, J4, J10, J21, J25, J36, J66, J67/2, J68, J69, J88, N9, N10.

**R.A.4 :** B12/3, D40, F6, G5, J1, J5, J17, J26, J55, J83, N4, N5/2, N8, N13, N14, V4.

**R.A.5 :** A5, A8, B1, B2, B17, C12, C13, C14, D16, F2, J2, J6, J11, J19, J20, J27, J52, J73, J94, K2, N1, N7.

**R.A.6 :** C15, C16, D10, D11, D20, D30, D33, D34, J35, J39, J50, K1, K4, N2, N15, O1, O2, O4, O7, Q6, V1, Y4.

**R.A.7 :** A7, B16/1, L1, L3, Q7, U1, V3.

**R.A.8 :** B16/2, B16/3, D49, J37, J38, K3, K5, Q1, S1, T1.

**R.A.9 :** A1, A2, A3, A4, V2, W1.

---

# CLASSIFICATION OF L.N.E.R. LOCOMOTIVES

The L.N.E.R. locomotive classification scheme was based on that used on the former G.N.R. Each wheel arrangement was allotted a letter, and the classes of that arrangement were numbered in groups according to the pre-grouping ownership, in the order G.N., G.C., G.E., N.E., N.B., G.N.S. L.N.E.R. classes were at first usually added at the end of the list, but later standard locomotives have been given the lowest number. Many classes are sub-divided into " parts," denoted thus : " D16/3." This division is not entirely consistent, as some classes with comparatively wide variation, such as " A4," are not sub-divided, but others, such as " D4," have some divisions dependent only on details such as brakes and whether or not the tender has a water scoop. In these cases, sub-divisions are denoted by " parts " where these exist, but elsewhere it is to be assumed that any variations between the locomotives in the class are not covered by the classification (e.g. " A4 ").